F AW Pool.

Christmas 1937.

RACING, CRUISING AND DESIGN

DORADE SWEEPS PAST DIAMOND HEAD TO WIN THE 1936 TRANSPACIFIC RACE

RACING, CRUISING AND DESIGN

BY

UFFA FOX

A Companion Volume to
"SAILING, SEAMANSHIP AND YACHT CONSTRUCTION"
"UFFA FOX'S SECOND BOOK"
and
"SAIL AND POWER"

With over 400 Plans, Photographs and Diagrams

LONDON
PETER DAVIES LIMITED

Published in 1937

PRINTED IN GREAT BRITAIN

INTRODUCTION

A GREAT many people have written to me expressing appreciation of my three previous books, and like Oliver Twist, have asked for more. In complying with their requests once again this year, I do not forget what I said in my Introduction to *Sail and Power* (1936), namely that I would let a year go by without publishing a book rather than, for lack of material, lower the high standard I have always tried to maintain. A glance through the pages of *Racing, Cruising and Design* will show that so far from suffering from lack of material, I have been able to include a very large number indeed of magnificent vessels of all types.

Was there ever a better type of large racing cutter than the *Astra*, the last big boat to the I.Y.R.U. Rule, or than *Helgoland* for driving night and day across wide oceans? Then *Lahloo* and *Valdora* are fine examples of two different types of power craft, and the 12-metre *Veronica* and the 8-metre *If* fill us with admiration as they show what a good type of craft can be produced under the I.Y.R.U. Rules. Here we must remember that there are many people in the world who prefer the speed of a thoroughbred as opposed to comfort, for while these last two vessels have, as will be seen, fine accommodation, speed has been considered foremost in them. The wonderful weatherly ability of the 8-metre *Carron II* saved her the night she was dismasted just outside the Needles, for had she not been a thoroughbred she would never have clawed off the dangerous shore at the back of the Wight in the gale blowing that night with only a spinnaker boom on which to set a rag of sail. As it was, she was able to weather the dangerous lee shore and save herself before being taken in tow by the Bembridge Lifeboat.

Later in the book *Evenlode* and *Golden Eye* bring to us the state of perfection reached by the cruising racer of to-day, and it is through the great kindness and generosity of the greatest yacht designers in the world that I have been able, once more, to produce in this book such wonderful examples of the designer's and shipwright's art. Every vessel in the book is a good type of craft for the work for which she was designed and built.

Throughout my life people have been very kind to me, and I hope that these pages, as those of my other books, are equally friendly, for then they reflect the generosity shown to me by all the people with whom I have come into contact in this world.

There are two ways of teaching :

(1) The bitter way, by taking bad examples and pointing out the faults in each case, and

(2) The better way, to my mind, of taking perfect examples and pointing out the perfection in the different details for people to admire and love. And this has been my way through life ; and so people will look in vain for hard criticism in these pages, for I have always only asked for the best types of boats, and once more can place my hand on my heart and say I would love to own any one of the vessels in this book.

CONTENTS

PART I

CRUISING

THIS section begins with plans and descriptions of the ships in which, a thousand years ago, the Vikings visited the whole of the Christian world from the far end of the Mediterranean to the North Cape. Iceland, Greenland and America also saw them, and it is fitting that they should head our Cruising Section, for these old rovers were fine seamen and their long ships very suitable for the uses to which they were put.

Next follows a chapter written round *Daedalus*, emphasising the truth that every vessel should be designed to suit the voyages her owner plans for her, after which I have tried to give reasons for choosing the rig.

We then have descriptions of cruisers of different nationalities, and designed for varying purposes, the first four being of German, Dutch, Norwegian and British origin. *Helgoland* shows a well-designed lay-out for ocean racing. Her lines and accommodation tell of a vessel that is designed with a view to being underway and driven hard 24 hours a day for a month on end, and her accommodation exactly fits this purpose and will be difficult to improve upon.

In *Tromp II* we have a family boat designed to cruise in shallow as well as deep waters. With *Noreine* we come to a racing cruiser type, ideal for fast passages and good sport in the day, but one in which her owner intends to be in harbour every night, though, of course, she could be sailed night and day and still be enjoyable ; while in *Heron II* we have the full-bodied comfortable type of craft of easy draught, suitable for cruising in all weathers around our coasts and those of France.

The chapter on long-distance racing, because it gives examples of the winning craft in all the races held this year, is particularly instructive, in the light of my contention that " the best ocean racer is the best cruiser ". When applying this to some of these vessels we have to remember that though termed ocean racers, many have been developed for long-distance racing throughout which they are never free of coasts ; such are popularly called off-shore races, whereas they are really long-shore races, as the vessels are never off soundings. Nevertheless, all these ocean racers are very fine craft, for unless well and truly built they would open up and leak when being driven, as they are, to windward when the normal cruiser would be hove to. While they have to be comfortable at sea in order not to exhaust their crews, this is to a certain extent cancelled out by the fact that no crew limitation is imposed. Such vessels as *Ortac* and *Maid of Malham* carry no less than eight or nine men when four should be ample to handle them ; and when in the years to come ocean racing rules restrict numbers on board, I would suggest that they consider that four only be allowed on all vessels with sail area up to 1000 square feet, as four enable the watches to be divided so as to give eight hours sleep below in normal weather. And when a vessel has over 1000 square feet of sail area she should be allowed two men for every extra 500 feet of measured sail area ; thus one with 2000 square feet would have eight men aboard, and all with 1000 square feet or less would have only four. However, in spite of this flaw in the present rules the vessels produced for ocean racing all make very fine cruisers.

After the ocean racers, vessels designed for the Baltic, the Norwegian coast, and Germany are described, and amongst them will be found a little transom-sterned cutter, 22 ft. on the water-line, of British origin.

This section finally ends with a lecture tour I made last winter through the countries bordering the Baltic. When a gate leading to new fields is opened for us, we wander in through the strange landscape, and though familiar objects such as the trees, streams and bushes are in a sense the same, yet they are different ; so on this lecture tour, staying in the homes of different people in the different countries, I saw their towns in a different light, for I was looking at them from within, whereas when we cruise to these places in our little ships, there is no doubt that while our vessels form the finest means of visiting different lands because they afford us a comfortable home, yet this very fact makes us all the while see the places from without and not from within, as we are really independent of the shore. I hope this land cruise will enable people visiting the Baltic countries to have greater understanding, and so derive more pleasure from their cruises.

For the rest, there are types of vessels to suit all tastes of all nationalities in this first section of the book, but the reader should not only look at the vessels he knows and is fond of, but at all of them, for all have been chosen because they teach us something.

A

· I ·
VIKING SHIPS

HOW they stir our blood, those long ships manned by fierce fighting freemen, and how their stories spell adventure, wonder and romance! Time has lent unequalled glamour to the tales of the Norsemen, so that we too would follow their example and sail away to roam the seven seas, seeking freedom and adventure in the unknown beyond the horizon, and the means to live (for one must live or adventure ends). Some day, time may

THE VIKINGS NOT ONLY GIRDLED THE OLD CHRISTIAN WORLD BUT ALSO SAILED WESTWARD TO GREENLAND AND
VINLAND = AMERICA

also weave a web of romance around our modern adventurers, who feel the same urge as the Vikings, who seek for greater colonies and expansion and the greater trade this brings. Science has only made the method different.

Shakespeare's Mark Antony, for his own purposes, said :

"The evil that men do lives after them,
The good is oft interred with their bones."

But this was an occasion for special pleading, and it is often the evil that is interred with men's bones—is not Charles

3

I now a saint? So we find (and take heart in finding) that the courageousness of the Vikings in undertaking their difficult voyages through uncharted seas, the way they surmounted their difficulties and endured the inevitable hardships entailed are uppermost in our thoughts when their name is mentioned, and we forget the evil they wrought in plunder and bloodshed.

Their voyages put a girdle round the old Christian World, for they sailed northward round the North Cape, eastward by Russia to the Caspian Sea, while westward they ravaged the coast of the British Isles and went south-

VIKING SHIPS IN THE BAYEUX TAPESTRY

ward plundering the coasts of France, Spain, the North African coast and the shores of the Mediterranean, their voyages through the Mediterranean linking up with the northern and eastern voyages. Farther westward they colonized Iceland, and settled in Greenland and in America. It is no wonder that their adventures have been the inspiration of many poems and legends and that with the passing of time we have forgotten the harm they did, and think of the good that has come from these Sea Rovers, and delight in the fierce joy of battle which breathes throughout all Viking stories.

We cannot expect all these legends to be true, but so much fact remains that it is easy for us to believe and enjoy every legend and saga relating to these old seafarers.

To them we owe the creation of the chief instrument and mainstay of our Empire, for had it not been for the ravages of the Norsemen, King Alfred, himself an outstanding example of the truth " that where there is the need for a giant he will be found ", would never have called into being the foundation of the British Navy.

The only permanent outcome of the Viking age in France was the settlement of Normandy by the Vikings. This Norse influence is clearly defined in that wonderful monument the Bayeux tapestry, for though the ships depicted in it are supposed to represent first an English ship coming to Normandy, and later the building of the ships for the conquest of England in 1066 by William, they, nevertheless, are Viking ships in form, and it is arguable that the Bayeux tapestry itself owes its existence to the Vikings, in whose courts the arts of the wood carver and the weaver were more highly prized than elsewhere.

The " Piraeus Lion ", a Greek carving now in Venice, has a Runic inscription on its flank, while away in America in the town of Newport there is a Viking Tower and these things give clear proof of the remarkable voyages undertaken by the Norsemen. No wonder that when I was fortunate enough to stand under the centre tower of the Viking Hall just outside Oslo, and with one glance was able to see three ships all over a thousand years old, the great rush of thoughts that came through my mind stirred my blood as it has seldom been stirred before. For standing there I thought of all the dangerous voyages through uncharted waters, desperate struggles with heavy breaking seas and with the human beings that opposed these ships, all the strange lands that these ships sought and found, and the fierce fighting men who manned the longships. Then calmer thoughts came, and I thought of those who had laboured so hard to excavate these ships which had lain in their burial mounds so long and who had so carefully brought and set them up as they were now, so that all who came after might marvel at the skill which the old shipwrights displayed in their construction. Looking at these old ships the first four verses of Longfellow's poem came to my mind.

> " Thorberg Skafting, masterbuilder,
> In his ship-yard by the sea,
> Whistling, said, ' It would bewilder
> Any man but Thorberg Skafting,
> Any man but me! '

" Near him lay the dragon stranded,
　Built of old by Raud the Strong,
　And King Olaf had commanded
　He should build another Dragon,
　Twice as large and long.

" Therefore whistled Thorberg Skafting,
　As he sat with half closed eyes,
　And his head turned sideways, drafting
　That new vessel for King Olaf
　Twice the Dragon's size.

" Round him busily hewed and hammered
　Mallet huge and heavy axe ;
　Workmen laughed and sang and clamoured ;
　Whirred the wheels, that into rigging
　Spun the shining flax! "

There before me were examples of the shipwright's art and craft over a thousand years old, examples of life and beauty and of excellent workmanship which for all their age are hardly excelled to-day, for such vessels would not only suit

FROM THE BAYEUX TAPESTRY

and be able to endure gales of wind at sea, but could also steal silently up creeks and rivers, through inland seas, and pass quietly through all armed camps on either side of a river in the black of night with their sixty fighting men on board. It is difficult to think of anything better than these ships for that same purpose to-day, while the clinker built construction used is still practised everywhere in the building of small boats.

　　In the wing to the left stood the remains of the Tune Ship ; there was very little of her excepting amidships, for the ends of her planks and her upper works had rotted away in the burial mound, but this fact enabled one to get a close view of the construction details in her bottom. The photograph I took will show how cleverly these old shipwrights fashioned their planks, and we must remember that the materials at the disposal of the workman decide and govern his method of construction.

As will be seen from the photograph, tiny cleats were left on the planking with holes through them with which to tie the planks with whalebone to the frames athwartships, and when one thinks that each of these planks has been hewn down from the solid to leave these cleats on, one realises the work entailed in the building of these old ships.

Directly in front was the Oseberg Ship, stretching away 70 feet 6 inches to the entrance of the hall, and as her plans show she is a very large open boat for sailing and rowing. Built entirely of oak, her timbers were so well preserved that after being taken from her burial mound they could be steamed and bent back to the original shape ;

THESE CLEATS EACH WITH ITS TWO HOLES FOR THE LASHINGS WERE LEFT AS THE
PLANKING WAS FASHIONED AND HEWN DOWN TO ITS REQUIRED THICKNESS

all the parts of the ship have been in turn boiled two or three times in a solution of alum before being re-erected. She is built throughout of all her old parts, and at least two-thirds of her old rivets have been used, the only important new timber about her being her figure head (an exact replica of the original that was found in such fragments and in such a state that it could not be rebuilt). It is easy to imagine why this rotted away, for when these ships were placed in the burial mound they were first of all buried in a soft clay, which sealed them and preserved them for all time, but the rising stem and figure head would be high and therefore in a more porous clay, so that in time these would decay.

The lines are those of a fast and very easily driven craft, her great length giving her speed and stability. As will be noted, she is very low sided, which shows that she was built for smooth water work inside the Fjords and Islands only, and was probably used by a Chieftain for State occasions in good weather. The date of her building is put at A.D. 800. Because she is so low in the water the holes to take the oars are in the top strake, and it will be seen that they are kept as small as possible and a slot making them rather like a key-hole is cut in the upper side to enable the oar blades to be slipped through the smallest possible space. At the forward oar, however, the boat was not beamy enough to allow the oar to be shipped from inboard, and as this oar would be shorter than the rest it was shipped from the outside, so the hole here is a perfect circle.

With thirty oars one imagines that she could be rowed along at a high speed ; she might have reached 10 knots sailing, and 8 knots under oars, though of course the rowing speed could not be maintained as the men would tire after a while. Seeing such a ship one regretted the fact that power has robbed the world of such sweet-lined rowing craft, for if our modern racing Eight shows us the poetry of motion, where the eight men work as one, how much more would we feel inspired by the sight of thirty men striking the water with their oars in perfect unison, and such a vessel flying along under their united efforts.

The mast step is amidships and is very long and well constructed, made to extend the thrust of the mast over a long length of the keel, while at the thwart there is a long fore and after spreading strains over four frames. This is shaped like a fish tail at each end, as were all the steps for masts and stanchions in these ships.

The after portion of the upper support is portable and enables the mast to be lowered in its step aft, for these spars were very heavy to step and unstep, and we have to remember that once a man is afloat he can only exert part of his strength, for he is not on firm ground, but has a moving platform underneath him so that half his strength and attention is used to balance and support his own weight, and only half can be used for hauling or setting up spars, unless, of course he sits down to work. This brings us back to rowing, and it is probable that the thirty men rowing this ship sat on loose seats on the floorboards.

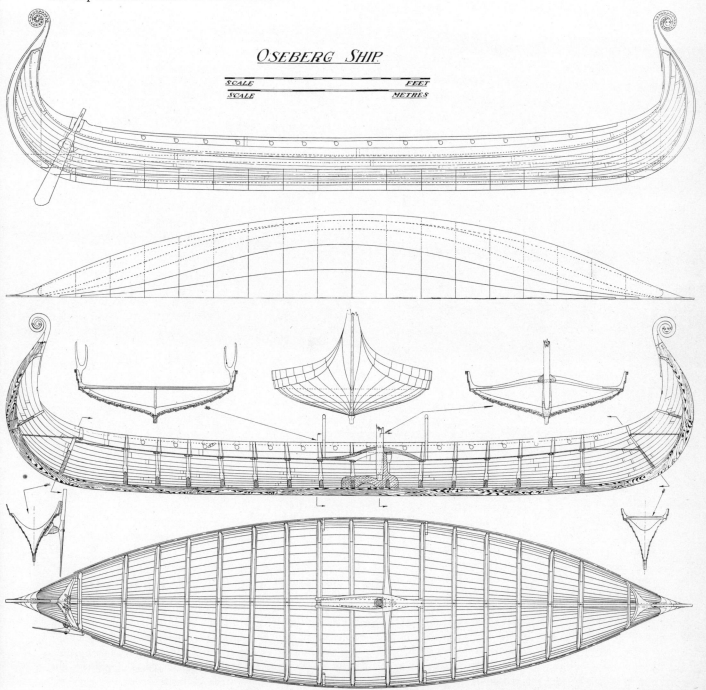

OSEBERG SHIP.

SCALE   FEET

SCALE   METRES

Aft on the starboard side is the steerboard, and I have always thought and believed that our word " starboard " comes from the Norwegian " steerboard " as the right hand was always the " steerboard side ".

In the right wing was the Gokstad Ship, and in her we have a far more seaworthy craft, as she is higher sided and deeper keeled ; in fact, everything about her speaks of the open sea rather than the waters inside the Skerries (Islands).

In her plans the upper parts of the stem and sternpost and the planking near these points are shown dotted, for these parts again were high and in a porous part of the clay with which she was covered in her burial mound, and so had to be renewed when she was rebuilt for the Museum.

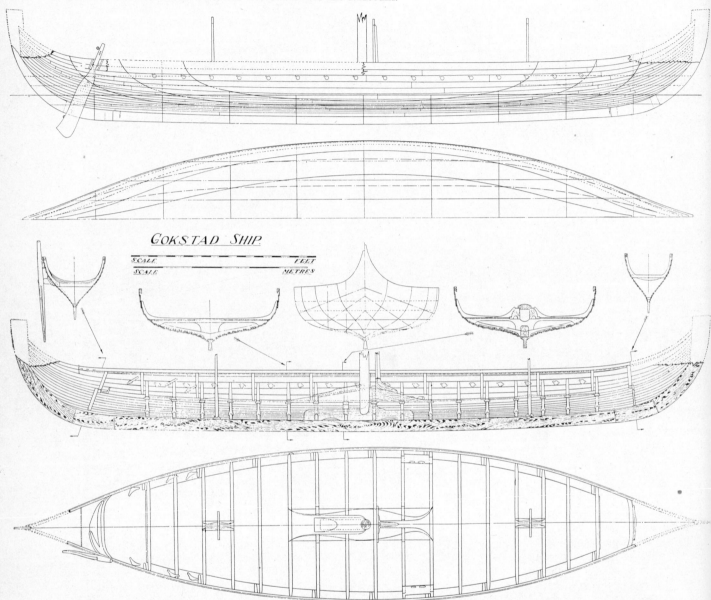

GOKSTAD SHIP

Her lines and sections fill us with admiration, and also remind us that the lifeboats aboard our giant liners to-day closely resemble this ship in shape, and that the whale boats of all nations in which men hunted whales weighing 80 tons were also very similar to this ship in model. The truth is that the sea has remained unaltered, and as the Vikings and their fathers before them had developed a ship that suited the sea, it is not surprising that their ships are still as good as can be devised and are similar to the vessels which are used on the north coasts of Norway for fishing to-day, on liners as lifeboats and around most of the coasts of the world as lifeboats operating from the shore. Even America, who it seems leads the way in many things, still retains vessels of similar type for her Coast-guard Service, which is similar to our National Lifeboat Institution.

The construction of the Gokstad Ship follows that of the Oseberg Ship and Tune Ship, for she is clinker built, and the sections show the cleats left on the botton seven strakes on either side for lashing these planks to the frames. Once again we see the long mast step supporting the mast amidships, and the fish tailed step on the deck with its after end portable to allow the mast to be lowered aft at sea, and the man lowering it to have perfect control of it the whole way down, just as men have when lowering a ladder, for when a ladder is being lowered one man always stands on the bottom rung to keep the heel steady, and here we see the bottom of this mast and the step rounded away to enable it to be lowered sweetly and evenly.

This ship has one more oar either side than the Oseberg Ship, and has her foremost oar farther forward. It will be seen that there is a slot in this for the oar to reeve through from the inside. These holes are all furnished with little shutters, which close them upon the inside, so that when sailing at sea no water finds its way through these holes. The steerboard is again on the starboard side, a tiller of course running athwartships. Looking at this I am reminded of the fact that when a replica of one of these ships was built to sail across the Atlantic those responsible for the building had no faith in the steerboard, and so a rudder was fitted on to the sternpost, but directly she was tried it was found that she answered her steerboard perfectly and the rudder was thrown away.

THE STEERBOARD OF THE GOKSTAD SHIP

A "PICTURE STONE" FROM HAMMARS GATLAND WHICH SHOWS HOW CULTURED THE VIKINGS WERE

As the sections show, these steerboards were fitted into two cleats and were fastened with a thick withy, which allowed the steerboard to be turned as the helmsman wished, and also to lift on its own in shallow water.

Though it will be difficult to discern it on these plans, the tenth or bilge strake, on which the upper ends of the ribs were fastened, and the fourteenth, which was bored for the oar holes, are both much thicker than the rest. This tells us that the craftsman strove for strength without undue weight and obtained it just as we do to-day. These and hundreds of other points about these vessels, that can only be appreciated by seeing them, tell us that these old craftsmen had brains as highly developed as ours are to-day, and that though we go forward we are no better than our fathers before us.

Along the sides of this ship are placed some half-dozen shields ; twenty-five of these were found when she was excavated. These Viking shields are made of fir and are some three feet in diameter with a solid wooden rim across the back which served as a handle, the shield being held together by a leather edging. When lashed along the rectangular openings in the top of the ship they gave her a highly decorative as well as a fierce look, and also served to protect those aboard from arrows when approaching the shore. Their colours were alternately black and gold, and as the bull's eye of a target for shooting with a bow and arrow is gold, one wonders if the black and gold used in archery to-day came from the shields of the Vikings. These shields are often depicted in the picture stones that are found in parts of Norway and Sweden. The Gotland Island is very rich in these stones. Ships, stones and carvings all tell us that the ruthless Vikings were a very clever and highly cultured race, as well as being probably the finest seafarers this world has seen.

· 2 ·

DAEDALUS

Length, overall - 28 ft. 0 in. = 8·534 m.   Length, water-line - 27 ft. 3 in. = 8·30 m.
Beam - - 9 ft. 2 in. = 2·794 m.   Draught - - - 4 ft. 4 in. = 1·32 m.
Displacement - 8·25 tons = 8,382 kilos.   Sail area - - 1,240 sq. ft. = 115 sq. m.

Owner, RATSEY & LAPTHORN LTD.   *Designer*, JOHN WHITE   *Builder*, JOHN WHITE

FIFTY odd years ago a great deal of the carrying trade was still in the hands of sailing ships, for steam had not yet come into its own ; and when Ratsey and Lapthorn wanted a small vessel to carry their bales of canvas from Southampton to Cowes, and the same material in the form of finished sails to various vessels or back to Southampton, they naturally chose a sailing vessel. *Daedalus* was designed and built by John White of Cowes for this purpose.

The reason for her coming into this book at this early stage is to impress upon us the fact that whenever we look at the design of any vessel in the following pages we must first of all consider the use to which that vessel is to be put, for it is that point that governs the owner's choice and ideas.

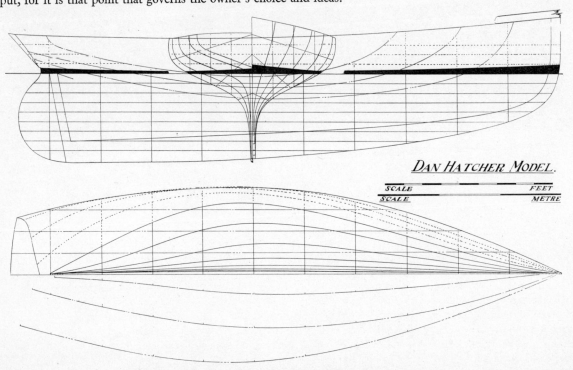

DAN HATCHER MODEL.

SCALE   FEET
SCALE   METRE

When the plans, proportions and characteristics of *Daedalus* were being considered, that famous old artist Dan Hatcher put up a model to Tom Ratsey for the job, and as Dan Hatcher models are now very scarce, the lines of this little craft are of great value, for they give us an opportunity of admiring his work.

Like most artists Dan Hatcher had great admiration for delicate soft easy lines, and the lines taken off this model show very easy waterlines and some of the easiest buttocks I have yet seen in a craft of this size. These make the sections also very sweet and easy. But the displacement of this vessel was only 3½ tons, so though she would no doubt have been very fast she was not chosen because she could carry so little in the way of sailcloth and sails. We must remember that the mainsail for a cutter like the old *Britannia* weighed close on a ton, and *Daedalus* had often tons of cloth aboard. Therefore, because of her inability to carry great weights, the Dan Hatcher model was reluctantly put to one side; I say reluctantly because Tom Ratsey had a great liking for a sweet lined craft, and all the family would have loved racing such a vessel as Dan would have produced, in the Regattas. But the job for which

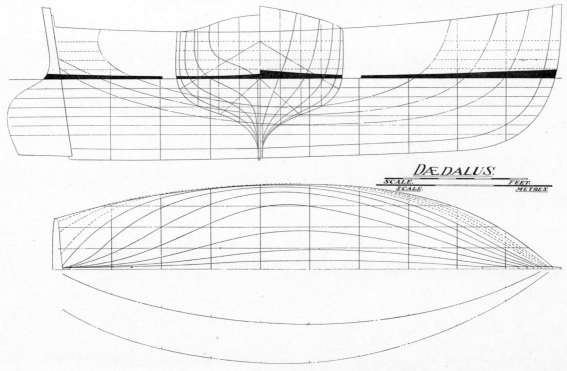

the craft was intended was most important, and the choice lay between a carrying craft and a racing craft. So *Daedalus* was built and in her we see a very small cargo craft, but nevertheless quite a fast one of her type and size as long as the water is smooth.

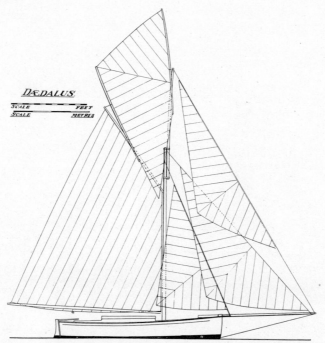

The displacement of *Daedalus* is 2½ times that of the Dan Hatcher model on the same length water-line, this telling us that her lines are that much coarser and her carrying capacity that much greater. Throughout these pages, then, we must consider every boat from the owner's viewpoint. Some owners wish for high speeds at all times, which can only be obtained from a fine-bottomed craft, while others do not care so much for speed as for comfort, so these have to have a coarser lined vessel as comfort means a heavier load for the vessel to carry in the way of cushions, stoves, cooking utensils, and all the things that make for comfort in this world, including a good cellar and ice box, as well as a well stocked larder, and only the owner can decide just what proportion speed shall bear to ability to carry a cargo of comfort.

The lines of *Daedalus* show that her under water-lines are hollow each end and her buttocks are fairly steep, while the sections show that she has a hard low bilge, all of which makes for a stiff boat able to carry heavy weights. The whole of her cabin top was portable, so that it could be lifted off, and the cabin turned into the hold for carrying her cargo ; but though designed and built expressly as a small cargo carrier, she has throughout her life given a great deal of pleasure to the Ratsey family, and I have had many an enjoyable weekend and race with them aboard her. One small cruise took Chris. Ratsey, "Chuckle" Brading and myself to Cherbourg and back, in March ; we also cruised to what used to be the quiet and unfrequented Lulworth Cove, all of which comes back to me when I look at these lines. Memories too come of anchoring in Swanage for a quiet night, and then the wind coming in hard from the east sending the steep breaking sea into the unprotected bay, a struggle to get our anchor in the darkness and the hard fight round Old Harry, and then rushing into Poole Harbour, with the wind abeam, for shelter as dawn was breaking. There also comes a memory of a race home from the west with a smart yawl three times her size in a light wind. Her owner could not understand why such an insignificant ship should be able to hold his fine great vessel, but the reason that we could hold her was that *Daedalus* had a large spread of canvas and in smooth water was boiling along at her utmost speed. Had the wind been a little stronger we should have slowed up as the sea would have killed her, while the yawl would have sailed on and soon had us hull down astern. These and other pleasant incidents come to mind, and so it will be seen that all the vessels that take us afloat give us joy and pleasant memories, whether designed as fast hulls or as cargo carriers. Unfortunately the one gains at the expense of the other, and a designer's greatest difficulty is in blending these two opposing features, the blending depending entirely upon the owner's wishes.

DAEDALUS

· 3 ·

SEA GOING RIGS

ONE of the hardest problems an owner has to solve is that of which rig to take to sea, for each has its advantages and its disciples. This chapter may be taken as an effort to help owners to decide upon the rigs for their vessels.

Large vessels can have large crews, but I am dealing with the question chiefly from the point of view of owners of small boats, although the larger ones have many of the same difficulties to contend with, so this can be used as a guide for all sailing craft. Most amateur yacht-owners have to consider the fact that at some time or another in their cruising career they may have to sail their boat single handed or with but two people on board, and I am writing with this fact foremost.

Forty-eight hours in a hard gale just to leeward of the Azores taught me two things about the ketch rig.

We had left the north west corner of Spain for the Azores. The night before making the land the wind increased with a very steep sea, and the two of us on deck had to reef the mainsail, which was 500 square feet in area. The other man steered, and I eased the mainsheet slightly, so that though close hauled the mainsail was not bung full of wind, but had just enough in it to keep it quiet and the boom steady and enable me to reef it fairly comfortably in spite of heavy seas sweeping over us. I put in one reef on top of the other, till the mainsail was close reefed, without undue difficulty, and from this learned that one man can handle 500 square feet in a gale. The increasing wind and sea then forced me to stow the mainsail. We drove into the seas throughout the night, and daylight revealed the island of San Miguel ahead but slightly to windward of our course. On we drove, making leeway due to our small sail, and with the houses in plain view some four miles away we tried to tack to get under the lee of the island.

All the people who argue for the ketch rig maintain that one has only to lower the mainsail and she will handle under staysail and mizen ; but though we tried some half-dozen times to get her about, we failed, for as soon as we eased the wind out of her sails the windage in her spars and rigging slowed her up, and the next sea would crash over her and knock her back on to the old tack. We set the close reefed mainsail to try and help her, but with this on she lay right down on her beam ends with the water forcing its way in through the closed hatchway amidships. So we took the main off her, and tried once more with the mizen and the headsail, only to fail again. We then gybed her, making the mistake of not taking the mizen off first, for in gybing we carried away the mizen mast, after which we quickly stowed the mizen and staysail, set the trysail and hove to, and did not reach the island until some days later. So, besides teaching me that one man could handle 500 square feet of sail, that forty-eight hours also taught me that a ketch will not tack with her mizen and staysail only, for when the wind is so strong that she can only carry that amount of canvas it is strong enough to slow her up as she comes into the wind through the windage in her spars and rigging, so that the very next sea knocks her back on to the old tack.

From a great deal of experience I have come to the conclusion that 500 square feet (47 square metres) is the largest sail that can be handled by one man in any weather, from calm to gale. All the rigs illustrating this chapter are designed with but 500 square feet in their largest sail, which means they can at a pinch be handled single handed, although two are really required to handle such craft as shown, one at the helm to ease her while the other is reefing or taking in the largest sail.

Experience has proved that the most efficient rig yet devised is the Bermudian cutter, and the following table gives an idea of the efficiency of this rig over others. For a ketch to have the same efficiency as a cutter she must have some 12 per cent. more sail area, and the main reason for going to a yawl or a ketch rig in a cruiser is that of making the sails smaller and more easily handled.

Cutter	-	-	-	-	-	-	100 per cent.
Yawl	-	-	-	-	-	-	97 ,, ,,
Schooner	-	-	-	-	-	-	88 ,, ,,
Ketch	-	-	-	-	-	-	88 ,, ,,

I have said that one man can handle 500 square feet, and so, to keep a vessel within his strength, the largest cutter rigged craft he can use single handed is 30 feet on the water-line. If his vessel is to be larger, then he has to

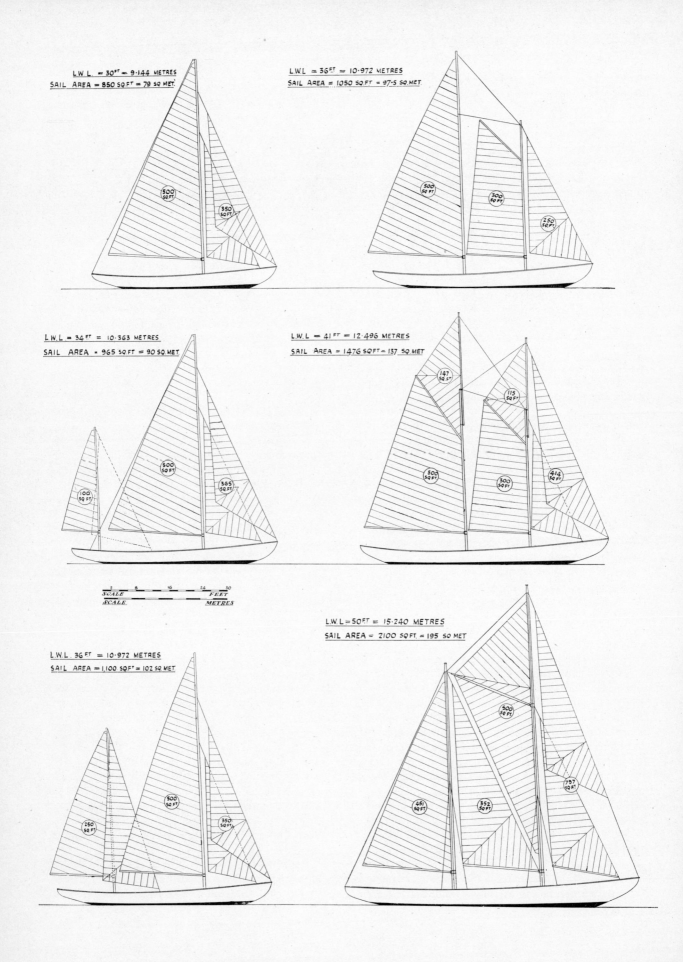

L.W.L. = 30 FT = 9·144 METRES
SAIL AREA = 850 SQ.FT = 79 SQ.MET.

500 SQ FT

350 SQ.FT

L.W.L. = 36 FT = 10·972 METRES
SAIL AREA = 1050 SQ.FT = 97·5 SQ.MET.

500 SQ FT

300 SQ.FT

250 SQ.FT

L.W.L. = 34 FT = 10·363 METRES
SAIL AREA = 965 SQ.FT = 90 SQ.MET.

100 SQ FT

500 SQ.FT

365 SQ.FT

L.W.L. = 41 FT = 12·496 METRES
SAIL AREA = 1476 SQ.FT = 137 SQ.MET.

147 SQ.FT

115 SQ.FT

500 SQ FT

300 SQ FT

414 SQ.FT

SCALE   FEET
SCALE   METRES

L.W.L. 36 FT = 10·972 METRES
SAIL AREA = 1,100 SQ.FT = 102 SQ.MET.

250 SQ.FT

500 SQ FT

350 SQ.FT

L.W.L. = 50 FT = 15·240 METRES
SAIL AREA = 2100 SQ.FT = 195 SQ MET.

500 SQ FT

451 SQ.FT

352 SQ.FT

757 SQ.FT

go to a two-masted rig, as this will enable him to rig her with the largest sail still only 500 square feet, and so, as the plan will show, he can have a yawl rig up to 34 feet on the water-line, then to keep his largest sail down to 500 square feet he is forced to a ketch or schooner rig for a vessel 36 feet on the water-line, all these four vessels having exactly the same area in their mainsails.

The fifth rig is one that gave me a great deal of pleasure to design. We go to sea for pleasure, and men, even when they are grown up, are still in a sense small boys with all a boy's imagination, and a great deal of our pleasure at sea is imagining that we have put time back to where man is at the mercy of the elements, and his joy is in battling against the winds, seas, fog and storms, which for all our scientific achievements still remain unharnessed, and exactly as they were in the beginning of the world. Without doubt the schooner rig is a rig which conjures up pirates, slavers, and the days when sail was the prime mover of everything that floated. But that schooner has to be a gaff schooner with topsails, and to find in this series of designs that a gaff schooner can be much larger than the ordinary Bermudian schooner and yet be handled by the same crew, has given me a great deal of pleasure, and I feel sure that many more will rejoice to see that the gaff sail has the advantage of dividing the sail plan into smaller and more easily handled units, so that a schooner 41 feet on the water-line can be handled by one or two men in any weather. So a gaff rig finds its way into this chapter, which for the rest is entirely devoted to the present day Bermudian rigs, excepting for the other schooner, which has a gaff foresail, because there is no finer sail than this for a schooner when the weather is so bad that she has to tuck her head under her wing till the gale has eased.

A new cruising rig appeared a few years ago, namely the "wishbone" ketch, and with this rig it is possible for one or two men to handle a 50 feet water-line vessel with 2,100 square feet (195 square metres) total area. This is possible because all the units that go to make up the total area are close to the limit that can be handled by one man, namely 500 square feet, as all the sails are near the same size.

I am afraid, however, that this rig will never be fully developed and made use of. Cruising men hate to admit it, but nevertheless it is a fact that almost every improvement made to their craft is due to the racing branch of this sport, just as in the motor cars on the road, the touring car owes almost every improvement that is made to it to the racing car.

The reason that the racing craft develop and perfect rigs is that their sailing mostly takes place in sheltered waters, in daylight and in good weather, and so they are able to experiment with new ideas at no risk to life or limb. Moreover, the keen competition found in racing makes owners want to try and develop and perfect new rigs, for the first man to perfect a rig has the advantage over his competitors. But where in racing the gain of a few seconds is of vital importance these seconds do not matter so much in cruising, and because the wishbone ketch rig is not a racing rig it will never reach perfection, which is a great pity, for it offers three great advantages for cruising men :

(1) Because of the shape of its sails, there are no backstays or runners to let go even when running. It will be seen that the topmast stay runs from the stemhead to the mainmast head and the mizen topmast backstay runs from the stern to the mizen head, while between the two masts the main topmast backstay is fitted, so that with a stay running from the stem clear over both masts down to the stern there is nothing to release or set up when tacking and gybing.

(2) Its other great advantage is that the units making up the total area are much the same size, which makes for a very easily handled vessel.

(3) All the space between both masts is very efficiently filled with sails, which makes for shorter spars than in any other rig. However, this rig cannot be considered as a proved sea going rig, for it is still in its infancy, and will probably always remain so because it is a cruising rig only, and therefore will never reach perfection, because it is valueless to our racing brethren.

So far I have considered the rigs with the strength of one man in view only, and from the fact that one man can handle 500 square feet in all weathers, and in doing so I have pointed out the advantages of the wishbone ketch rig when it is perfected. We might now consider the advantages of other rigs. The cutter is the fastest and most efficient for sailing, but unless the mast is stepped well into the vessel she will be light headed so that her bow falls to leeward when under a trysail and staysail, whereas a yawl with mainsail and staysail set, because of the windage in her mizen mast, would tend to hold higher into the wind. This applies also to the ketch, only more so.

To my mind, of the four rigs the schooner is the most seaworthy, for this reason, that in bad weather when the mainsail is stowed and a trysail set on the mainmast she is in fact a ketch, so that in the very worst of weather she has her largest sail amidships where it can be handled and wrestled with safely and easily. Then when the weather gets even worse and she has to tuck her head under her wing, she takes in her trysail and staysail, and she will then heave to with her foresail only. So her foresail should always be of the best of materials and kept in first class condition.

Once with a schooner we were hove to on a lee shore on the American coast in an October gale under our foresail only, and all night long we slowly worked to windward with the helm a lee and the fore sheet started slightly.

Another great advantage of the schooner is that both masts are tied together and support each other.

The schooner's disadvantages are, that in running, her mainsail being aft tends to drive her up in the wind and causes her to broach to, and also the mainsail being aft has the disadvantage that when reefing one is generally in the way of the helmsman and working on a very broken up part of the deck. From forward there is the deck house and the sliding hatch down to the saloon, then one drops down off this into the cockpit, and still farther aft one steps up again to the deck once more ; but in spite of all this my favourite rig for really hard service at sea is still the schooner.

· 4 ·

HELGOLAND

Length, overall -	59 ft. 4 in. = 18·084 m.		Length, water-line -	42 ft. 7¾ in. = 13·00 m.
Beam - -	13 ft. 5 in. = 4·089 m.		Draught - - -	8 ft. 6 in. = 2·590 m.
Displacement -	26·5 tons = 26,924 kilos.		Sail area - -	1,480 sq. ft. = 137·60 sq. m.

Designer, HENRY GRUBER

EVERY book of mine so far has had a design in it by Henry Gruber, and because Henry combines a great mathematical brain with his artistic ability, I hope that he will always be kind enough to let me include his best plans in my books throughout the years to come, for besides being plans of fast weatherly hulls they are a great joy to look upon and study. This is not surprising when we think that Henry has helped to design successful defenders for the *America's* Cup, and many successful ocean racers, as well as good wholesome cruisers. Germany is indeed fortunate in having such a man within her borders, for after designing a great many years in America Henry has returned once more to his native land.

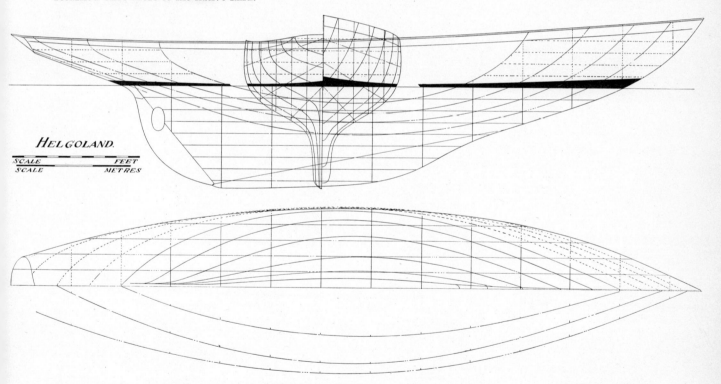

HELGOLAND.

SCALE — FEET
SCALE — METRES

The lines of *Helgoland* show a wonderful combination of speed, seaworthiness and comfort, for, though designed as a cruiser, she is of the fast type encouraged by the ocean and long distance races, which are growing in popularity year by year. For a vessel to win these long races she must be seaworthy as well as fast, and also fairly comfortable to live on board, otherwise her crew are unable to drive her at all times. The comfort of the crew is very important, for generally in small vessels such as this it is the human element which gives out first, and as the strength of a chain is in its weakest link, the human element must be studied all the while. It is for this reason that many years ago I said that the best ocean racer is the best cruiser, for while we might drive a fast uncomfortable hull round a short 200 mile course, once the distance gets over a thousand miles, comfort on board with the ability to carry food and water becomes of primary importance. When speaking of ocean races, I do not mean the short races such as our Channel race of 200 miles, which is often spoken of as an ocean race, though it does not take the vessels off soundings at all.

Every line in *Helgoland* tells of the designer's consideration for all of the above facts, and future years may see *Helgoland* winning a transatlantic race just as her predecessor, the *Roland von Bremen*, from the same designer's board, did last year, for *Helgoland* is undoubtedly based upon the knowledge gained from the *Roland* and her victorious race across the Atlantic in 1936.

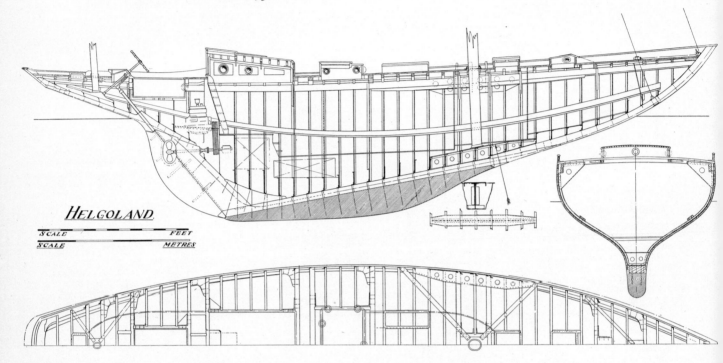

HELGOLAND.

SCALE   FEET

SCALE   METRES

The construction plan shows that in *Helgoland* we have a composite hull, the frames being steel angles and the planking of wood, and as is usual with such a construction the floors and mast step are also of steel. In *Helgoland* there should be no fear of leaking at the mast step, for it will be seen that this is a substantial girder some 9 feet in length, and immediately above the step will be seen strong steel plates of the same length giving the same girder effect to the topsides, as most vessels tend to strain and lift their topsides at the mast where the pull of the shrouds is very heavy.

Another point of interest is that the forestay runs through the deck to the stem just above the water-line, thus taking all the strain off the deck; while aft we see that the mizen step is utilized as a bearing for the steering wheel spindle, and the bevelled gearing, working on the quadrant, is the stronger and better for this bearing at the mast step.

In the deck plan we see a diagonal steel strap at the forestay, two diagonals on the mainmast, and between them the girder-like deck stringer to take the strains abreast the mast sideways as well as up and down, and two more diagonals back at the mizen.

These and many other details show great appreciation for strains and stresses set up at sea, and in *Helgoland* we have a strong workmanlike hull that can be driven without fear of her opening up through any weakness in constructional details.

The accommodation plan shows that immediately abaft the fo'c'sle she has a double stateroom with a washroom at its after end. From here we go into the main cabin, which is a very cosy place, and I have often wondered that we do not make such cosy little places in our houses ashore, for this cabin, like many others, breathes a feeling of contentment and rest. One sits all the way round as there is no room to stand or walk about, so one must sit and relax, and the U-shaped settee round the table is very soothing, for everyone on it is sharing the same seat and such an arrangement gives a spirit of friendliness to the cabin which is often lacking in houses on shore.

On the starboard side there is an ordinary sofa with a wardrobe forward, and a wine locker aft. Behind the cosy seats on either side is a sleeping berth, hidden and out of the way in the day, and yet ready for instant use, in fact as long as he did not snore a man could be asleep in this and no one know he was there, as the drawing shown of the port and starboard side will illustrate.

The port side drawing shows the U-shaped settee, and beyond it with the curtains drawn is the sleeping berth. On the left is seen the china cupboard closed, while on the right the locker door is also shut. This sleeping arrangement I have met on board the Norwegian pilot cutters where it proves most useful, as a pilot can come aboard, turn into his bunk behind the curtains, and be out of sight and mind at once.

Another drawing shows the starboard side, and here we see the full length wardrobe at the left hand of the bunk, while at the right hand or after end of the cabin will be seen the wine locker with a bottle, two glasses and a box of

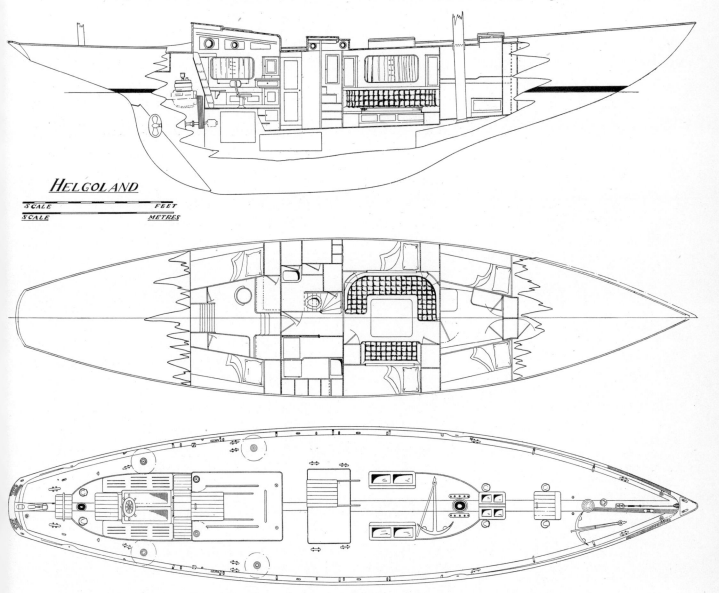

cigarettes all to hand ready for use. Such drawings as these give an idea of Henry's artistic ability, for he is able to visualise every detail of the vessels he designs and to convey this to the builders before any work is started at all.

Immediately abaft the saloon we have the pantry, stove, dresser and sink, in fact everything needed for the cooking, preparation and clearing up of meals. From the passage way there is a winding stairway, which forms a companion way to the deck, and so the smells of cooking easily find their way out of the ship, and the man cooking gets a good deal of fresh air down. This arrangement too keeps the cook in the middle of the ship, in the centre of the see-saw where there is the least motion and so he is able to cook in all weathers. All of us who have been to sea know how difficult it is to cook right forward when a vessel is being driven hard into a head sea, for not only are we left in mid-air as she crashes down into a sea, coming back to the floor with a dreadful jolt, but all out pots and pans jump about on the stove and cannot be controlled. So this arrangement, while it has the disadvantage of occupying the best part of the ship, is an arrangement which shows a thorough knowledge and understanding of the way of such a small ship at sea.

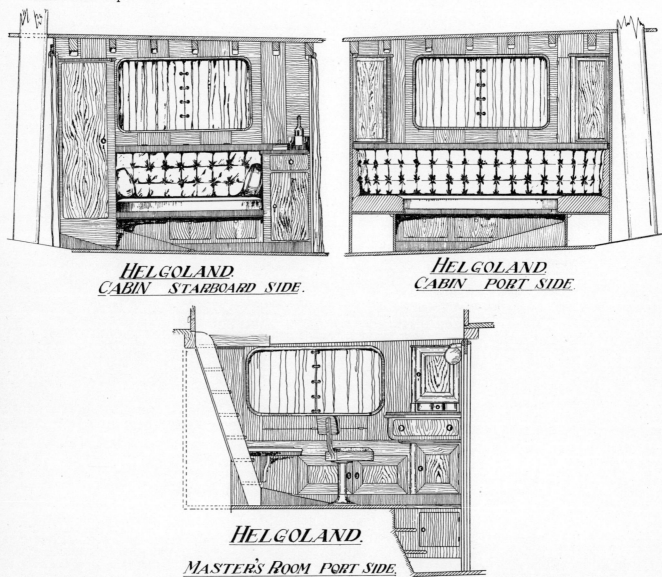

HELGOLAND.
CABIN STARBOARD SIDE.

HELGOLAND.
CABIN PORT SIDE.

HELGOLAND.
MASTER'S ROOM PORT SIDE.

Stowed away opposite under the companion way are oilskin lockers, linen lockers and a washroom, so that on coming below the crew can get rid of their oilskins and seaboots before entering the saloon, which for this reason can be kept dry and snug in the worst of weather instead of becoming as is usual a sloppy and dispiriting place.

Farther aft some steps lead up into the skipper's room, which has a berth in the wings either side. The master's room is also the navigator's room, for here the navigating officer does his work, and such an arrangement enables the skipper and the navigator to share a cabin and be in constant touch with the man at the wheel, for the steps on the after end of this cabin lead directly out over the bridge deck into the cockpit. To port is the navigating table with a swivel chair, and as will be seen from another excellent drawing the men in these berths can pull their curtains and be hidden away from the world until they wish to come back to life once more, so that a navigator can work at his table with the skipper turned in out of sight.

The watertight cockpit has the wheel at its after end, and the motor room is formed by the cockpit floor and the bridge deck and takes no room at all away from this ship, so we see that as in the construction the accommodation plan also makes for a ship that can be used at sea in all weathers with the greatest degree of ease and comfort.

The deck plan shows that cleats, winches, anchors and dinghies have all been considered and placed in the best possible positions, and the result is that the *Helgoland* has a clear and comfortable deck.

A yawl rig has been chosen to drive this ship. The twin headsails and the mizen all make for ease at sea, as various combinations of sails can be set, and finally with the staysail and a close reefed mainsail set *Helgoland*

HELGOLAND.

SCALE FEET

SCALE METRES

becomes a very snug cutter, and with these two last sails to be stowed her crew would stand little chance of being swept overboard, as in stowing them they are not very far from the centre of the boat.

The impression one gets from these plans is that they have been drawn by a man with a thorough knowledge of the sea and that the vessel can come straight from the builder's yard into the race capable of winning it, or she can sail straight from the builder's yard round the world, for these plans, without doubt, represent a very fine cruiser that would also make a good ocean racer, a vessel on which men can live in comfort for months on end. Seaworthiness, speed and comfort all combine to make her a perfect little ship.

· 5 ·

TROMP II

Length, overall -	55 ft. 7¼ in. = 16·95 m.		Length, water-line -	40 ft. 8¼ in. = 12·40 m.
Beam -	12 ft. 9½ in. = 3·90 m.		Draught - - -	5 ft. 9 in. = 1·75 m.
Displacement -	20·67 tons = 20,991 kilos.		Sail area - -	1,280 sq. ft. = 118·90 sq. m.

Owner, A. E. DUDOK VAN HEEL *Designer*, G. DE VRIES LENTSCH, SEN. *Builder*, G. DE VRIES LENTSCH, SEN.

WHEN lecturing in Amsterdam this winter, Dudok van Heel very kindly invited me to stay at his home, and so I saw Amsterdam and life in Holland at its very best, for Dudok, besides owning a lovely house and estate just outside the capital, is also as we all know a great yachtsman, owning and racing various craft to the International rules as well as being a keen cruising man. Holland with all its inland waterways is a nation with a great love for the sea, and it will be recalled that our pleasure craft or yachts come from that country, the word " yacht " being a Dutch word and the Dutch by presenting Charles II with his first yacht introduced yachting into England.

LEFT TO RIGHT: THE BUILDER, OWNER AND MYSELF UNDER STERN FRAMING OF TROMP II

TROMP II GLIDES ALONG

At lunch one day Dudok suggested I should visit the yard of G. de Vries Lentsch, Senior, to see his new boat being built. Having raced against him in many different craft I rather expected to see a racer, but though his six-metre was hauled out in this yard, the vessel I was to see was *Tromp II*, a steel cruiser that, as well as being comfortable, would have a fair turn of speed, would be capable of standing up to a gale in the open Atlantic, and yet have shallow draught so that she could sail in the Zuyder Zee and up to his estate on its shores. So as can be imagined this visit was full of interest, for a design to meet so many conflicting conditions was bound to be interesting.

The lines are those of a comfortable shallow draught cruiser with moderate overhangs fore and aft, the long centreboard continuing the keel line to make the long deep heeled craft so easily handled at sea. The buttocks, water-lines and diagonals all tell of an easily driven vessel, while the sections speak of one that is good in a sea way, for her bow will cleave into the sea without any fuss or bother whatever, and the counter being well V'd will not pound as so many do. The lines therefore are very pleasing to our eyes.

I imagine it is because Holland has very few trees suitable for shipbuilding that she has developed steel vessels faster than most countries, and as one would expect this cruiser is built of steel, and though a lover of wood I can admire steel craft for a great many reasons. They are not affected by the weather so much, their bilges are always free of water, and steel gives greater room inside, for the steel plating and the frames are much smaller dimensioned for the same strength as wood, and though *Tromp II* is of a size where steel comes heavier than wood (above 80 feet steel is lighter than wood, but below 80 feet wood is lighter than steel construction) she has these things to offset this disadvantage.

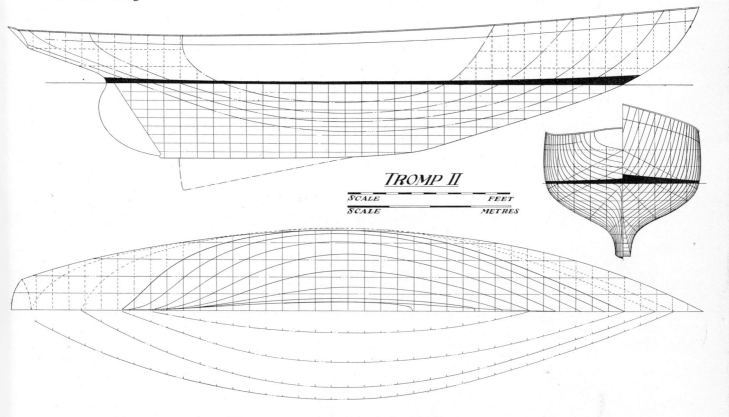

When studying her accommodation plan we must remember that Dudok is fortunate in having a large and healthy family, and as all of them love the sea he needs a great deal of sleeping accommodation for them, and so we see berths one above the other in three of the sleeping cabins.

There are two pipe cots forward, and a washroom separates the fo'c'sle from the galley, which is on the starboard side abreast the mainmast, while straight across the ship from the galley we have a small double berthed cabin. From here, as we go aft, we find two more sleeping cabins, each with one berth above the other, and abaft this we have the main cabin, which is very spacious and cosy. There is no outlet directly into the cockpit, but instead at the after end there is a U-shaped settee round a table, which is a very cosy arrangement. At the fore end of this main cabin will be seen two winding stairs leading out on to the deck to port and starboard, while the table in the fore half of the cabin is formed by the top of the engine room, and this accommodation tells us that *Tromp II* is first and foremost a family cruiser, one in which Dudok can cruise with all his merry men in perfect comfort.

The centreboard too tells us that she is not designed as an ocean racer, for though it would seem that a good bonus should be given for shallow draught with centreboards, our ocean racing rules have not gone into the problem that deeply yet. Without doubt such a boat as *Tromp II* with her shallow draught has much to recommend her and should be encouraged, yet nevertheless the rules have not yet thought of encouraging such a vessel.

Most of the prettiest havens left are those with a difficult shallow approach, and it is the difficulty of making such inlets and rivers that has kept them quiet and peaceful, but such a boat as *Tromp* can enjoy these havens, and it is well to remember this when looking at her centreboard.

The idea behind the centreboard is that it continues the keel line down to the deep heel, and it will be noted that even if the lifting gear carried away, the centreboard would not drop out through, as it has a notch on its top after end, which will engage on a similar one at the keel just forward of the rudder post, and as she came on the slipway to repair her hoisting gear, if ever it did carry away, the centreboard would go back into its case as the cradle was hauled out and *Tromp's* draught would be lessened inch by inch. With centreboards designers and owners must always prepare for the carrying away of their hoisting gear, as sooner or later this occurs, for we have to remember that the average yacht lives fifty or more years, which is a long time to go without any trouble. So in this drop keel we have one that does not interfere with the accommodation at all, as it is stowed below the floor,

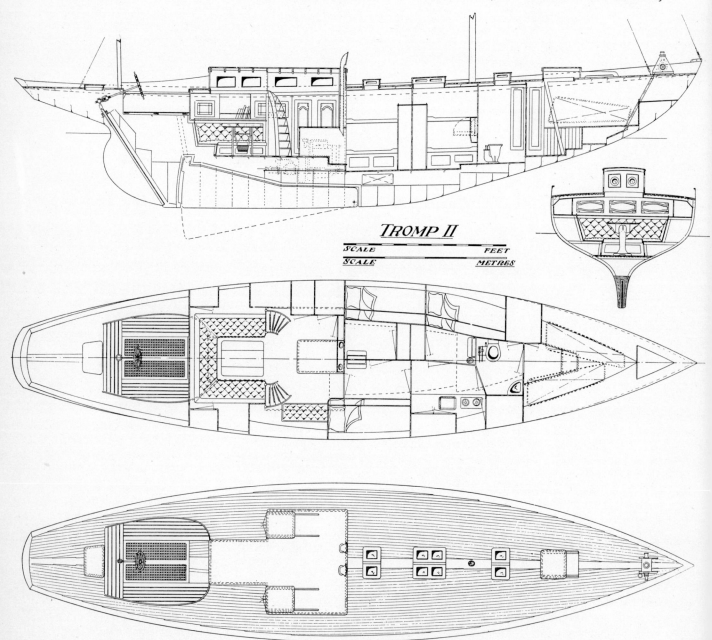

TROMP II

SCALE   FEET

SCALE   METRES

almost all of its case being formed by her ballast keel, and also one that will give little trouble, but which in the event of the hoisting gear parting, can be beached or put on a slipway and repaired without undue difficulty.

Abaft her main cabin *Tromp* has a very large but self bailing cockpit, and here again we get a picture of the chief with all his gang gathered around him enjoying the freedom of the seas.

In the past much has been written, and much will be written in the future about the best rig for sea work, all of which is a good thing, but at the moment almost every cruiser built has a yawl rig. This is largely due to the Ocean Racing rule under which the mizen with its mizen staysail is given free. Besides this there is no doubt that the rig is very efficient, as one really has a short boomed cutter with an additional tiny cutter rig put abaft it, and even America, a country which most of us thought would remain faithful to schooner rig for evermore, has adopted the yawl rig. No matter what country a design comes from in these days it is almost sure to have the British yawl rig. So it is not surprising that Dudok chose it, for he is a racing man, and though *Tromp II* was not built with ocean racing

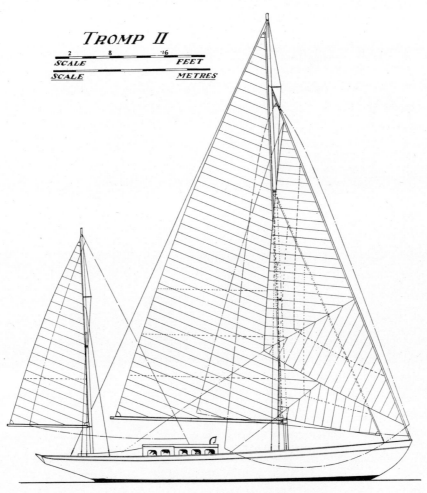

in view, nevertheless, at the back of Dudok's mind is the hope that one day she will enter into some of the long distance races, and then unless the rule has been altered his yawl rig will stand him in good stead as it is an efficient rig and the rule is very kind towards it. In this little craft we can easily picture Dudok and his family enjoying sailing inland water-ways as well as the open seas for many years to come, whether the wind be light or strong, and always at the back of her owner's mind will be the thought that one day he will enter long distance races with her and enjoy the fun of racing, for such a racing man cannot be expected to give up racing even though his heart is now given to such a comfortable cruiser.

· 6 ·

NOREINE

Length, overall - 55 ft. 1½ in. = 16·80 m.   Length, water-line - 37 ft. 5 in. = 11·40 m.
Beam - - 11 ft. 0 in. = 3·36 m.   Draught - - - 7 ft. 3 in. = 2·22 m.
Displacement - 15 tons = 15,225 kilos.   Sail area - - 1,130 sq. ft. = 105 sq. m.

Owner, R. G. PERRY   *Designer*, JOHAN ANKER   *Builder*, JOHAN ANKER

EARLY this summer, as I looked out of my office window over Cowes Harbour, I saw a lovely blue ship moored within a hundred yards of me, and in spite of the warm sunshine my thoughts travelled swiftly back to Oslo in

THE CROWN PRINCE
AND JOHAN ANKER

JESPERSEN'S BLACK COAT
IN STRONG CONTRAST TO
OSLO'S WINTER MANTLE

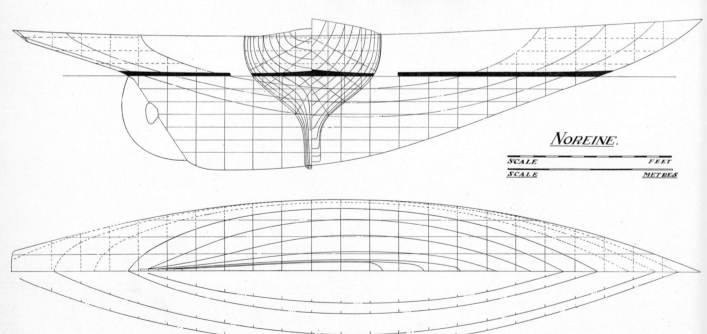

NOREINE.

| SCALE | FEET |
| SCALE | METRES |

the dead of winter with the thermometer 20 degrees below zero, snow ploughs at work, and the fjord, where it bordered Anker's Yard, covered with ice. For it was a winter's day when Johan Anker first showed me *Noreine*:

Prince Olaf, Engineer Oppegard, Yngvar Jespersen and I had called on Anker to view the Crown Prince's new six metre *Norna VI*, which was nearing completion, and also this lovely little cruiser. As I looked out of my window I felt, as I had when in Norway, a great deal of gratitude to these kindly Norwegians for speaking English throughout the days I spent amongst them. The picture of *Noreine* with her deck beams across and a great deal of her interior work completed came back to me, and I saw once more her lovely blue hull nearing completion on the slipway ready for launching. All who look at these sweeping graceful lines will understand why this cruising racer impressed herself so much upon me. Her stem and keel line are a delight, and the easy sweeping buttocks all tell us that *Noreine* is a fast hull, while her diagonals and easy water-lines confirm this.

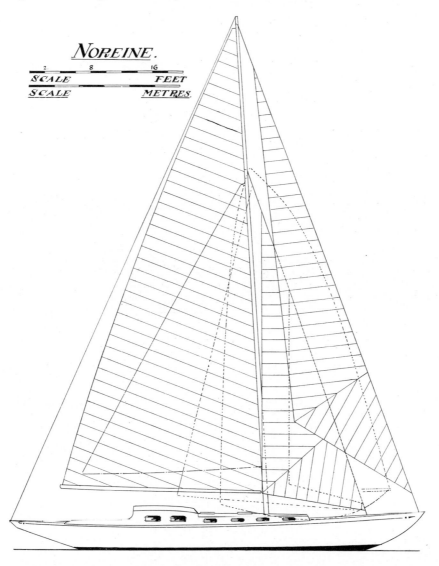

As we look at the lower water-lines we see a change in the shape, for these belong to the keel of *Noreine*, and so are practically true streamline in shape. We see that every line has been drawn with a perfect understanding, so it is no wonder that R. G. Perry, the owner, is delighted with his vessel.

Before commissioning Anker to design this little ship Perry searched the market trying to find something to suit him, but failed to do so, and then wisely ordered this vessel to suit his ideas.

To drive this sweet set of lines Johan Anker has designed a tall Bermudian cutter rig with the jib going to the mainmast head, and a staysail set inside and almost parallel with it reaching to a spot three-quarters of the way up the mast, the head of the trysail reaching to this same spot.

The mainsail has a luff just over twice as long as the foot, so though this rig is highly efficient it is yet moderate in its proportions, and therefore highly suited to the open sea, for while taller and narrower rigs are more efficient, it will still be a few years before they are ideal for sea work. The rig of *Noreine* has been carefully developed and is as near perfection as can be devised to drive such a hull.

When we look at *Noreine* the long clean looking sides of her cabin top take our eye, and when I saw these in the shipyard they looked as long as a wet day, and one wondered just how they would look when fitted on *Noreine*. But they improve her appearance enormously, for this long piece of bright varnished mahogany above her blue topsides gives her a very pleasing appearance and of course adds greatly to the accommodation and comfort below.

It will be seen that the mast is stepped down through this long cabin top and it has given no trouble whatever, for nowadays first-class builders with the materials at their disposal are able to build such a top so that it endures any side loads imparted to it from the mast.

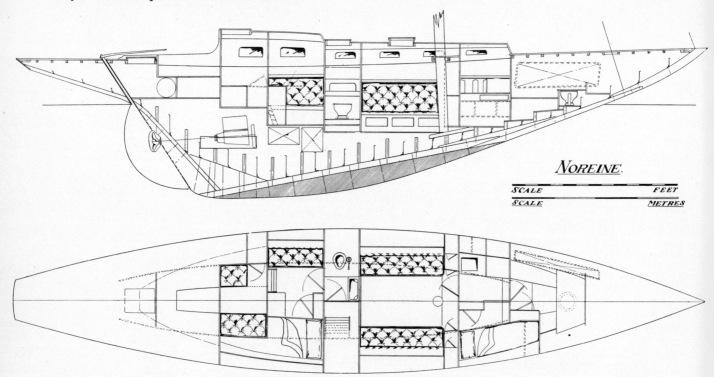

NOREINE.

SCALE   FEET
SCALE   METRES

Starting from forward we have a pipe cot, immediately abaft of which is a single cabin to starboard with the pantry and galley to port, the pantry leading immediately into the saloon abaft the mast. The long coach roof gives head room in the galley and pantry, and if only for this reason would be well worth while.

There are no sleeping berths arranged in the saloon, which tells us that the owner has all the accommodation he needs without turning the saloon into a sleeping cabin at night. From the saloon a companion way leads up on the starboard side to the deck and underneath this is a sail locker, while to port is the washroom. Immediately abaft this is the owner's cabin with his sleeping berth to starboard and a sofa to port, and this arrangement makes it a cosy, comfortable stateroom.

A short flight of three steps takes the owner from this into a small sitting room, situated immediately over the engine, from which one can enjoy everything that is happening on deck without being on deck, and from here it is one step into the cockpit.

As will be seen from the plans the engine is out of sight and mind until it is required and with its fuel tank at the after end of the cockpit it is arranged as safely and conveniently as it is possible aboard such small craft.

The backbone of *Noreine* formed by the stem, foregripe, keel, sternpost, sternknee and horn timber, all tell us that as well as being a designer, Anker is also a builder and able to appreciate the builder's difficulty in obtaining the main framing of any vessel. For though this backbone arrangement is wonderfully strong, and is as good as can be devised, it nevertheless shows great sympathy towards the builder, for every piece is as simple as possible. Where designers have had no experience in building we see construction plans without thought for those who have to obtain the timber and fashion it into the vessel designed.

Many years ago when all flying machines were made of wood and linen fabric, a friend of mine, who was successful at designing flying boats, told me he never considered the builders at all, he drew his machine and thought it was the builders' job to develop the wooden construction to suit his ideas.   As I was one of the gang building to his designs I saw the difficulty we had at times to do this, and had also talked to him about it.   This forcibly impressed

NOREINE'S LONG COACH ROOF BESIDES GIVING ROOM BELOW IS PLEASING TO THE EYE

upon me the lesson that designers should always keep before them the limitations imposed on them by the material and the workmanship available.   In these plans of Johan Anker we have the wisdom of this lesson before us, and if all designers had his understanding of building there would be less trouble in yachts in their old age, for every part of their construction would be simple and natural with no member straining against the rest of the ship.

· 7 ·

HERON II

Length, overall - 46 ft. 3 in. = 14·079 m.   Length, water-line - 35 ft. 0 in. = 10·693 m.
Beam   -   - 11 ft. 4 in. = 3·454 m.   Draught -   -   - 6 ft. 6 in. = 1·981 m.
Displacement - 12 tons = 12,192 kilos.   Sail area   -   - 1,041 sq. ft. = 96·70 sq. m.

Owner, STANLEY W. COOPER   *Designer*, FRED SHEPHERD   *Builder*, WOODNUTT & CO.

IN *Heron II* we see that, as usual, Fred Shepherd has produced a very roomy cruiser, for though only 35 feet water-line she has the accommodation and comfort of a much larger craft. When we look at the sections we see how this has been accomplished, for they show her very wide garboards which give great floor space and headroom, and at the same time make for an easily driven vessel as there is very little wetted surface to such sections. These sections naturally give steep buttock lines fore and aft, but these are wonderfully fair and the water-line and diagonals are very easy and sweet to the eye. As I have said before, Fred Shepherd always manages to put a quart into a pint pot, and almost all of his craft are big little ships. No one else, it seems, is quite as good at this as he is.

The construction plan shows that *Heron* is well and truly built, and a hundred years from now she may easily be sailing and giving pleasure to some owner.

The specification gives an idea of the excellent materials and workmanship which Woodnutts put into this little vessel, and her owner is justly proud of the lovely timber collected and built into his ship.

SPECIFICATION OF A 19 TONS T.M. AUXILIARY CUTTER FOR STANLEY W. COOPER, ESQ., OF ETTRICK LODGE, TOWER ROAD, BRANKSOME PARK, BOURNEMOUTH

To a design supplied by Fredk. Shepherd, M.I.N.A. of 199 Piccadilly, London, W. 1

PRINCIPAL DIMENSIONS

Length, overall -   -   - 46 ft. 3 in.   Length, water-line   -   - 35 ft. 1 in.
Beam, extreme -   -   - 11 ft. 4 in.   Draught -   -   -   - 6 ft. 6 in.

GENERALLY.—The layout and appearance of the yacht to be generally in accordance with the Drawings supplied by Architect as approved by Owner. To be insured by the Builders during construction against fire and usual building risks. To be measured for tonnage and Registration—fees paid by the Builders. Lloyd's fees to be paid by Owner.

HULL.—To be strongly constructed, the scantlings to be to Lloyd's requirements for a vessel of this class. All planking and timber to be carefully selected, well seasoned, reasonably free from knots, shakes and other defects. All fastenings to be copper or yellow metal. The boat to be built under a substantial shed, protected from sun and rain during construction. To be laid off and faired up as nearly as possible to the approved lines or sheer draught. The whole of the work to be sound, well finished and of the best quality. The Hull to be built with selected Burma teak planking on grown English oak frames, with one steamed American elm timber between. The stem, dead-woods, breasthooks, knees, etc. to be of English oak. Teak sternpost. Keel of English elm. Raised deck coamings, main companion, hatches and deck work of best Burma teak. All faying surfaces to be laid in genuine thick white lead paint. Scarphs to be of proper length, to be well fastened and finished off smoothly. The caulking of the outside and deck planking to be well executed. The best quality caulking cotton, oakum and marine glue to be used on each seam. Butts of outside and deck planking are not to be closer together than 5 feet unless there be a strake wrought between them, and then a distance of 4 feet will be allowed. No butts are to be on the same timber unless there be three strakes between. The butts of garboard strakes are to be kept clear of each other and of the keel scarphs. The planking to be in as long lengths as practicable.

SCANTLINGS.—All scantlings and materials to be in accordance with the approved Lloyd's Scantlings Midship Plan, and to be to the usual working plans supplied by the Owner's Architect.

WOOD KEEL.—Of English elm, 6 in. moulded.

TEAK STERNPOST. FRAME, STEM AND DEADWOODS.—Of best English oak.

FRAMES.—Of well grown seasoned English oak.

FLOORS AND HANGING KNEES.—Of galvanised wrought steel or plate floors at ends of yacht as indicated on construction plans.

DECK.—Of selected Burma teak laid in narrow widths, parallel to covering board to have bead run on under edges.

COACH ROOF SIDES.—Of selected Burma teak.

COACH ROOF DECK.—Of selected Burma teak in narrow widths to have bead run on under edge.

BEAMS.—Of selected English oak, extra strong beams of oak where shown. Lodging knees of English oak. All dovetailed and through fastened to shelf.

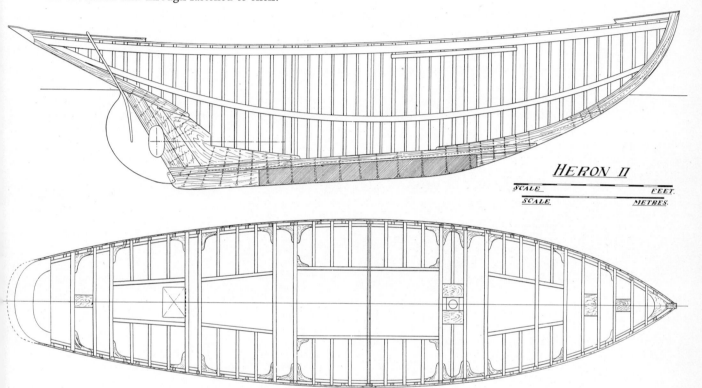

HERON II

PLANKING.—Of selected Burma teak $1\frac{1}{4}$ in. thick.

HATCHES AND MAIN COMPANION-HOUSE.—Of well selected Burma teak.

BULWARKS.—Of teak, with teak rail on top $2\frac{1}{4}$ in. $\times \frac{7}{8}$ in.

SHELF AND STRINGERS.—Of selected pitch pine.

CABIN SOLE.—Of 1 in. teak flooring supported on pine bearers.

WINDLASS.—To be a Thomas Reid & Sons galvanised marine winch of suitable pattern. Complete with all necessary fittings, chain pipe, etc.

KEEL.—To weigh $7\frac{1}{4}$ tons well fastened to main keel with $1\frac{1}{4}$ in. naval brass bolts. The inside ballast to be one ton lead cast in handy pigs of about 25 lb. to trim yacht to designed line.

PAINTING.—Topsides after fairing to receive three coats of paint and finished in white enamel. Gilt line to be worked in caveta and name and yacht club gilded on stern. Bottom to have two coats of Kobe priming and two coats of green antifouling composition. All deck work and spars to have four coats of best Copal Yacht varnish. Bilges to receive two coats of good red lead paint. Accommodation to receive, where painted, three coats and one of enamel, and where not painted internally, to receive two good coats of oil and varnish.

PUMPS AND PLUMBING.—One suitable copper chambered bilge pump (Tarbert pump 3 in. barrel) with spares and levers complete, to be fitted where shown on deck and to discharge below the L.W.L. with screw brass deck plate complete. A brass pantry pull pump (No. 455B manufactured by Messrs. Simpson Lawrence & Co., Glasgow) to be supplied, together with all the usual air pipes and piping of galvanised iron with lead branches to taps, etc. The bilge pump to draw from all compartments including engine room compartment, and provision made accordingly.

RUDDER.—Of teak-blade, to be fitted as shown on plan. Stock to be 1¾ in. forged bronze with the usual fittings, stuffing gland, etc. carefully fitted and all made watertight. Strong rudder band of hardened copper about 2 in. × ¾ in., and a properly fitted brass bearing at heel. Rudder head to be fitted with a suitable Edison Patent Oscillating steering gear, with teak box and teak wheel, to have the name of yacht engraved thereon, also that of the designer and builder. An emergency tiller of galvd. iron also to be fitted. Particular care to be taken in fitting and hanging rudder, to ensure perfectly free and easy working when afloat.

FRESH WATER TANKS.—Of galvd. steel of about 125 gallons. To have baffle plates and to be well cement washed inside before use with usual pipes, connections, as before described.

MAST AND SPARS.—The main mast and roller boom to be of hollow silver spruce complete with usual ironwork, metal tracks, cross trees, Woodnutt reefing gear, etc. The spinnaker boom, bowsprit and staysail boom of solid silver spruce. All in accordance with the sail plan.

CHAIN PLATES.—Of wrought steel to be fitted through covering board and well fastened to the grown oak frames.

RIGGING.—The rigging (wire) to be of best make, neatly fitted. The shrouds and backstays being of extra plough steel. The wire running gear of " best flexible steel rope " all according to rigging plan. The rope running gear to be of best make and quality of suitable sizes and complete with all sheets, tackles, etc. usual in a first class cruising yacht of this tonnage. Whole to be neatly fitted and finished.

BLOCKS.—The yacht to have a complete set of blocks, the wood blocks to be of well seasoned English ash with galvd. steel internal binding or strops. Steel pins and patent sheaves to principal blocks. The steel blocks where required to be of best material galvd. and all of good workmanship, pattern and fitting. All with good swallows for easy running.

SAILS.—To consist of a complete working set of best material and workmanship of Egyptian cotton by Ratsey & Lapthorn of Cowes, as follows :

 1 Bermudian mainsail of 15 in. cloths diagonal cut.
 1 Boom foresail with spring hanks.
 1 Balloon foresail.
 First jib of 12 in. Egyptian cotton.
 Second jib of 12 in. Egyptian cotton.
 Third jib of 12 in. Egyptian cotton.
 Trysail of 12 in. Egyptian cotton.
 Spinnaker of 12 in. Egyptian cotton.

 Also the usual and necessary sail bags, tiers, hanks, etc. Cover for mainsail dressed with Ratsey's flexible waterproof composition.

DECK FITTINGS.—To be complete in all details and according to deck and other plans. The companion deckhouse, raised deck, hatches, cockpit coamings, crews and sail hatches, to be of the best teak with suitable oval portlights to the cabin, raised deck hatches, fitted with necessary brass fittings and fastenings. All to open except the centre ones at saloon and aft cabin hatches. Other fittings to include 12 in. hand forged main sheet buffer, one pair of galvd. iron " Worth " collapsible davits, with sockets, falls, etc., complete. One suitable cathead to ship on either bow. Wrought steel ridge rope stanchions painted white with metal sockets, and white cotton ridge ropes, gangway stanchions with manropes of white cotton, meat safe. Teak folding accommodation ladder, fittings both sides, skylight rods and guards of chromium metal, gunmetal warping cleats on bows and taffrail of good size, steel bowsprit heel plate, steel runner hooks and sheaves, necessary deck lights. Teak permanent boom gallows, the necessary jib sheet leads, and all the usual eye bolts, cleats and pin rails. Also two gunmetal sheet winches, about 3½ in. high. Necessary ventilators as shown. Teak hand grips to tops of hatches where required. Stove deck plate. A small " clip on " portable seat about 14 in. × 9 in. to be made so as to clip on either side of cockpit coaming. Cockpit to contain the engine controls, to be lead lined with teak gratings and drained to sea with two drain pipes each fitted with " shut off " cock at ship's side. Provision to be made for stowing flares, pilot and danger signals, deep sea log and other necessary ships gear which may be required quickly.

ACCOMMODATION

To be laid out according to cabin plan and to include two of Blake & Sons " Victory " water closets. The main W.C. to be the model " Special Three " chromium plated with oval pan and usual fittings, fitted in the bathroom. The other W.C. to be a Blake " Baby " pattern of slightly smaller make fitted as shown, together with all necessary fittings, " shut off " cocks, etc.

BATHROOM.—This compartment to be well ventilated and to have a neat fold up wash basin at back of W.C. discharging into same. To be Simpson & Lawrence No. 2702 fitted with a chromium plated service pump. A tub bath of suitable size to be fitted at aft end of bathroom supplied with salt water tap discharging into sea. To be well fitted and connected with necessary "shut off" sea cocks. The whole compartment to be finished in white enamel.

SALOON.—To be fitted in polished oak, panelling and fittings. Sideboards to be fitted as shown on plan with corner cupboards, all according to plan. Sofa seats at each side to be well made and properly fitted with drawers

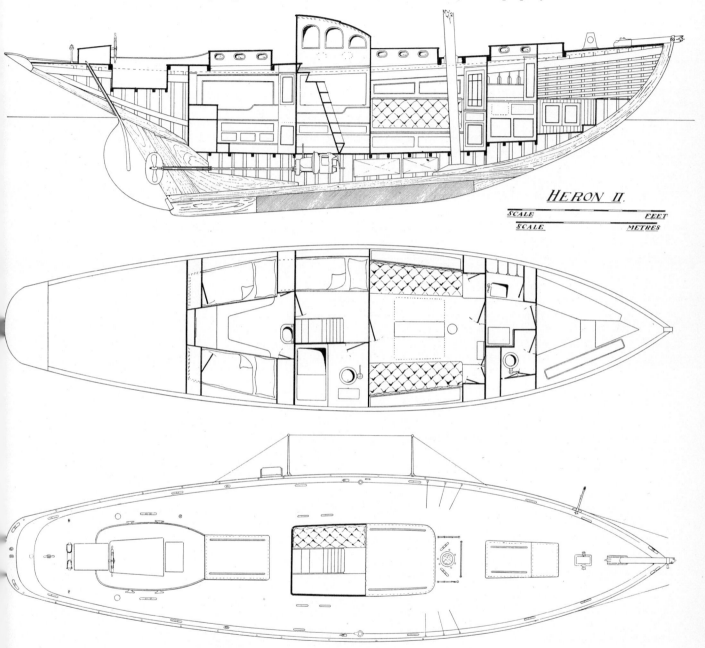

HERON II.

under and fold up Pullman berths at back. A polished oak swing table with lead ballast to be supplied and fitted. A neat Calor stove or other approved make to be fitted at fore bulkhead. The chimney leading up to the deck, through the linen cupboard. Vi-spring settees to sofas and Vi-spring mattresses to be fitted to fold up Pullman beds.

STEERAGE.—To be of polished oak panelling and bulkheads, with teak ladder and rubber treads to stairs. The port side to be fitted with a bed 6 ft. 2 in. long with recess for feet under the after cabin wardrobe. The back of bed to contain a fold up chart table all as shown on plan, and a recess under bed for portmanteaux. The bed to be fitted with a Vi-spring mattress, one bolster and one pillow. Remainder of bedding to be supplied by Owner.

C   F.R.C.D.

SLEEPING CABIN.—Bulkheads and sides to be fitted in polished oak panelling, and to have beds with drawers under as shown. Each bed to have one Marshall Patent Vi-spring mattress, one bolster and one pillow ; the remainder of bedding to be supplied by Owner. Dressing table with cupboard and mirror at back. Hanging cupboard at foot of beds, with full length wardrobes on starboard side, and wardrobe above recess, and cupboard below on port side. All locks, keys, catches, etc. in the cabin and saloon, etc., to be chromium, also all fittings to oval port lights, etc. A porcelain W.B. Simpson, Lawrence & Co. No. 287, size 2, to be fitted at fore bulkhead with service pump drawing from fresh water tanks, and mirror at back.

UPHOLSTERY.—The seats and sofas, with the usual squabs, backs and ends, to be upholstered in approved material chosen by Owner at a price not exceeding 12s. 6d. per yard. Brussels carpet to floors of saloon and cabin at an average price of 10s. 6d. per yard. Lino of approved pattern in W.C. and bathroom compartments.

PANTRY.—To be fitted with the usual teak top dresser and with an enamelled sink, and a good counter pull pump No. 455B Simpson & Lawrence, drawing from main tanks. Plate racks to be fitted at back and cupboards under dresser. At the fore bulkhead a " New Clyde " cooker No. 0, two ovens (Simpson & Lawrence) or other approved make to be fitted as shown. Woodwork behind cooker to be protected with asbestos and iron plate. Pantry to be finished in white enamel.

FORECASTLE.—To be teak battened, and to contain teak locker and seat on starboard side with fold up iron cot at back. On port side a teak bench to be fitted to take sails, etc. The top to form bed. Each cot and bed to have the usual mattress, bolster and pillow. One galvd. iron ladder about 12 in. wide. A chain locker to be fitted to contain chain cable and shelves fitted in bows for lamps, etc. A separate compartment fitted as shown to contain the crew's W.C. (Blakes " Baby ") and a fold up iron ring W.B. together with small mirror also to be fitted. The W.C. compartment to be finished in white enamel.

CABIN FLOOR.—To be of teak $\frac{7}{8}$ in. thick. A grating to be fitted at foot of main companion and all necessary hatches in floors to be teak framed and of ample size, to get at tanks, etc.

CABIN WORK GENERALLY.—To be of good class and character, the materials and workmanship to be of the best and no *iron* nails or sprigs are to be used anywhere. Decks above head in saloon and sleeping cabins to be well finished with proper mouldings and painted flat white. Glass mirrors where supplied to be bevelled, and a layer of felt placed at back to absorb moisture.

ELECTRIC LIGHT AND CABIN LAMPS.—No candle lamps are required anywhere—but the yacht is to be wired in suitable lead covered cable to take about 14 points placed in positions as indicated. The electric fittings and globes also to be supplied, together with set of Nife accumulators.

LOCKS, KEYS, ETC.—Metal work such as locks, taps, keys, etc., throughout the cabin accommodation of chromium plate and one patent key to fit all drawers, etc. in saloon. Spring catches to prevent cupboard doors from opening to be to approval. The door handles, plates, escutcheons, etc., to be of chromium metal.

NAVIGATION LAMPS.—Two copper sidelights and one galvd. riding light to be supplied as usual. The necessary screens for sidelights to be fitted.

ANCHORS AND CHAINS.—To be of Thomas & Nicholson pattern (or equivalent weight in C.Q.R. type anchor if required by Owner) and to consist of :

> 1st bow anchor 88 lb. with stock.
> 2nd bow anchor 75 lb. with stock.
> 1 kedge anchor.
> Chain cable 50 fathoms of $\frac{7}{16}$ in. stud link chain.
> Hemp hawser 45 fathoms of $2\frac{1}{2}$ in.
> Hemp warp 45 fathoms of 2 in.
> All to Lloyd's requirements.
> Also 1 light chain 25 fathoms cable of $\frac{5}{16}$ in. diameter for light mooring work.

BOAT.—A suitable spruce dinghy about 9 ft. 6 in. long finished in mahogany to be supplied complete with oars, gratings, brass rowlocks, rudder and tiller. Y.C. badges on bows and slings for hoisting. All complete for sea.

BINNACLE AND COMPASS.—Supplied by Owner.

MACHINERY.—A 12 H.P. Coventry Victor Diesel Motor with 3 to 1 reduction gear, complete with all electric equipment, electric starting gear, and batteries, etc. Together with stern tube, shafting, $22\frac{1}{2}$ in. diameter, 2 blade propeller, engine controls to cockpit, generating set, switchboard, and 35 gallon fuel tank, all complete and ready to run. Copper trays to be fitted under motor and fuel tank to prevent oil getting into bilges. Exhaust to be carried aft and the water outlet to be taken out well above water level or a trap must be made. It must not be possible for water to get into the engine. All to be supplied and carefully fitted by Builders to approval. A few iron bars to form an emergency ladder to be fitted to the bulkhead.

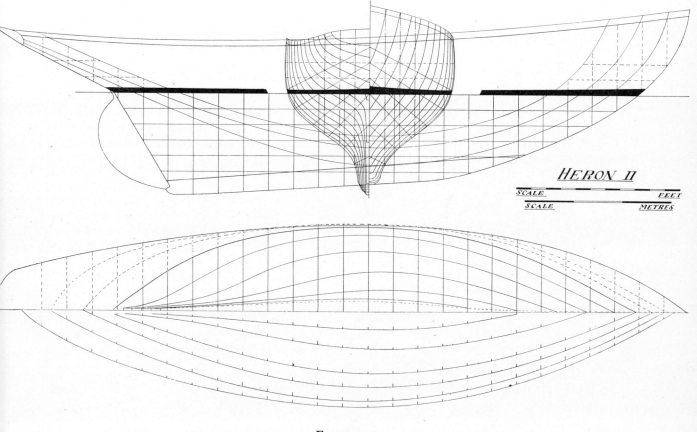

HERON II

SCALE   FEET
SCALE   METRES

EQUIPMENT

Navigation lamps, comprising port and starboard, masthead and riding light for oil.

1 Verticle teak folding gangway ladder.

2 Gangway fenders.

2 Lifebuoys with yacht's name and yacht club.

1 Canvas bucket.

1 Galvd. iron bucket.

1 Mop.

1 Squeegee.

1 Deck scrubber.

1 Marline spike.

1 Hand lead and line.

1 Fog horn.

1 Long boat hook for mooring.

2 Rubber mats with yacht's name.

Deck boat chocks for boat.

Side light boards port and starboard.

1 Bell.

1 Small vice to be supplied.

1 Boatswain's chair.

1 Ensign staff.

GENERALLY.—The vessel to be built and finished to the satisfaction of the Owner and his Representative, and in accordance with this Specification, plans and detailed drawings furnished by his Architect. The whole of the materials and workmanship for the vessel, and her equipment and outfit to be to approval.

The accommodation plan is at first startling until we look back once more at her sections to see how all this room has been obtained.   First of all we have a roomy fo'c'sle with a small washroom to starboard, abreast of which, partitioned and isolated from the rest of the ship, is the galley, which leads immediately into the main cabin, and here one is struck by the wide floor space and the comfortable seats either side of the table, above which are the owner's books.   And as he is fortunate enough to have a wife who cruises with him, this saloon has a cosiness about it which is lacking in ships where a woman's hand is never seen, for without doubt their kindly touches in such things as curtains and cushions enable us awkward males to go through life with a feeling of restful contentment.

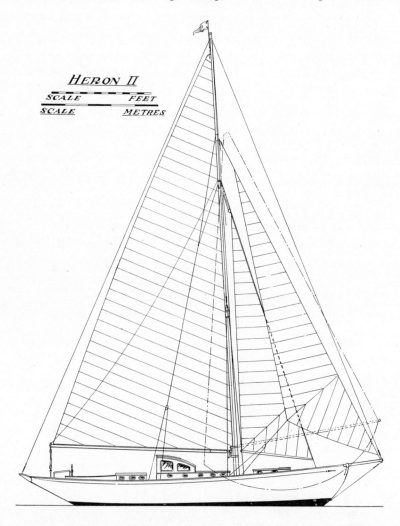

HERON II
SCALE   FEET
SCALE   METRES

Abaft this is the companion way to the deck and to starboard is the bathroom with W.C. and washbasin as well as the bath, while to port is a single berthed cabin.   Further aft is a double berthed cabin for the owner and his wife, and as there is no companion way to the cockpit this is the most private part (as it should be) of the ship.

Next aft we have the cockpit and the steering wheel, and so we see that *Heron II* is designed as a comfortable cosy cruiser for a man and his wife with a single cabin for their daughter or a stray guest.

With all these virtues it is difficult to conceive a more suitable craft than *Heron II* for this job, for as well as having this accommodation she has quite a good turn of speed, as her cutter rig, while being easily handled, is very efficient, and *Heron II* as one would imagine sails very well indeed.   When she has arrived at the haven where she would be her owner has all the comforts of home with a few more added, for he is able to choose the site for his home in whatever harbour or part of the world he wishes, knowing full well that once he arrives he can enjoy a peaceful home there for just as long as he cares to stay.

This summer the owner's son took her for a cruise and if we read between the lines, this rough log tells us what a comfortable and weatherly cruiser *Heron II* is.

"YACHT *HERON II*

July 11th-July 24th from Brixham, Salcombe, Yealm River, L'Abervrach, Brest, Morlaix, Lézardrieux, Guernsey, Poole ; about 480 miles

Sunday, July 11. Left Brixham at 7.00 a.m. Light S. breeze outside. Breeze increasing and visibility deteriorating during morning. Hove to in Start Bay, inside Skerries, for lunch, and to shorten canvas for a beat round the Start on a weather-going tide. Since conditions were not good enough to go across Channel, visibility becoming bad, we put into Salcombe. We were there until Tuesday midday, as on Monday there was a fresh wind and much fog.

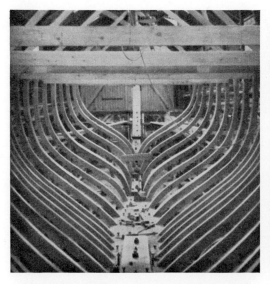

AS WELL AS SHOWING THE FINE TIMBERS BUILT INTO HERON II

THESE PICTURES TELL US HOW FASCINATING IT IS TO BUILD A SHIP OF OUR OWN

HER TRANSOM

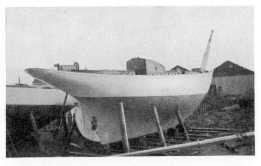

ALMOST READY TO LAUNCH

On Tuesday, July 13 we left in the fog with little wind for a change of scenery, steered for Mewstone Rock to E. of Plymouth and found our way into Yealm River. The leading marks, not mentioned in the Books, make this now an easy entrance.

Wednesday, July 14, with a forecast of " Light S.-S.E. wind, visibility becoming good " we streamed the log with the Eddystone Lighthouse on our starboard beam, and set a course of S.S.W. for Isle de Vierge Light. [We would then have to make a very big error to miss Ushant altogether, and sail into the Bay of Biscay!] At 10.00 p.m. we had covered 60 miles. 10.45, wind whipped round from S.E. where it had been all day, to W. × S. and so we proceeded on our course on the starboard tack. 11.00 p.m., ran into fog, which continued until 8.00 a.m. the next morning. Being in the lane of shipping coming up from the Bay of Biscay we had steamers fairly near us. The wind at times fell away completely.

7.00 a.m., July 15. Wind increasing from N.W. and having estimated out position altered course to S.W. and then at 7.54 to S. At 8.03 picked up Isle de Vierge Lighthouse, looking very weird in the fog. Dropped the hook in L'Abervrach, after heaving to for breakfast and rolls (in the mainsail). Found the pilotage most interesting, with rocks close on either hand. Distance 125 miles.

Friday, July 16. Fine day with little wind, had to be through the Chenal du Four by 5.30 p.m. to avoid head tide, to do which had to shove engine on. After passing Pt. St. Mathieu had delightful sail into Brest, where we anchored at 10.00 p.m. Distance about 40 miles.

Saturday, July 17. Sailed around the Rade de Brest in bright sun, and ran 8 miles with spinnaker set to River de Chateaulin, where we spent night.

Sunday, July 18. Got away at 9.30 to catch tide at 7.30 p.m. up Chenal du Four. Sunny, hot day, light wind. Reached Chenal du Four early and beat against last of ebb in company of French fishing boats. [This is where you can work twelve hours' tide like at Land's End if coming down Channel and going up Bristol Channel.] Wind dropped away and fog came on and at 8.05 on Monday morning we started engine after slatting about in what was for us a big swell coming in from the Atlantic. Visibility was poor, but at 3.00 p.m. we picked up the Isle de Bas light-house, and just fixed our position by a 4 pt. bearing before a thick blanket of fog blotted it out. It cleared in time for us to get into Morlaix all right, where we anchored at 6.00 p.m. Distance 90 miles.

Tuesday, July 20. We decided to have a night sail to Lézardrieux, so we got away at 3.00 p.m. in a light breeze, which unfortunately fell away, so we had to motor through the channel between Les Sept Isles and the mainland, the lights proving simple to understand. We finished up with a nice sail up to Lézardrieux (we anchored just below, to N. of Perdrix Pt.). 50 miles.

Wednesday, July 21. Again we had a night sail as we did not want to get away too soon, nor too late, and weighed anchor at 8.00 p.m. Once outside we took some rolls in and sailed away for Guernsey with W. wind. We soon picked up Les Hanois, and passed Roches Douvres to starboard, as there was a weather-going tide, which I preferred should push us clear of them. For easy steering to avoid gybes, we pointed for Les Hanois and then wore the ship round into the starboard gybe until in the white sector of St. Martin, where we went on to port gybe. At 5.30 we dropped the hook in St. Peter Port and went to sleep until about 11.00. So we still had the best part of the day there. 50 miles.

It was blowing hard all the Friday, but on

Saturday, July 24, we had a magnificent sail to Poole. Getting away at 7.00 a.m. we got hooched through the Little Russel, by the spring tides, up to the Casquets, having to point as high as we could with the wind N.W. to avoid being put down on them. About 9.30 bore away and steered N.E. × N. for Anvil Pt. Big foresail set, big jib and doing 7 knots without shirts on. Picked up Portland Bill and Anvil Pt. at about 3.35 and got our moorings at Branksea Island at 9.00 p.m. 75 miles in 14 hours in perfect warmth and comfort was very pleasant.

Crew.—Owner's son and three friends and a Brixham skipper, who had not been to that part of the French coast at all.

Last year, 1936. Scillies and back from Poole—12 days.

J. H. COOPER. 9.8.37."

Tucked away below the floor level is a small Coventry Victor Cub, and this engine, being placed so low, tells of the space under the floor, and also how compact and easily installed this engine is. The controls and starting button are all up in the cockpit, and throughout this summer the owner has only had to press the button in the cockpit for the engine to burst into life and drive *Heron II* along at 4 knots. But though the engine is so easy to start and uses little fuel the owner sails most of the time, calling, however, upon his little iron topsail whenever it is needed. Because of the cheapness of fuel oil combined with the ease with which *Heron II* sails, his fuel bill for the whole of 1937 came to only 11s. 10d.

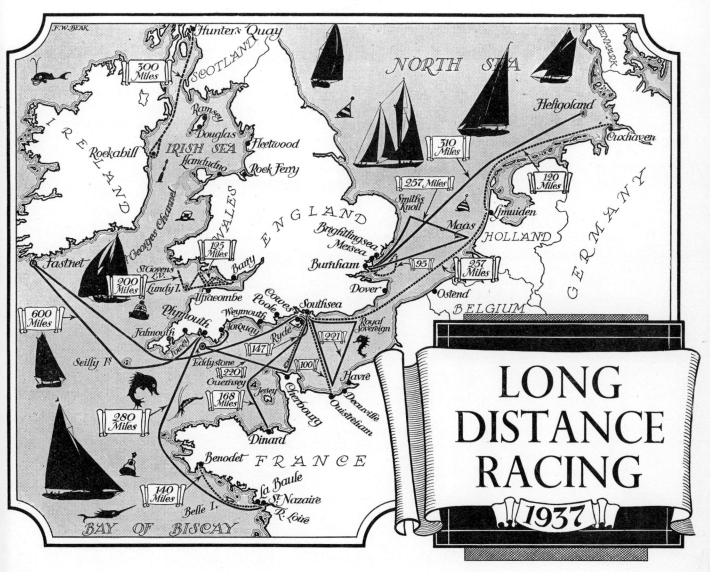

ORTAC

Length, overall	-	49 ft. 0 in. = 14·90 m.	Length, water-line	-	35 ft. 0 in. = 10·66 m.
Beam	- -	11 ft. 1 in. = 3·38 m.	Draught	- -	7 ft. 6 in. = 2·29 m.
Displacement	-	14 tons = 14·224 kilos.	Sail Area	- -	940 sq. ft. = 87·30 sq. m.

Owner, COLONEL C. F. KING   *Designer*, ROBERT CLARK   *Builder*, MORGAN GILES

WHEN we look at *Ortac's* lines it is difficult to think that she is only the second boat designed by Robert Clark, his earlier boat being the cruiser *Mystery*, 26 ft. on the water-line.

Ortac is 35 ft. on the water-line, as this is the magic length for Royal Ocean Racing Club events. This length water-line enables an owner to race in either the larger or the smaller of their classes, and so gives him choice of either the Channel or the Fastnet race. There is no doubt the Royal Ocean Racing Club were wise in making a link between

39

the two classes, this link being a boat able to enter either class, for it meant that there would be many built to the length, so forming a really keen racing class, with all the attributes of, we will say, an 8-Metre class, combined with weatherliness enough to go round the Fastnet Rock, and the comfort to be found aboard such a sized vessel. So it is not surprising that many of the ocean racers built this year were to this length, *Ortac* being one of the most interesting of them.

The lines show a very easily driven yet powerful hull, and the more one looks at these lines and studies them the more one admires them.

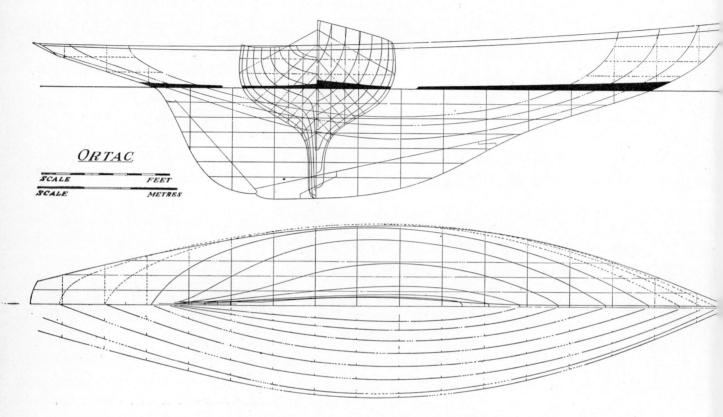

ORTAC.

SCALE ———— FEET

SCALE ———— METRES

The construction plan tells us that she has 45 per cent. of her total displacement in her lead keel, and this is, I think, the best proportion one could have. The mast, being well inboard, comes down on top of the fore end of the lead, so the lead keel is actually helping to take some of the downward thrust of the mainmast.

As well as her lead keel and mast being well amidships, it will be noticed that her water tanks (under the cabin floor) are also amidships. Thus with all her heavy weights in the middle *Ortac* is able to lift her bow and stern to the seas, which should make for safe and fairly dry decks.

With our present-day knowledge of construction it seems a pity that the cabin top did not run past the mast, and so keep full headroom at this point, for while everywhere else she has 6 ft. under beams, in way of the mast she has only 4 ft. 10 in. So while her present arrangement is undoubtedly a strong and comforting one to her owner on a dark night at sea, for he knows that any side thrust of the mast is being taken directly to the powerful mast clamp fitted inside the shelf, there will be many days on which, after they have bumped their heads, his guests will wish the cabin top had been continued past the mast. A designer is continually balancing strength and comfort in his construction plan, and only the owner can decide which he shall do.

Her accommodation plan shows that she has four berths in the main saloon. This has proved very successful, and, as can be imagined, makes for comfort and tidiness below.

The galley, though forward, is very convenient, for *Ortac* has such an easy motion that though an arrangement is made for cooking aft, it was not called into use in the Heligoland Race, even when she was logging 7 knots on the wind. So the after galley has been abolished and an additional large drawer fitted in its place.

The large forehatch enables spinnakers and headsails to be passed up and down comfortably, and, as will be seen from the deck plan, *Ortac* has been carefully thought out for ocean racing, winches and spinnaker booms, as well as the dinghy, all being placed exactly right for work at sea.

Ortac is a Bermudian cutter, and her mainmast is stepped well into her—so far, indeed, that the base of the fore-triangle and the length of the mainsail on the boom are almost the same, and with her mast so far aft she should have no trouble from this in a seaway, for it is back where she is well able to carry it.

Her stemhead jib goes to the top of the mainmast, 55 ft. above the deck, while the staysail halyard is 41 ft. above the deck, the luff of the two sails being almost parallel and $4\frac{1}{2}$ ft. apart, a space which enables the jib to work over the forestay fairly comfortably.

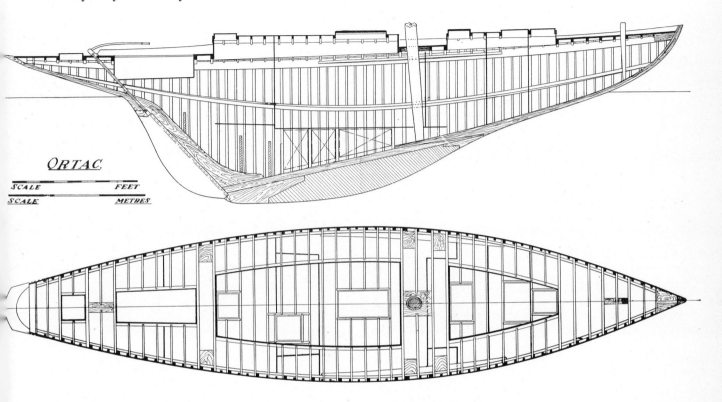

ORTAC.

SCALE   FEET
SCALE   METRES

The sail plan shows she has a combination of sails to meet every kind of weather from calm to a gale, and it is not surprising that this little vessel won the Heligoland, her maiden race, without any tuning-up, in spite of the fact that such well-known ocean racers (built to the rule) as *Latifa, Trenchemer, Roland von Bremen* and *Hamburg* were ranged against her. Col. King is to be congratulated on the success of his venture, and his courage in going to a new designer has been well rewarded.

HELIGOLAND RACE

Because of the narrowness of the River Crouch, the Committee wisely started the fleet in three groups, at ten minute intervals. *Ortac* started in the last and smallest batch in an enjoyable breeze, which allowed them to lay out through the Whittaker Channel on the starboard tack.

Ortac's crew consisted of Colonel King, owner, skipper and navigator, J. B. Kirkpatrick, F. B. R. Brown, Mates, and J. Christmas, Robert Clark (designer), E. G. Moore, J. W. Ridsdale, A. H. Paul and H. T. S. Clouston. By the time they had reached the Sunk *Ortac* was close aboard *Ilex, Sentra* and *Bamba*, who had started in the middle class some ten minutes earlier. Here the wind was very light and easterly. During the night the wind increased and backed so that by early morning it was north east which meant a dead beat to windward, and so *Ortac* was tacked at every change of watch, making seven knots through the water, $4\frac{1}{2}$ points off the wind. Though there was a fair sea she took no heavy water aboard at all, but as can be imagined at that speed there was a continuous shower of spray thrown over her, and as they had the misfortune to break the armour plate glass of the galley skylight when demonstrating its unbreakability to some friends before the start it was as well that no heavy water came aboard ; this meant that the cook had to work in oilskins and a sou'wester, but even so he produced first class meals.

The wind here was so strong that *Zeearend* and *Roland* had two reefs in their mainsails, but *Ortac* carried on with full sail and was fairly comfortable, in fact she seemed to those aboard far more comfortable than the *Joice*, who had carried away her topmast. The motion in the forward galley was so little and so little different from that aft, where the auxiliary galley for use in a seaway was situated, that it was decided there and then to abolish the after galley.

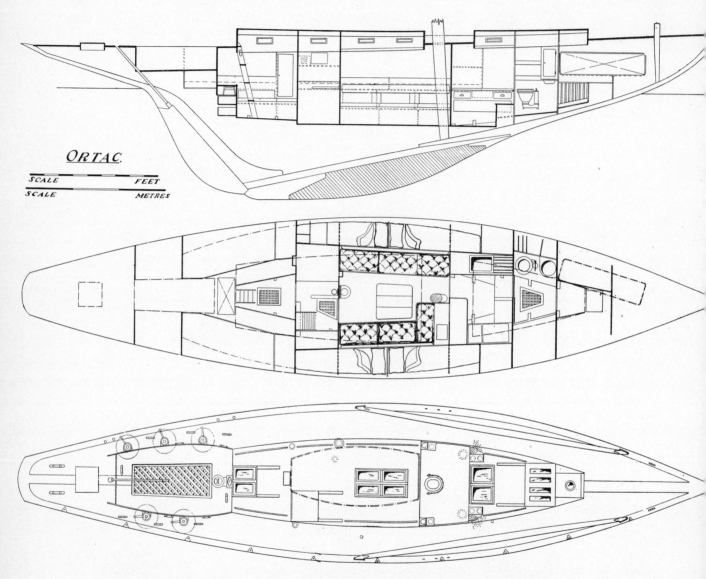

ORTAC.

SCALE ———————— FEET

SCALE ———————— METRES

Round her bow *Ortac* has rails some three feet high in the form of a pulpit continuing and connecting the port and starboard lifelines, and this was a great comfort in changing headsails, for it was possible to jamb one's self between these and the topmast stay and stow and set sails in comfort. At 21.30 with the wind and sea having further increased *Ortac* had the *Haaks Lightship* abeam, and tacking to the north sighted the Terschelling light just before dawn. By 8 o'clock on Sunday morning she was able to bear away for Heligoland.

The wind was still fresh, but it moderated and backed throughout the day. *Roland von Bremen* was sighted on the port quarter during the morning, and these two kept in close company. *Ortac* set her genoa before noon, and as the wind came farther aft in the afternoon the spinnaker was run out and so she was kept at 7 knots. Although the *Roland* was drawing ahead of her very slowly the owner and designer were, as can be imagined, very pleased at *Ortac's* performance.

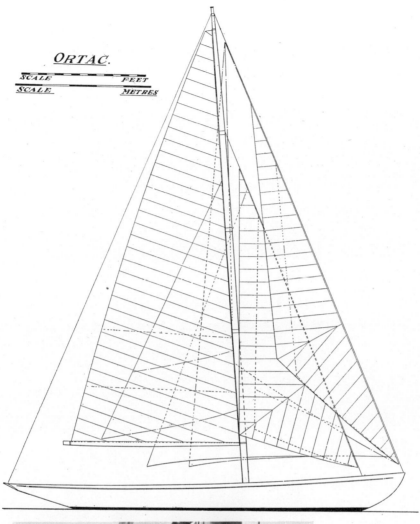

ORTAC.

SCALE ——————— FEET
SCALE ——————— METRES

ORTAC'S VENTILATORS HOUSE HER
PORT AND STARBOARD LIGHTS

ORTAC'S FOREDECK SHOWING THE PULPIT

ORTAC (140), THE WINNER, IN CLOSE COMPANY WITH PELIKAN

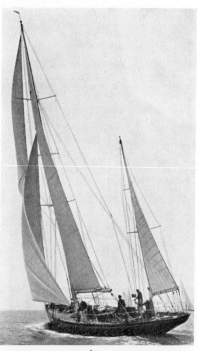

MR. W. D. M. BELL'S BERMUDIAN YAWL,
TRENCHEMER, WAS PLACED THIRD

Visibility in the Heligoland Bight was poor, but the fog signal was heard at 20.00 and soon after the high land was seen, and after a gybe and a short reach *Roland* and *Ortac* crossed the line close together, *Ortac* being only 58 seconds behind *Roland von Bremen*, at 22.15 o'clock. One can imagine the cheerful surprise *Ortac's* crew had

ELLA AND ILEX LEADING THE WISHBONE KETCH SENTA AT THE START

when, making the harbour, they discovered that only *Asta, Latifa, Trenchemer* and *Roland* had finished ahead of them :

		ELAPSED TIME		CORRECTED TIME	
		H.	M.	H.	M.
1.	*Ortac* - - - -	55	48	43	2
2.	*Roland von Bremen* - -	55	47	46	51
3.	*Trenchemer* - - - -	53	45	47	47
4.	*Latifa* - - - -	53	38	49	21
5.	*Zeearend* - - - -	61	19	50	10
6.	*Ilex* - - - - -	66	9	52	15
7.	*Rose* - - - - -	59	12	53	30
8.	*Asta* - - - - -	52	7	56	25
9.	*Larry* - - - - -	76	56	58	11
10.	*Tai-Mo-Shan* - - -	80	16	60	51
11.	*Joyce* - - - - -	62	53	61	17
12.	*Senta* - - - - -	76	50	62	32
13.	*Hamburg* - - - -	76	48	63	37
14.	*Pelikan* - - - - -	76	25	63	9
15.	*Ibis* - - - - -	77	24	64	28
16.	*Banba* - - - - -	76	54	66	8
17.	*Dyarchy* - - - - -	—	—	—	—

Cruiser Class : *Rose, Asta, Larry, Tai-Mo-Shan, Joyce, Banba.*

Retired : *Aralus, Boekanier, Ella, Saladin, Marianna, White Heather, des Wagner von B, der Goldene Lowe, Iseuet.*

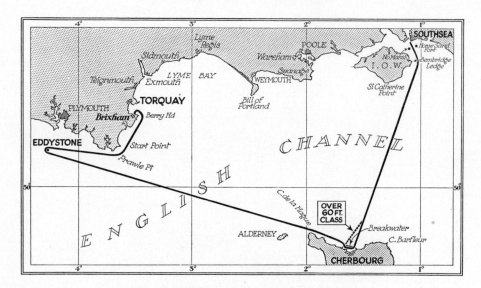

MAID OF MALHAM

Length, overall -	- 48 ft.	= 14·63 m.	Length, water-line -	35 ft. 0 in. = 10·688 m.
Beam - -	- 10 ft. 6 in. =	3·20 m.	Draught - -	- 7 ft. 6 in. = 2·286 m.
Displacement -	- 13·50 tons =	13·716 kilos.	Sail Area - -	- 992 sq. ft. = 92·15 sq. m.

Royal Ocean Racing Club Rating - 35·74 *ft.*

Owners, LT.-COMMDR. ILLINGWORTH AND NORMAN JONES   *Designer*, LAURENT GILES
Builder, KING & SON

WITH *Maid of Malham* we come to the Coronation Race, her maiden race, which she won. Her lines are those of a fast cruiser. In the buttocks we see the designer has gone for a long clean run which starts forward of midships, and as all the racing craft I have designed and built have had this feature, and have been most successful because of it, this pleases my eye, as I am one of those who believe that the longer and cleaner the run the higher the maximum speed of any hull.

These long clean buttock lines (their fore ends are called the bow lines) give a flat angle to the run of the transom, which it will be seen has been sawn off. This at first gives the *Maid* an ugly expression, but like most other things we shall in time get used to it, and in looking at this transom we must remember several things :

First of all, one of her owners, Lt.-Commdr. Illingworth, is a Navy man, and has grown used to the sterns of destroyers, which are chopped off square immediately they can be to save weight and the sea from clinging to them, and as destroyers are to our battle fleet, ocean racers are to our cruising fleet. Secondly, though it would look prettier very little good would come of extending the counter, for its weight would counteract the good of the longer length given to the buttock lines. Thirdly, the *Maid's* designer, Laurent Giles, is not bound by traditions of any sort and rather takes a joy in shocking our ideas of what is right. Such sterns have been used in America on ocean racers and the cheaper one-designs, in France on the 6·50 metres, and in this country in days gone by, but, nevertheless, every time we see it it strikes us hard and anew, perhaps because it tells us that the vessel is designed with certain objects in view, all else being cast to one side.

Her sections, water-lines and diagonals are easy and sweet, but it is to her buttocks that my eye keeps going back with delight. When I first saw her, *Maid of Malham* was moored, and she looked no longer than 26 ft. or 27 ft. on the water-line. Though this is partly due to her black hull (black always makes things seem smaller, girls wear dark shoes and light stockings to give the effect of tiny feet), most of it is due to a well proportioned hull, and this fact brought home to me that the chopped off stern was not as ugly as I pretended it was.

Her construction is of wood with steel floors and straps where they are needed, and from the plan we can pick out any constructional detail we are interested in.

The lay of the deck shown in the plan is unusual, as forward it is parallel with the centre line; from midships aft we see it is following the line of the covering board.

The cabin top, it will be noticed, stops abaft the mast and starts again forward of it, and though this is a very strong and well proved feature years will, I think, see the mast coming through the cabin top (as shown in the Anker

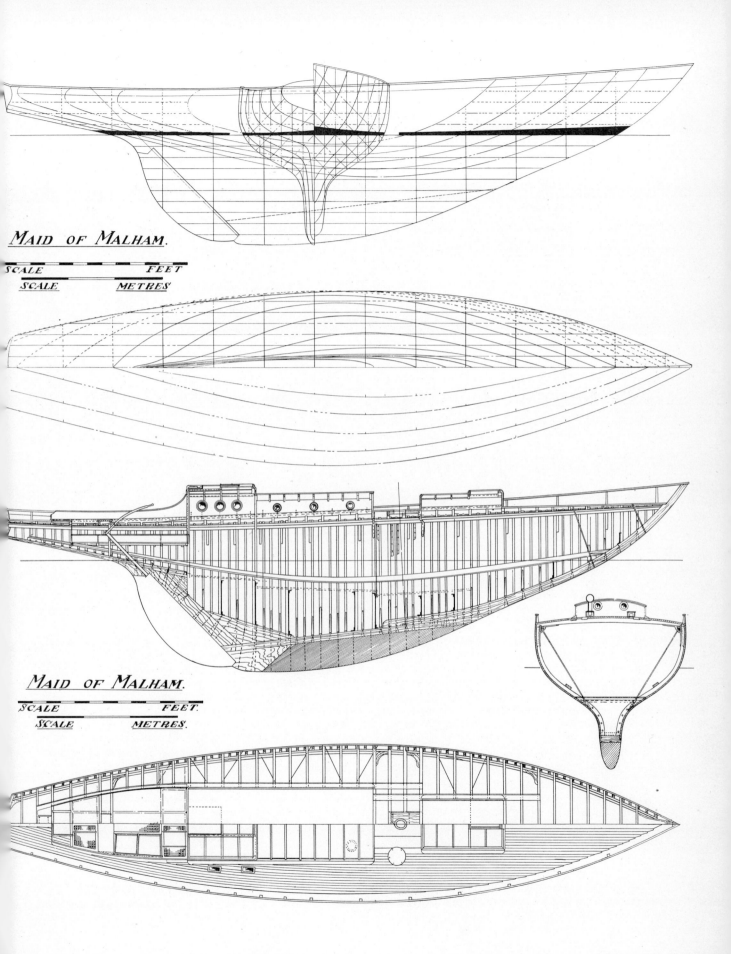

MAID OF MALHAM.

SCALE   FEET

SCALE   METRES

MAID OF MALHAM.

SCALE   FEET.

SCALE   METRES.

designed *Noreine* earlier in this book), this method being used greatly in America, Norway and Sweden. But we Britishers are noted for our conservatism and old fashioned ideas, and things must be proved over and over again before we adopt them ; and the fact must be borne in mind that strength is of the utmost importance to an ocean racer such as the *Maid*, for to win her races she has to be driven to the utmost all the while, which means that

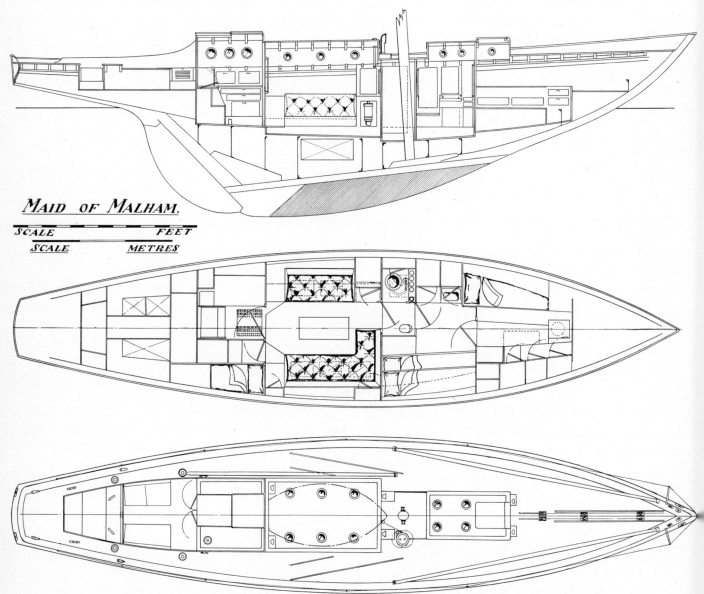

MAID OF MALHAM.

SCALE   FEET
SCALE   METRES

heavy strains have to be endured by her throughout her racing career, and on the midship section will be seen stays from the shelf down to the steel floors to spread some of the strains over as much of the hull as possible.

Her accommodation plan shows she has a fo'c'sle with a built in berth for one. Immediately abaft this is the double-berthed cabin to starboard, and though in the plan there seems little room here, actually on board it is quite comfortable, for the upper berth is a root bunk. To port of this is the washroom, immediately abaft is the saloon with an L-shaped bunk to starboard and an ordinary settee to port, so designed that her entire crew of eight can sit down at once to a meal.

Abaft the saloon to port is the navigating room, with a sliding chart table, and over to starboard is an oilskin locker and a small cabin with a one recess bunk. Then comes the double cockpit, the helmsman having a small single cockpit, while the crew working sheets and backstays can have a cockpit all to themselves, so that the helmsman is free from all turmoil, and able to keep his mind on sailing the *Maid* at her very best.

There are two quarter cots under the cockpit sides, and so we see that the *Maid* can sleep nine all told, three in the saloon as there is a root cot above the port settee, and as her normal racing crew is eight she has one spare berth when in port, whereas many yachts that take part in these races have to house some of their crew ashore when in harbour.

The *Maid's* sail plan shows that her mast is well aft ; had it been another 2 ft. 6 in. farther aft, it would have been exactly midway along her water-line, and one would have wondered then whether to have called her a single masted schooner or a cutter.

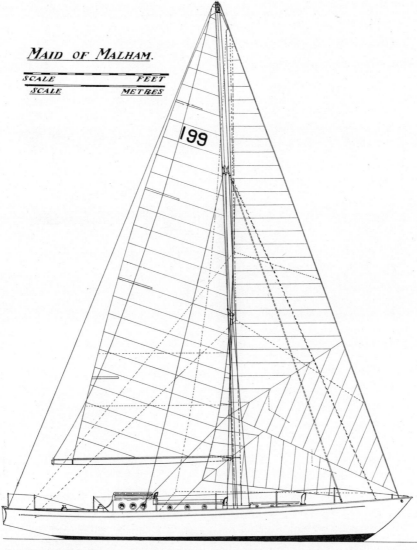

MAID OF MALHAM.

SCALE ——————— FEET
SCALE ——————— METRES

199

The mast so far aft makes the base of her fore triangle exactly the same length as the base of her mainsail, which means that she has more area in her headsails then in her mainsail. Without doubt such a rig makes for a seaworthy vessel, as the mast being so far aft enables her to carry it with very little effort ; it is also in a more beamy part of the vessel where the shrouds can have a better spread, but above all it gives a wonderful combination of headsails so that the mainsail need seldom be reefed, for, as will be gathered from the plan by changing headsails the *Maid* can easily reduce her canvas by this means alone.

It will be seen that the jibstay runs to the top of the mainmast, and she is able to carry this long-luffed headsail because the mast is fairly short. It will be noticed that three different jibs are shown on this one stay to suit various wind conditions. Her forestay has two positions, these being dotted in on the plan, and as these are twin stays hove down by Highfield levers they can be changed in a few seconds.

We will suppose the port stay is going to be taken into the forward position ; then the port Highfield lever is slacked up, and the port stay unhooked and taken forward to the forward leg of the lever and hooked on again, and the lever being hove down the port stay is set in the forward position, and the starboard stay can follow suit in a few seconds.   In light weather, when her large genoa is set from the topmast head to the stemhead, both of these forestays are let go and taken into the mast and the *Maid* becomes a single headsail cutter.   These and many other devices tell one that the designers, owners and builders have all striven hard to produce the perfect small racing cruiser, for new winches have been made specially for her, the topmast backstay leading over the sheave at the end of her short counter registers the tension on it all the while.   Everywhere a great deal of thought has been given to

THE MAID ON A WIND

every detail, as one would expect, for both Laurent Giles and Lt.-Commdr. Illingworth are members of the Royal Ocean Racing Club Committee.   Her rating is very small indeed, for throughout her design the rule has been very carefully studied, so much so that when she is dead before the wind her mainsail is stowed and two fine great spin-nakers are set, and as can be imagined such a rig only pays when the length of the spinnaker boom is equal to that of the main boom, for all the time the main boom is longer the mainsail will have more area in it than the spinnaker. Though these twin spinnakers are such an expense that they have never been allowed in international class racing, nevertheless, they have the great advantage that there is no gybing and no chafe to any gear, for they fly out forward of the mast and stays, so that the chafe always experienced in a fore and aft vessel when running is non existent with such a rig.   The disadvantage to this flying of two spinnakers is the fact that they are held at three points only, the deck, clew and head, and thus put a great deal of strain on the mast in a breeze of wind.   Though at first sight it would seem there would be a great struggle to get them in, directly the mainsail is hoisted one of them is blanketed behind it and can be taken in, then, if the vessel is run by the lee slightly, the other is also blanketed by the mainsail and blown clear of all stays and will come down as quiet as a lamb.   So with all the thought and care devoted to her it is not surprising that the *Maid* has had a most successful 1937 season.

THE CORONATION RACE

With 51 entries this race proved the most popular of the whole series held for the 1937 Season. The idea at the back of it was to take all the racing cruisers down to Torbay for the Coronation Regatta there.

ORTAC'S SPINNAKER LIFTS HER ALONG

SAIL NO.	YACHT	CRUISER	RATING	OWNER	RIG
			CLASS I		
—	*Elk* - - -	Cruiser	—	Alan Mackay - - - - - -	Gaff schooner
—	*Sumerun* - -	Cruiser	—	F. W. Shenstone - - - - -	Gaff yawl
211	*Cynara* - -	Cruiser	63·50	Marquis of Northampton - - -	Gaff ketch
193	*Cachalot* - -	Cruiser	51·43	Lt.-Col. C. Beddington - - - -	Gaff ketch

SAIL NO.	YACHT	CRUISER	RATING	OWNER	RIG

CLASS II

SAIL NO.	YACHT	CRUISER	RATING	OWNER	RIG
33	Iyruna	—	53·28	Dr. N. F. Adeney	Bm. cutter
121	Latifa	—	51·87	Michael H. Mason	Bm. cutter
22	Firebird	—	51·64	Ralph Hawkes	Bm. cutter
132	Rose	Cruiser	49·51	Royal Artillery Y.C.	Gaff yawl
177	Trenchemer	—	48·78	W. D. M. Bell	Bm. yawl
151	Aralus	Cruiser	46·61	E. Gore Lloyd	Bm. yawl
202	Adria	Cruiser	—	W. J. Chinneck	Bm. schooner
14	Seaward	—	—	M. Atkinson Adam	Bm. schooner
210	Fairwind	Cruiser	45·76	L. A. Hart	Gaff yawl
101	Bloodhound	—	44·37	Isaac Bell	Bm. yawl
111	Ella	Cruiser	44·05	W. R. S. Bond	Wishbone sch.
144	Banba	Cruiser	—	A. Rosling	Gaff cutter
126	Foxhound	—	43·40	The Comte de Gasquet-James	Bm. cutter
7	Varuna	Cruiser	41·16	R. R. C. Vernon	Bm. cutter
92	Rosemary	—	38·45	S. S. Taylor	Bm. cutter
200	Waterwich	—	—	D. Curtis	—
31	Zoraida	Cruiser	35·22	Capt. Franklin Ratsey, R.N.	Gaff cutter
124	Yeoman	—	34·83	O. A. Aisher	Bm. ketch
168	Windstar	—	—	Lt.-Col. P. D. Ionides	Bm. cutter
216	Primrose	Cruiser	—	Dr. Neville Bradley	Bm. schooner
140	Ortac	—	32·62	C. F. King, D.S.O., M.C.	Bm. cutter
199	Maid of Malham	—	—	Lt.-Comdr. J. H. Illingworth and Norman Jones	Bm. cutter
209	Quest III	Cruiser	—	J. Allan Herrow	Bm. ketch
146	Tai-Mo-Shan	Cruiser	31·26	The Admiralty	Bm. ketch
196	Dolly Varden	—	30·93	T. C. Ratsey	Bm. cutter
150	MacNab	—	28·88	J. J. Joass	Bm. cutter
208	Farewell	Cruiser	26·64	Capt. W. R. West	Gaff cutter

CLASS III

SAIL NO.	YACHT	CRUISER	RATING	OWNER	RIG
162	Spica	—	39·98	Mrs. A. M. and Mr. J. T. Hunt	Gaff cutter
125	Glance	Cruiser	35·68	F. A. Haworth	Bm. cutter
172	Armyne	—	35·00	Henry Trefusis	Bm. sloop
176	Marianna	Cruiser	32·03	Major Ralph Blewitt	Bm. sloop
184	Aline IV	Cruiser	30·84	G. Kimber	Gaff cutter
25	Oenone	—	30·72	E. G. Wardrop	Bm. cutter
173	Viola	—	29·07	A. R. Lapthorn	Bm. cutter
180	Lady Maud	Cruiser	27·82	A. G. Wilson and H. C. Devitt	Bm. cutter
160	Keryl	Cruiser	25·72	Miss M. E. Wiles	Bm. cutter
109	Driac	Cruiser	25·43	M. Hackforth Jones	Bm. cutter
171	Little Windflower	Cruiser	—	C. S. Blundell	Gaff cutter
221	Saïda	—	—	Capt. J. H. Elwes	Gaff cutter
189	Craignair	Cruiser	—	Drs. Girling and W. Snell	Gaff ketch
185	Brambling	—	23·33	G. D. Lock	Bm. cutter
194	White Heather	Cruiser	23·30	J. H. N. Wrohan	Gaff cutter
167	Alethea II	Cruiser	20·98	R. Radcliffe	Gaff cutter
217	Black Duck	Cruiser	—	P. H. Gordon Clark	Gaff cutter
84	Cameo II	Cruiser	—	E. G. Friend	Bm. sloop
212	Wanda	Cruiser	19·62	Capt. B. G. A. Scott	Gaff cutter
152	Alethea III	Cruiser	18·81	J. G. H. Cockburn	Bm. ketch
163	Dozmare	Cruiser	18·55	G. C. Barrow and L. L. Chatwin	Gaff yawl

As can be imagined the start on Friday, June 18 at 5.00 p.m. from Southsea beach was worth going miles to see, and one realises that to win this 220 mile race from 50 starters calls for a great deal of knowledge of the sea on the part of the crew as well as a good vessel. By winning this race the *Maid of Malham* showed that not only was she well designed and built, but also that her owners, now that it was their turn, were doing their part, for a vessel has to be well designed, then well built and then well sailed in order to prove herself to be a good ship, and the failing in any of these three spoils her in the eyes of a seaman.

In the first stage of the race the boats were close hauled to Cherbourg in a fairly smart breeze, but after a while the wind came freer and finally over the quarter, so this part of the race was enjoyed by all. But off Cherbourg the wind was light and the tide foul, so where vessels had been travelling at a high speed they now slowed down. This light sailing calls for different qualities, and the ability to slide along with little wind was now needed, for the wind continued very light between Cherbourg and the Eddystone. *Bloodhound*, *Latifa* and *Ella* were the first at the Eddystone, but *Maid of Malham* was close astern. They finished at Torquay in this order, and when the times had been worked out it was found that *Maid of Malham* was first, with *Bloodhound* second and the old *Dolly Varden* third, *Ortac* being fourth. Though *Maid of Malham's* success shows that she is a racer that will have to be reckoned with always, we should also bear in mind the fact that *Dolly Varden's* third is a great achievement, for being built 70 years ago, to no rule at all, it is amazing that she can win a prize amongst so many modern vessels.

As our thoughts wander from her designer to her builder and then to her owner we suddenly face the fact that the Royal Ocean Racing Club rule, which is framed to measure boats fairly, is far better than most of us realise, because it rates the things that make for speed so well that such an old ship is still able to win. So this race brought all the racing cruisers to Torquay.

		FINISH		CORRECTED	
		H.	M.	H.	M.
CLASS I					
Cachalot - - - - -		23	46	49	44
Cynara - - - - -		21	16	52	06
Sumurun - - - - -		21	58	61	25
CLASS II					
Maid of Malham - - -		20	41	39	20
Bloodhound - - - -		15	18	39	53
Dolly Varden - - -		22	05	39	57
Ortac - - - -		21	55	40	36
Ella - - - - -		17	38	41	40
Foxhound - - - -		18	27	42	15
Latifa - - - - -		16	02	43	03
Rosemary - - - - -		21	54	43	19

MacNab, Yeoman, Banba, Trenchemer, Aralus, Tai-Mo-Shan, Fairwind, Iyruna, Adria, Firebird, Zoraida, Rose, Seaward.

Cruiser Class : (Winner) *Ella,* (2nd) *Banba,* (3rd) *Aralus,* (4th) *Tai-Mo-Shan, Fairwind, Adria, Zoraida, Rose.*

		FINISH		CORRECTED	
		H.	M.	H.	M.
CLASS III					
Brambling - - - - -		23	40	37	00
Viola - - - - -		22	13	39	08
Wanda - - - - -				41	57
Keryl - - - -				42	16
Driac - - - -				42	59
Spica - - - - -		21	25	43	33

Armyne, Lady Maud, Marianna, Oenone, Aline IV, Glance.

Cruiser Class : (Winner) *Wanda,* (2nd) *Keryl,* (3rd) *Driac,* (4th) *Lady Maud.*

COWES-DINARD RACE

3.00 p.m., Friday, July 16, saw the start of this race under a blue sky, in bright sunshine and with a brisk nor'-west wind, and as it was not yet high water the racers took a fair tide away with them on the course round the Bembridge end of the Island to Dinard, near St. Malo. *Larry, Red Gauntlet, Beatrice* and *Skoiern* did not start.

Though the conditions were ideal for sailing, the breeze was strong enough to make *Karin* put a reef in her mainsail, which, however, she shook out after the five-minute gun had gone.

With such a large interesting fleet it was difficult to follow the thoughts and manœuvres of them all, but at the ten-minute gun *Ortac*, who decided not to set any headsails at all as it was a run, was reaching up and down the line under her mainsail only while her crew got her spinnaker ready to set to port.

THE START OF THE CORONATION RACE

Aile Noire, the new French Fastnet possible, looked full of life and energy as she reached up and down, tacked and gybed in her efforts to get the best start, and one was struck with three things aboard this boat : she had very fine winches for setting up and slacking her backstays. The man on deck knelt between the two and ground them in or eased them off as she tacked.

The other noticeable things about her (besides her speed) were her main and mizen booms. These were merely skeletons, designed to give an airfoil shape to the foot of the sail, and they looked rather like a long stream-lined pair of snow-shoes.

At the five-minute gun *Maid of Malham* decided it was going to be a run so she took in her genoa, set a small jib topsail and started getting her spinnakers ready. This sudden change and its excitement would be far too much for a peaceful chap like me, though it seemed to be a lot of fun for those on board.

Rose, with her topsail being set, made a lovely picture, and there is no doubt these old-timers are still very pleasing to our eyes.

Tai-Mo-Shan, the Navy's entry, which was sailed home by Naval officers from Shanghai, seemed to need more wind to liven her up in contrast to *Aile Noire*, who was still dashing about full of energy. *Foxhound* made a very fine sight as she reached in towards the Squadron and then tacked out to go along the line on the starboard tack just before gunfire, but though she was fairly close to the line, for it must be remembered that all had a strong flood trying to push them over, *Wanda* was actually first away with *Maid of Malham* and *Ortac* in close attendance either side. Then came *Foxhound* and *Keryl* and the rest in a bunch close astern. *Driac*, who had been luffed to the wrong side of a buoy, was 8 minutes late.

Ortac was the first to set her spinnaker, but *Maid of Malham* was not far behind with hers, and these two soon took the lead.

Now, though aboard *Foxhound* no preparation had been made to set the spinnaker, she kept well up with the *Maid* and *Ortac* owing to her superior speed and though it was not until the Old Castle Point Buoy was reached that she set her spinnaker she was still abreast of the *Maid* and *Ortac*.

At this point the *Maid* luffed out to the northward, set a second spinnaker and dowsed her mainsail for the run down through the Forts. Watching this being set I wondered if there was something not quite consistent in the Ocean Racing Club rules, for these rules, in order to keep the cost down, say that " No headsail may exceed one and a third times the base of the fore triangle ", when it would be far better if they were one and a half, as the American rule, or twice the base, as the International Six-Metre rule. By allowing two spinnakers to be set there is no doubt the Ocean Racing Club are opening up a great field to be exploited, for even the International racers do not permit such extravagance, and there is no knowing where these double spinnakers and the numbers carried will stop.

All the racers carried their mainsails to starboard except *Karin* and *Rose*, while *Maid of Malham* had no mainsail set at all. So this fleet sailed away out of the Solent, making a lovely picture, the white sails standing up well against the blue sky while the two tanned sail boats, *Foxhound* and *Aile Noire*, helped to complete a colourful picture.

THE MAID'S WOMANLY CURVES   WHEN THE FORETRIANGLE BASE EQUALS THE LENGTH OF THE MAIN BOOM IT PAYS TO TAKE IN THE MAINSAIL AND SET TWIN SPINNAKERS

After seeing this fleet off we put a crew of four aboard the French 8-metre *France*, which had come over, and in three straight races had easily defeated and outsailed our own 8-metre *Felma*, for she, too, was bound out through Bembridge across Channel. Her port was Havre, and as we towed this crew of unconcerned Frenchmen with their bottles of wine out clear of the harbour one could not help thinking that had the Y.R.A. rules been all that was hoped of them there would have been no room for the Ocean Racing Club's rule. The Y.R.A. boats would have been such fine ocean racers that there would have been no room or need for the Ocean Racing rule at all, for this 8-metre looked a lovely little cruiser, and one knew and felt she would arrive at the haven where she would be. The only preparation her crew deemed necessary being the supply of wine and food and the removal of collars and ties before setting sails.

So future years will, I think, see the Ocean Racing Club learning from its older sister, the Y.R.A., many things, and the Y.R.A. itself also learning a great deal from the Royal Ocean Racing Club rule and its activity, and one greatly hopes that these two clubs will work together in harmony and peace throughout the years to come.

DINARD RACE

This race was sailed fast, and *Maid of Malham* finishing ahead of all the fleet won fairly comfortably.

When clear of the Island it was a beat to windward against a fresh breeze and the usual Channel chop, then the wind dying away the racers had to sail against a dying wind and sea. Finally the wind coming north they had a run into St. Malo with the lightest of breezes. The *Maid* with her double spinnakers up made an interesting sight as she ran down through Spithead, and this helped her to such an extent that she had lost very little to *Foxhound*, who led through the Forts, while *Aile Noire*, the interesting French racer, showed her speed on the reach to Bembridge Ledge, where she passed *Ortac* and nearly caught the *Maid*.

Rounding Bembridge Ledge the breeze was strong enough to give an exciting test of weatherliness amongst the fleet, and *Foxhound* here went away to windward, outpointing and outfooting the rest, while *Maid of Malham* and

Ortac kept close company till dark, going at a great speed for their size in such a seaway. With the darkness came less wind, as it is so often does, but it was now south west, and the different vessels enveloped in darkness were lost to each other, and as usual the night sorted out the various ships. Rounding the Caskets the *Maid* led, with *Foxhound* second, while *Ortac* had fallen astern. However, with daylight *Foxhound*, who was now able to see what she was doing, went ahead, but the wind dying and then coming in very gently from the north west did not seem to be to her liking, and *Maid of Malham* once more took the lead and held it to the end, and so won her second long distance race, which was similar to the Coronation Race, in that almost every condition of wind and sea, from a fresh breeze to a calm, was experienced.

RESULTS

YACHT				OWNER					ARRIVAL TIMES SUNDAY		CORRECTED TIMES	
									H.	M.	H.	M.
Large Class												
Maid of Malham	-	-	-	Lt.-Comdr. J. H. Illingworth and Norman Jones					0	53	25	55
Foxhound	-	-	-	The Comte de Casquet-James	-	-	-	-	1	20	29	29
Ortac	-	-	-	C. F. King, D.S.O., M.C.	-	-	-	-	6	2	29	58
Aile Noire	-	-	-	M. G. Baldenweck	-	-	-	-	9	3	34	59
Rose	-	-	-	Royal Artillery Y.C.	-	-	-	-	18	36	46	37
Small Class												
Laita	-	-	-	M. Georges Reviere	-	-	-	-	20	17	39	19

Retired : *Pelleas II, Tai-Mo-Shan, Karin III, Nyse, Keryl, Driac* and *Les Gemeaux.*

ROYAL THAMES YACHT CLUB'S MORGAN CUP RACE

This proved yet another success for the *Maid*. Though there were as many as 16 starters in this race from Ryde round Cherbourg breakwater and back, *Dolly Varden* and the *Maid* led the fleet out through the Forts, but later the larger vessels could not be denied and they came through into the lead.

The race was held in a good breeze which proved to be too much for the old *Dolly Varden*, for though she was holding up well with her more modern sisters like the *Maid* and *Rosemary*, the hard driving was too much for her, as the water came in faster than it could be pumped out, and so she reluctantly left the race, which it seemed she might very well have been successful in, as her showing early on proved that it was possible for her to be in the prize list.

Though *Bloodhound* and *Trenchemer* led the fleet, the *Maid of Malham* and *Rosemary* hung on well, and the *Maid* saved her time, to put the Morgan Cup in her locker with the others she had won, and her owners should be congratulated on sailing such a fine race.

Corrected times were :

YACHT			OWNER							CORRECTED TIMES		
										H.	M.	S.
Maid of Malham	-	-	Lt.-Comdr. J. H. Illingworth and Norman Jones							17	16	52
Rosemary IV	-	-	Mr. S. S. Taylor	-	-	-	-	-	-	18	12	37
Bloodhound	-	-	Mr. I. Bell	-	-	-	-	-	-	18	15	29
Banba	-	-	Mr. A. Rosling	-	-	-	-	-	-	18	23	32
Trenchemer	-	-	Mr. W. D. M. Bell	-	-	-	-	-	-	18	48	13
Neith	-	-	Major G. Henderson	-	-	-	-	-	-	18	53	43
Varuna	-	-	Mr. R. R. C. Vernon	-	-	-	-	-	-	19	25	24
Cachalot	-	-	Lt.-Col. C. Beddington	-	-	-	-	-	-	21	23	38

Retired : *Dolly Varden, Aralus.*

BRAMBLING

Length, overall -	- 36 ft. 9 in. = 11·201 m.	Length, water-line -	30 ft. 6 in. = 9·296 m.
Beam - -	- 9 ft. 6 in. = 2·895 m.	Draught - -	- 5 ft. 6 in. = 1·676 m.
Displacement -	- 10·80 tons = 10·972 kilos.	Sail Area - -	- 595 sq. ft. = 55·27 sq. m.

Owner, G. D. LOCK   *Designer*, BERTHON BOAT CO.   *Builder*, BERTHON BOAT CO.

THOSE who followed the fortunes of the Royal Ocean Racing Club's Annual Channel Race from the Solent round the *Royal Sovereign* and *Havre* Lightships and back, were not a bit surprised at *Brambling* winning this race, as in the past boats of her type have been very successful in this event. *Brambling* is a gauntlet, and the

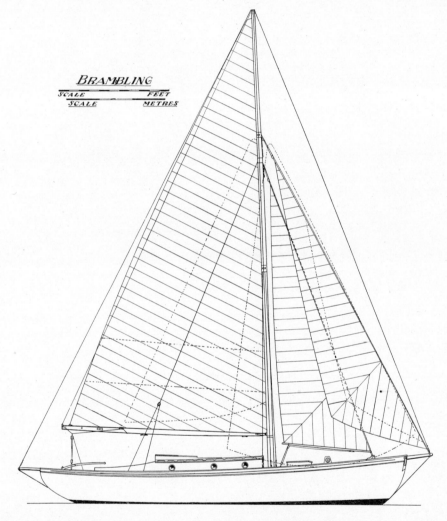

original gauntlet was second in the Channel Race in 1934 and *Greengage* (another Gauntlet) won it in 1935. So we are not surprised that *Brambling* should win this year ; the more so as, if we look back to the Coronation Race from the Solent to Torquay via Cherbourg and the Eddystone, we see that she saved her time on every vessel in the race.

The gauntlets were designed without any thought of ocean racing, but simply to produce a good comfortable solid cruiser, one with easy draught, comfortable accommodation and easy motion in a sea, so that a man could be happy entering a shallow unfrequented creek or harbour or out at sea in a breeze of wind, yet, added to all these admirable qualities, and in no way taking away from them, we have speed, and speed enough to win places in the Channel Race more often than not.

The lines show that the gauntlet is canoe sterned with very short overhangs fore and aft, with easy and fair buttocks and water-lines, the sections making for room and comfort below decks.

The construction plan shows her long strong keel, the foregripe being connected to this with a long scarph and the sternpost by a strong sternknee, while to her $2\frac{3}{4}$ in. $\times 2\frac{1}{8}$ in. oak frames the pitch pine $1\frac{1}{8}$ in. planking is fastened

GREENGAGE IS A GAUNTLET LIKE BRAMBLING

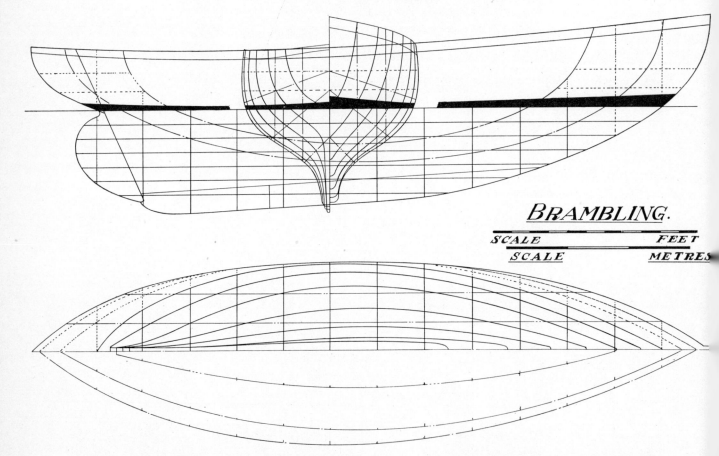

BRAMBLING.

SCALE   FEET
SCALE   METRES

with $\frac{1}{4}$ in. diameter copper bolts. Her decks are of teak the same thickness, while the cabin top is one inch thick, canvas covered and painted.

Her galley and pantry are abreast the mast, while forward of this is a single pipe cot in the fo'c'sle, and immediately abaft the mast comes her saloon with its settee either side and Pulman berths above, this leading into the

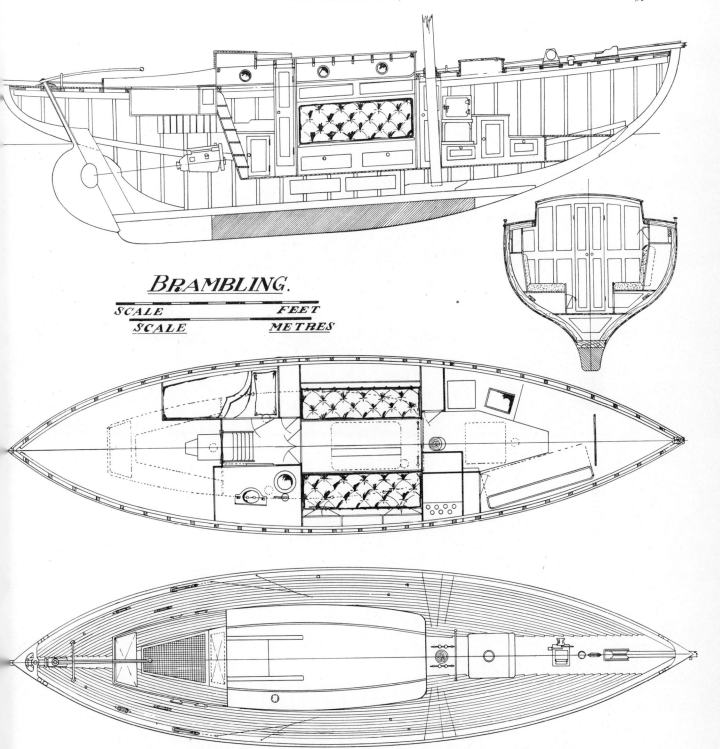

BRAMBLING.

SCALE   FEET

SCALE   METRES

companion way which has a washroom to starboard and a single berthed cabin to port, her engine being tucked away under the stairway leading out on deck.

The whole of her watertight cockpit is forward of the after end of her water-line, so aboard one feels safe and sound.   Because of her short overhangs *Brambling* has a small bowsprit and a bumpkin aft, the bowsprit taking the jib and the topmast stay, and the 3 ft. 9 in. bumpkin carrying the permanent topmast backstay far enough aft to clear the main boom.

The luff of the mainsail is exactly double that of the main boom, so we see that throughout *Brambling* is designed with cruising rather than with racing in view, while her jibstay, which is only 31 ft. 6 in. above the deck, just $\frac{3}{4}$ in. off the mast height, makes for a snug rig.   Possibly this snug rig has done more than we think for the gauntlets in the

HAPPY FROM START TO FINISH

THE CHANNEL RACE STARTED ON A CLOSE REACH IN IDEAL CONDITIONS

Channel Race, for this being held at the end of July almost always takes place in a good breeze of wind when anything delicate would tend to crumple up.   So in these plans of *Brambling* we see a sturdy comfortable little cruiser with speed enough to win the Channel Race.

THE CHANNEL RACE

The Channel Race for vessels 25 ft. to 35 ft. designed water-line is the great event of the year for the smaller ocean racers, and to win this is their great ambition.

The start this year was on Friday, July 30, at 5.00 p.m. from Southsea Beach. The idea of starting these races on Friday evenings is to give those taking part a chance to complete their week's work before the race, and as almost all taking part are workers this idea can hardly be improved upon.

The conditions were good, as it was lovely and sunny with a breeze east north east, which made it a close reach to the Owers. But the breeze increased as darkness came down, so that by 11.00 p.m. there was a smart wind and a fairly steep sea due to the tide, and when we remember that it was impossible to lay the Owers we can imagine all the class hard on the wind jumping at the seas and eager to get round the *Sovereign* when the wind would be abaft the beam.

Brambling was very wise when she tacked to the northward at practically right angles to the shore and the *Sovereign*, as in doing so she went for smoother water and an earlier fair tide, for we all know the tide turns earlier under any shore, and as well as getting the earlier tide she also had the advantage of smoother water for the wind was slightly off the land. *Brambling* did very well over this part of the course.

The run from the *Sovereign* to Havre with sheets well off and a good breeze was most enjoyable, for every vessel was travelling at her top speed, and it is always fun to chase away before the wind under such conditions. But after the *Havre Lightship* the racers were on the wind once more, laying the *Nab Lightship* close hauled on the starboard tack. The weather conditions made for a fast-sailed race indeed. At the same time there was a race underway round the same course for the larger class, and *Latifa* set a new record for the course, completing it in 29 hrs. 6 min., which gives her an average speed of just under $7\frac{1}{2}$ knots for the course, telling us that every vessel in this race was travelling at a high speed. As well as *Brambling* winning this race it also proved a triumph for the gauntlets, as they took 1st, 3rd, 6th, 10th and 11th places, which must be encouraging for those who evolved the Royal Ocean Racing Club's rule, for it clearly shows that the rule tends to produce as well as speed, comfort and sea worthiness.

CHANNEL RACE, 1937—CHANNEL CLASS

YACHT	FINISHING TIME	CORRECTED TIME		PLACED	PLACED CRUISER CLASS	YACHT	FINISHING TIME	CORRECTED TIME		PLACED	PLACED CRUISER CLASS
		H.	M.					H.	M.		
Brambling -	Aug. 1 09.27	27	37	1st	1st	Marianna -	Aug. 1 09.57	31	22	9th	3rd
Larry -	,, 06.27	28	19	2nd		Gauntlet -	,, 16.15	31	35	10th	
Greengage -	,, 10.47	28	32	3rd		Osprey -	,, 15.29	31	44	11th	
Viola -	,, 09.03	29	36	4th		Allegro -	,, 15.25	32	51	12th	4th
Spica -	,, 05.54	30	41	5th		Keryl -	,, 16.48	33	56	13th	5th
Guiding Light	,, 15.15	30	55	6th		Moti Hari -	Aug. 2 05.59	39	38	14th	6th
Armyne -	,, 10.22	31	14	7th		Alithea II -	,, 11.25	43	38	15th	7th
Wanda -	,, 17.38	31	16	8th	2nd						

Retired : *Sylvia, Barbara, Mavis, Saida, Lady Maud, Iris.*

CHANNEL RACE, 1937—BIG CLASS

YACHT	FINISHING TIME	CORRECTED TIME		PLACED	PLACED CRUISER CLASS	YACHT	FINISHING TIME	CORRECTED TIME		PLACED	PLACED CRUISER CLASS
		H.	M.					H.	M.		
Ortac -	Aug. 1 3.04	25	55	1st		Aile Noire -	Aug. 1 04.39	28	24	6th	
Trenchemer -	July 31 23.49	26	57	2nd		Banba -	,, 03.43	29	23	7th	2nd
Firebird -	,, 23.22	27	12	3rd		Thanet -	,, 03.30	32	28	8th	3rd
Latifa -	,, 23.06	27	19	4th		Taimoshan -	,, 15.45	34	54	9th	4th
Macnab -	Aug. 1 06.38	27	23	5th	1st	Rose - -	,, 09.09	35	49	10th	5th

Retired : *Maid of Malham* (broke spreader) ; *Dolly Varden* (too much water below) ; *Clyde* (trouble with topmast) ; *Rosemary.*

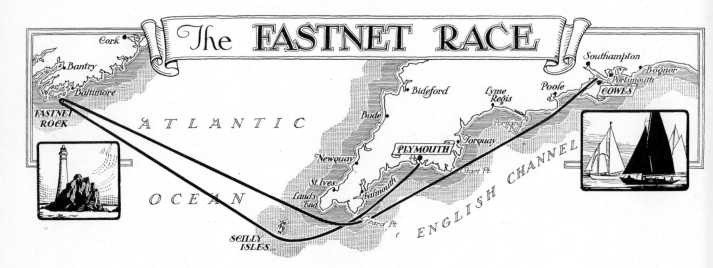

ZEEAREND

Length, overall -	- 54 ft. 7½ in. = 16·649 m.	Length, water-line -	40 ft. 0 in. = 12·192 m.
Beam -	- 12 ft. 0 in. = 3·658 m.	Draught - -	8 ft. 4 in. = 2·54 m.
Displacement -	- 45260 lb. = 20·528 kilos.	Sail Area - -	1380 sq. ft. = 128·20 sq. m.
Lead Keel -	- 19260 lb. = 8·617 kilos.		

Owner, C. BRUYNZEEL, JNR.   *Designer*, OLIN OF SPARKMAN & STEPHENS   *Builder*, DE VRIES LENTSCH, JNR.

As usual Olin has drawn a wonderfully sweet and fair set of lines for *Zeearend*, and we cannot but help being struck by the easy sweeping diagonal lines of this ocean racer, while her water-lines and buttocks all give an

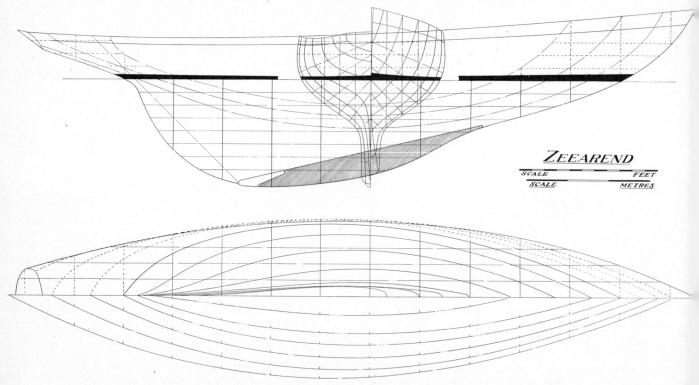

impression of speed. The sections, while giving the same impression, also tell of a comfortable boat at sea, so once again we see that Olin has combined speed, seaworthiness and comfort in a remarkable way, and one can see that

Zeearend is a boat that would always have to be reckoned with in an ocean race, no matter what the weather conditions were.

She has two pipe cots in her fo'c'sle, and immediately abaft this is a double berthed cabin abreast the mainmast taking the full width of the ship, abaft of which are two single cabins, one to port and one to starboard. At the after end of the starboard cabin is the washroom. Next aft comes one of the most unusual arrangements yet seen

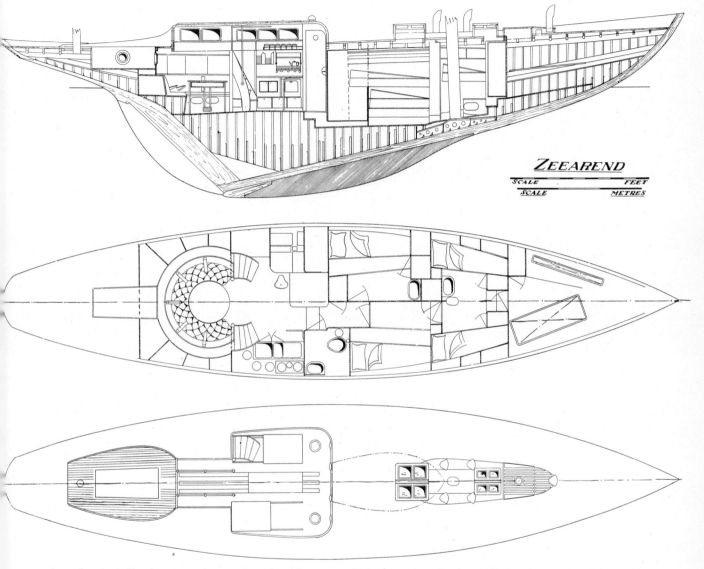

ZEEAREND
SCALE ———————— FEET
SCALE ———————— METRES

afloat, for the galley is arranged to starboard, while to port is the pantry, and two winding stairs, one on either side, leading out to the deck ; between them one walks straight into the dining saloon, where the circular seats are arranged around a round table. Though these round tables are getting rare it is difficult to think of anything more companionable, for, sitting at a round table, one is able to see the faces of all without bending and leaning forward, and such a table takes one's mind back to King Arthur and his knights. There being no head to a round table there can be no thought of one man occupying a better seat than another, and one would like to see round tables used more than at present.

The arrangement proved so comfortable and cosy that we see a similar edition of it in Dudok van Heel's *Tromp II*, though in his case he has made the table square.

Abaft this is the watertight cockpit and the mizen mast.

Like most ocean racers designed these days *Zeearend* has a yawl rig, and looking at her rig and the rigs of practically every ocean racer, whether American, German, Dutch or any other nationality, our mind goes back to a few years ago when there were a great many arguments, as there always will be, on the rig for sea work.

The cutter rig is undoubtedly the fastest, and therefore the best whenever it can be used, but this rig is penalised, and quite rightly, because of its efficiency; and so, as the next best thing, everyone goes for a yawl rig because of its allowance. These yawls are practically the same as we have used in British waters for a great many years, and have

ZEEAREND AT SEA

proved to be very good rigs for sea work as well as being fast, for they have the advantage of what we used to call a short boomed cutter rig, and added to this a mizen mast and mizen staysail given practically free under the rule. If one deplores the fact that America has forsaken her schooner rig for the British yawl rig, one must take comfort in the fact that here at least a point which has been argued about for many years has been proved, that point being " Which is the better rig, the yawl or the schooner? " for the yawl has proved so efficient at sea that all American designers have dropped the schooner rig in favour of it in spite of the fact that the Bermudian yawl rates at 98 per cent. and the schooner at only 92 per cent. But for all that the schooner rig has still much to recommend it and will always be seen upon the sea.

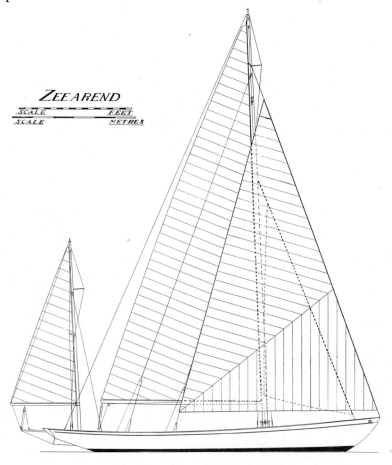

ZEEAREND
SCALE   FEET
SCALE   METRES

THE FASTNET RACE

The major ocean racing event in European waters is written around *Zeearend*, for *Zeearend* won this event from the finest fleet that has yet been seen. Amongst the entries were American, Dutch, German, British and French vessels, many of them designed especially for the race. When we look at the different types designed to the rule we are astonished, for it is amazing that designers should arrive at such widely varying results, the difference in most cases being the way they have ended their lines fore and aft. In *Latifa* we have one of the loveliest canoe sterned craft yet seen, while in *Bloodhound* we have a fine example of a normal counter stern for sea work, in the *Maid of Malham* there is the sawn-off counter found in all the French 6·50 metre class vessels and in older six-metres, while in *Phryne*, designed by Malden Heckstall Smith, we have the raking transom stern met with on the French crabbers, four distinct types by four different designers ; and Malden, it will be remembered, had a great deal to do with the forming of the rule, and is one of the greatest students of yacht racing rules. But though a square stern and a plumb bow gets past the rule and measures extremely well, I do not believe that they can prosper in rough water races, for while in smooth water such a vessel is fast (for at such times the overhangs of the other craft are just waving about in the fresh air and doing nothing except to stop them through their weight), once they get into a sea these overhangs increase the fore and aft lines and the fore and aft stability, so that they more than make up for the penalties the owner takes for them ; and as the rule tends to measure the sailing length of vessels, the better type with seaworthy over-hangs will come to the forefront in the years to come, and transom sterned and short bow vessels will slowly cease to exist, for it will still take several years for people to realise that the only time a well designed overhang fore and aft is of any value is in a seaway, whereas many people in the past have especially decried them for sea work.

The list shows what a fine fleet came to the line, and it will be seen that though not staged as an international event, the Fastnet Race is proving to be one of great importance, one that will do a great deal of good because the racers and crews gather together at dinners and have yarns before and after the event.

E   F.R.C.D.

SAIL NO.	YACHT	CRUISER CLASS	RATING	OWNER	RIG
142	Pam - - -	—	74·60	Lt. E. A. Woodward, R.N. - - -	Gaff yawl
XIX/2	Asta (G) - -	Yes	74·39	Marine Regatta Verein - - - -	Gaff yawl
121	Latifa - - -	—	52·41	Mr. Michael H. Mason - - -	Bm. yawl
22	Firebird - - -	—	50·60	Mr. Ralph Hawkes - - - - -	Bm. cutter
132	Rose - - -	Yes	49·51	Royal Artillery Y.C. - - - -	Gaff yawl
XIV/4	Ettsi IV (G) -	Yes	—	W. V. Alter Corpsstudenten E.V. - -	Bm. ketch
177	Trenchemer - -	—	—	Mr. W. D. M. Bell - - - -	Bm. yawl
218	Stiana - - -	—	45·28	Lt. J. F. B. Gage, R.N.V.R. - -	Bm. cutter
—	Elizabeth MacCaw	—	—	Mr. R. J. Reynolds - - - -	Bm. yawl
101	Bloodhound - -	—	44·37	Mr. Isaac Bell	Bm. yawl
144	Bamba - -	Yes	43·53	Mr. A. Rosling - - - -	Gaff cutter
123	Neith - - -	—	—	Major G. Henderson - - -	Gaff cutter
3	Roland von Bremen (G) - - -	—	40·86	S.K. Das Wappen von Bremen - -	Bm. yawl
X/4	Hamburg (G) -	—	39·47	Hamburger Verein Seefahrt - -	Bm. yawl
206	Zeearend (d) -	—	38·88	Herr C. Bruynzeel - - - -	Bm. yawl
XI/25	Peter von Danzig (G) - - -	—	37·84	A.S.V. Danzig - - - - -	—
201	Aile Noire (F) -	—	36·97	Mons. G. Baldenweck - - -	Bm. yawl
IX/37	Senta (G) - -	—	36·84	Herr H. Schmidt - - - -	Wishbone ketch
237	Nanette - -	Yes	—	Mr. Norman King - - - -	Gaff yawl
31	Zoraida - -	Yes	—	Capt. Franklin Ratsey, R.N. (retd.) -	Gaff cutter
4	Arktur (G) -	—	34·83	Herr V. Deutchlander - - -	Wishbone ketch
133	Ilex - - -	—	34·81	Royal Engineer Y.C. - - -	Bm. cutter
140	Ortac - - -	—	—	Colonel C. F. King, D.S.O., M.C. -	Bm. cutter
205	Saladin - -	Yes	—	Highland Brigade Y.C. - - -	Gaff cutter
199	Maid of Malham -	—	31·91	Lt.-Comdr. J. H. Illingworth and Mr. Norman Jones - - - - -	Bm. cutter
146	Tai-Mo-Shan -	Yes	30·78	The Admiralty - - - -	Bm. ketch
149	Phryne - - -	—	30·68	Messrs. R. A. P. Bevan and H. W. Paton	Bm. cutter
156	MacNab - -	Yes	28·88	Mr. J. J. Joass - - - -	Bm. cutter

AILE NOIRE HAS RACED
HARD THIS SUMMER

The day came in with a clear blue sky and a lovely northerly breeze, strong enough to give the racers a great deal of life, yet not so strong as to cause any sea at all ; in fact, the conditions were ideal for stretching the new mainsail of the American *Elizabeth MacCaw* which was waiting for her when she arrived in British waters.

THE SPARKMAN AND STEPHENS YAWL ELIZABETH MACCAW ON HER WAY FOR THE FASTNET

ZEEAREND, THE WINNER, HAS TWO TUCKED UNDER HER LEE AT THE START

We towed *Zoraida* out to the starting line, and there is no doubt this old-timer made a lovely picture with her tanned sails and a jackyard topsail set aloft.

It was some two hours before high water, and a strong flood was running up the Solent against the racers, but from the Squadron to Egypt Point the eddy tide was away in their favour, and so it was difficult for the ocean racers to judge whether to start at the northern end of the line and make straight for the slack water over the Lepe Shoals or to work this eddy tide along the Island shore to Egypt Point, and then luff across to the Lepe Shoals once they had reached Egypt Point, for the distance here is very short.

A great many of the boats had been specially built for ocean racing, such as *Latifa, Firebird, Trenchemer, Stiarna, Elizabeth McCaw, Bloodhound, Roland von Bremen, Hamburg, Zeearend, Peter von Danzig, Aile Noire, Ortac, Maid of Malham,* and *MacNab.*

In contrast to these were the fine ships of the old school, such as *Zoraida. Senta*, one of the German entries, a wishbone ketch, was another vessel built before the Ocean Racing Rule was formed, but she is of modern type with modern overhangs and delights in light weather, when she can set a great deal of light canvas from her wishbone gaff.

Before the five-minute gun there could be seen two distinct schools of thought, one was for going across the weather end of the line and the other the lee end, those at the weather end being *Zoraida, Bloodhound* and the ketch with two wishbone booms. At the start down to leeward was John Gage's *Stiarna*, the American yawl, *Latifa, Maid of Malham* and others.

There was a great deal of yelling at the weather end of the line from *Zoraida* and *Pam*, for the dinghy on the mark barge to be pulled up. Of those at this end of the line *Asta* made the best start, with Ikey Bell's *Bloodhound* close up on her weather quarter, but it was *Zoraida* who luffed out for the weather berth and the slack water over on the northern shore, the others holding their course down through the strength of the tide. When *Zoraida* had crossed the line her crew hauled in her mainsheet and stole out to the weather of the fleet.

Of those who took the eddy tide under the R.Y.S., Michael Mason's *Latifa* led the way soon after the start, with John Gage's *Stiarna* second, *Maid of Malham* third, the gaff boat fourth, and the American yawl fifth. The latter had been recalled, but failed to respond. *Saladin*, also recalled, lost some nine minutes making a fresh start.

Once Egypt Point had been reached Michael Mason, with a strong lead, luffed across for the northern shore, and when there had a strong lead from the rest of the fleet. Being a R.Y.S. member he was bound to put his faith in the Squadron eddy, and it did not fail him, and I really enjoyed seeing him right out ahead of all the fleet.

Soon after passing Egypt Point the American yawl, which also followed *Latifa's* lead, had gone up into the fourth place, but some of the fleet made the mistake of sticking to the Island shore after passing Egypt Point. So this fleet went away for their long race to the Fastnet and back, 29 ships of the line making a wonderful picture.

It, however, seemed to me after they had got half-way out into the Solent that most of those who had started on the Island shore made the mistake of charging down against the full strength of the tide, and one wondered if *Zoraida*, holding on to the north shore, could not pass them before the tide eased in the middle and let them through. And so the finest fleet yet, set sail for the Fastnet Rock.

Two yachts at the inshore end were over the start at gunfire. One of them, the American, failed to answer the recall signal, and so, according to the rules, was out of the race. This brings us to one point. The R.O.R.C. can learn something from its older sister the Y.R.A., for in the Prince of Wales' Cup the rule for the start says there will be no recall, but any yacht over the line *may* be disqualified.

No committee in the world can recall yachts with any satisfaction once there are more than twenty in the race, and so in future the R.O.R.C. will have to use the Y.R.A. starting rule for the Prince of Wales' Cup. The committee can use their discretion as to whether they disqualify a yacht for being over the line at the start, whereas now the R.O.R.C. must disqualify the *Elizabeth MacCaw*, and their rules have placed them in a rather stupid position, for this little vessel, having sailed across the Atlantic, must by the rules be disqualified.

However, thank Heaven, the Royal Ocean Racing Club's Committee was big enough to be able to admit the mistake in the starting rule and say, that in such a long race a few seconds at the start are of so little importance that we shall not disqualify *Elizabeth MacCaw*, and all was well with the world, for the *Elizabeth* sailed so well that she finished ahead of the fleet, and one only hopes that for all future ocean racing events the starting rules will have a note :

" Recalls—Exception to Y.R.A. Rule No. 28.

There will be no re-calls and any vessel over the line at the start may be disqualified without being recalled."

Thinking this over I wondered if the Y.R.A. rule itself could not be altered so that recalls are done away with entirely, and any vessel over the line disqualified unless she returns of her own accord, for surely it is just as much a breach of the rules to be over the line and starting before time as it is to hit a mark, and one has to retire on hitting any mark on the course, so why should not vessels be forced to retire if they beat the gun across the line, for on board they still have the chance of re-starting if they see they are over the line, and such a rule would take a great deal of worry away from all starting committees, and only those who have started races and run them know the work involved.

ZORAIDA MAKES A LOVELY PICTURE

Going down the Solent *Latifa* led the fleet with *Asta* second and *Zoraida* third, these choosing the north shore which is almost always right when working against a foul tide, for there one is able to ease the tide over the banks, while on the island shore it is impossible to ease the tide at all, for instead of banks there are ledges of rocks jutting well out into the tide, the Gurnard, Salt Mede and Hamstead ledges being obstacles that have to be avoided whereas over on the north shore there is only soft mud, which shoals gradually so that the lead can be used and is a good guide.

The order through the Needles was *Latifa, Asta, Zoraida, Bloodhound, Elizabeth MacCaw, Pam, Trenchemer, Zeearend, Ettsi, Roland, Peter von Danzig, Aile Noire, Firebird, Stiarna, Senta, Bamba, Arktur, Nanette, MacNab, Maid of Malham, Ortac, Neith, Phryne, Saladin, Chough,* and *Tai-Mo-Shan.*

As the fleet sailed away a friend remarked " It is remarkable that all the foreign-designed rigs are yawls and all the British cutters", and so it would seem that ocean racing is boiling down to a contest between yawls and cutters, and time alone will tell if the rig allowance should be adjusted to level this up, for though this year's contests have been equally shared between them, the majority of long distance races have been taken by the yawls.

Latifa led the fleet the whole way to the Fastnet and right back to practically within sight of the finish line, and only bad luck robbed her of a well deserved victory, for she was anchored for eight hours off Ramehead within sight of the line.

On the outward journey *Trenchemer* was second at the Lizard, almost an hour astern of *Latifa*, *Asta*, the great German ketch, third. Next came *Firebird, Bloodhound, Elizabeth MacCaw, Stiarna, Bamba, the Roland, Rose* and *Zeearend*. *Zeearend* at this point was two hours astern of *Latifa*, and after her came *Zoraida*, the old jackyard cutter, then the rest of the fleet. The *Maid* and *Ortac* had a ding-dong race, first one and then the other taking the lead, *Zoraida* doing particularly well throughout the race until she had the misfortune to lose her topmast through the carrying away of the topmast shroud plate. Though the jury topmast was set, she not only lost a great deal of time over this, but was unable to sail as well as she had done before, and so lost her chance of the trophy.

WISHBONE BOOMS IN THE FASTNET

ZORAIDA, PAM, SENTA AND OTHERS, SOON AFTER THE START

As in the past, there were some who did not fetch the Fastnet, but hit the Irish Coast to the eastward and leeward of it. Generally speaking, because our races are coastal races where points have to be weathered and winds are generally westerly, one should keep the weather gauge of all headlands and points, which means keeping them under the lee whenever possible.

All this time *Latifa* was leading the fleet, and rounded the Rock at 1.30 p.m., *Stiarna* rounding second at 4.18, while *Zeearend* came round third, these three having made good landfalls, while others had gone to leeward and had to beat along the Irish coast. The *Elizabeth MacCaw* was next round it at 4.28 on Monday, *Bloodhound* at 5.05 and *Firebird* at 5.30, *Asta* not getting round till 5.45. *Trenchemer* meanwhile, who had been second at Land's End had been led astray by her compass; and while steel ships have many advantages, one always wonders just what is happening to the compass aboard them, for on such small vessels it is extremely difficult, in fact impossible, to get the compass very far away from the hull.

BLOODHOUND AND THE ULTIMATE WINNER, ZEEAREND, FINISHED IN CLOSE COMPANY

Fog and the lightest of airs prevailed along the Fastnet coast and held many prisoners there, some of them being kept prisoners for 11 hours.

At 7.00 p.m. on Tuesday *Latifa* had arrived back at the Lizard, having experienced from moderate to light westerly winds as had the rest of the leaders. Second at the Lizard was the American yawl *Elizabeth MacCaw*, at 2.55 a.m., some seven hours astern of *Latifa*. Surely no vessel has had the heartbreaking experience after having a seven hours' lead and sailing along as far as Ramehead, only 20 miles away from the finishing line, to be becalmed and anchored for eight hours. This is just what happened to *Latifa*. Eight hours, in which time the American yawl, sailing very very slowly and farther out to sea with her spinnaker set, slowly ghosted ahead and led *Latifa* over the finishing line by just over half an hour.

However, neither of these took the cup, for *Zeearend* was sailing remarkably well, and rounding the Bishops close to, she saved as many yards as possible on her course, sailing extremely well in the light airs from the Lizard onwards, finishing with *Bloodhound*. Crossing the line a second ahead of *Bloodhound*, and saving her time on the fleet, she won by over two hours from the next best, John Gage's cutter *Stiarna*, which throughout had sailed a wonderfully good race. *Maid of Malham* took third place in spite of being becalmed so long at the Fastnet, and *Bloodhound* fourth. *Elizabeth MacCaw* took the cup for the first home, while the scratch boat *Pam*, an ex 15-metre, was the last to finish. So ended the Fastnet race of 1937, and again it was a triumph for Olin Stephens, for there were two vessels to his design in the race. the *Elizabeth MacCaw* taking the cup for the first vessel to finish, while *Zeearend* won the Fastnet Cup. Olin, as we all know, is still in his twenties, yet even so has made a great name for himself as a designer, not by one vessel but by many, for the last four Fastnet Races have been won by vessels to his design and as these are the only Fastnet Races in which we have seen vessels to his design, he has scored a possible.

YACHT	OWNER	FINISH			CORRECTED TIME	
		H.	M.		H.	M.
Zeearend - -	C. Bruynzeel, Jun. - - - -	17	32	(11th)	85	29
Stiarna - - -	Lt. J. F. B. Gage - - - -	14	17	(11th)	87	46
Maid of Malham	Lt.-Comdr. J. Illingworth and N. Jones	07	06	(12th)	89	46
Bloodhound -	Isaac Bell - - - - - -	17	33	(11th)	89	54
Elizabeth McCaw -	R. J. Reynolds - - - -	13	24	(11th)	90	09
Ortac - - -	C. F. King - - - - -	07	53	(12th)	91	13
Latifa - - -	M. H. Mason - - - -	14	03	(11th)	92	40
Hamburg - -	Hamburger Verein Seefahrt - -	09	09	(12th)	98	54
Firebird - -	Ralph Hawkes - - - -	00	30	(12th)	109	56
Bamba - - -	A. Rosling - - - -	07	15	(12th)	101	01
Ilex - - -	Royal Engineer Y.C. - - -	18	03	(12th)	101	55
Aile Noire - -	G. Baldenweck - - - -	16	57	(12th)	101	58
Neith - - -	Major G. Henderson - - -	11	21	(12th)	102	57
Trenchemer - -	W. D. M. Bell - - - -	09	36	(12th)	106	35
Rose - - -	Royal Artillery Y.C. - - -	09	17	(12th)	108	00
MacNab - -	J. J. Joass - - - - -	18	44	(13th)	112	49
Asta - - -	Marine Regatta Verein - - -	20	14	(11th)	113	08
Roland von Bremen -	S.K. Das Wappen von Bremen - -	03	31	(13th)	115	41
Phryne - - -	R. A. Bevan and H. W. Paton -	19	53	(13th)	116	12
Nanette - - -	N. King - - - - -	26	31	(14th)	121	20
Zoraida - - -	Capt. Franklin Ratsey - -	18	58	(13th)	121	59
Senta - - -	H. Schmidt - - - -	18	37	(13th)	123	21
Chough - - -	W. A. Wetherby-Mein - - -	12	48	(14th)	124	48
Saladin - - -	Highland Brigade Club - - -	11	15	(14th)	130	02
Arktur - - -	U. Deutchlander - - - -	08	11	(14th)	131	32
Peter von Danzig	A.S.V. Danzig - - - -	05	47	(14th)	133	41
Ettsi IV - - -	W. V. Alter Corpsstudenten E.V. -	18	28	(14th)	140	42
Pam - - -	Lt. E. A. Woodward - - -	22	54	(13th)	167	08

TAI-MO-SHAN AT THE START OF THE FASTNET RACE

L A T I F A

Length, overall	-	-	70 ft. 0 in. = 21·33 m.	Length, water-line	-	52 ft. 0 in. = 15·85 m.
Beam	-	-	15 ft. 3 in. = 4·72 m.	Draught	-	10 ft. 2 in. = 3·10 m.
Displacement	-	-	41 tons = 41,656 kilos.	Sail Area	-	2200 sq. ft. = 204·39 sq. m.

Owner, MICHAEL MASON *Designer*, WM. FIFE & SON *Builder*, WM. FIFE & SON

*L*ATIFA has been a great delight to lovers of sailing vessels, for she is one of the loveliest of sailing craft yet seen, and I can see her now smoking up through the Solent with a north west breeze over her quarter, everything set even to the mizen staysail, and all her cloud of canvas seeming to lift her out of the water. She looked so airy that she reminded me of Mother Cary's chickens flitting along the tops of the waves with just their feet touching them, and the sight of her dancing over the seas that day will always live in my memory. The brightness of white sails

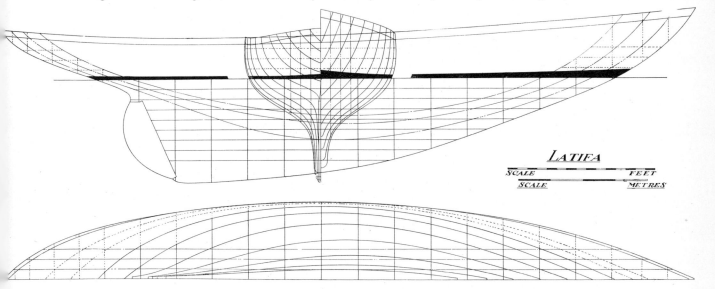

LATIFA

SCALE — FEET
SCALE — METRES

and a white hull in strong sunlight is always inspiring and cheering, and when added to that we have white breaking water caused by wind strong enough to give such a vessel as *Latifa* a bone in her teeth and a long clean white wake, then we have seen a sight that is satisfying to our senses, and we feel that the world indeed is a lovely place to live in. Here before us we have the lines and plans of Michael Mason's wonderful *Latifa*, and looking at them my mind flies back to that day on which she made such a splendid picture, and one ceases to wonder that she won the Queen's Cup then, for her clean buttocks and water-lines are a delight to look upon. Her sections show she has seaworthy overhangs, the bow and stern sections being well V'd so that they will cut through and not slam into the seas as so many do. These develop sweetly into her powerful and yet easily driven midship section, and one realises that in *Latifa* Fife has once more produced a lovely vessel, and my mind wanders back to all the wonderful yachts he has designed.

We all of us know that inspiring photograph of the schooner *Suzanne* by Beken, in which she is flying along beneath a great cloud of sail, a picture that will probably live for all time. *Suzanne* was designed by Fife, and with all his successes behind him we expect and always find lovely lines in all his vessels.

I was fortunate enough to see *Latifa* as she was being built, and therefore was not at all surprised that, when she was laid up last winter after a long and strenuous season, including a voyage down to Madeira and back in the autumn through gales of wind, which severely shook up the giant liner *Berengaria*, she showed no sign of strain whatever. No matter how hard she is driven *Latifa* is always absolutely watertight. This strength is another feature of Fife's vessels, and in *Latifa*, as always, he has combined beauty with strength which latter at sea in a gale of wind is a source of comfort, for so often we hear of yachts leaking badly whenever they get into a strong wind and sea.

Below she has four pipe cots in the fo'c'sle. Her paid crew have a separate washroom of their own, and abaft the fo'c'sle we have the galley and pantry abreast the mast, from which the doorway leads into the dining saloon, where we find a settee behind the seat on the port side.

Farther aft, as the accommodation plan shows, she has three single-berthed cabins, a washroom with a companion way leading up into the deck house, which is separated from the watertight cockpit by the bridge deck, and this deck house is a very cosy place, whether at sea in a gale or anchored in harbour, and one imagines the owner and his friends spending many a pleasant hour here.

The sail plan is that of a Bermudian yawl with a three-headsail rig, and as this rig can be changed to a double-headsail rig quite easily, the owner has a great number of sail combinations in the fore triangle, to suit every wind from the lightest of airs to a gale, *Latifa's* light weather ability can be gauged from the fact that though light winds prevailed throughout this Fastnet Race her average speed from Cowes round the Fastnet and back to the Lizard was so high; while her hard weather ability stood the owner in good stead on the way from Madeira last autumn when *Latifa* brought him safely through the worst of weather.

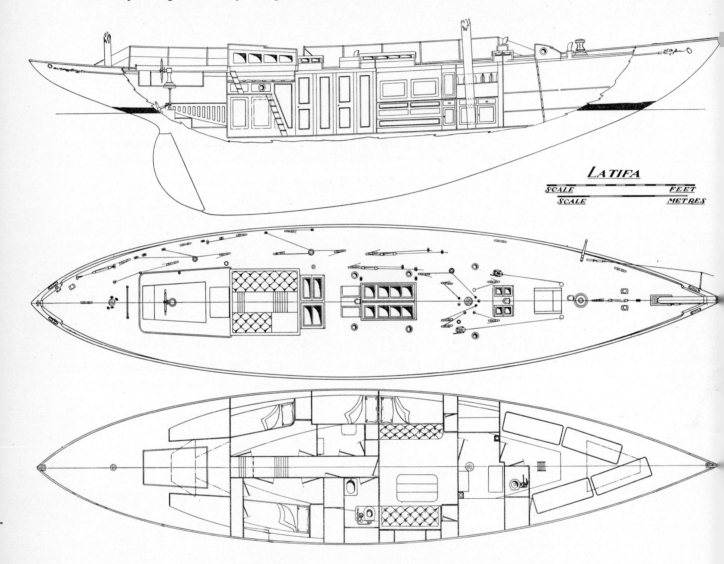

LATIFA

SCALE   FEET
SCALE   METRES

LA BAULE AND BENODET RACE

11.00 a.m. on Monday, August 16, saw the start of the race from Plymouth to La Baule, and *Latifa*, expecting the wind to come to the south west, tacked to the south west while the others stood away north west.   However, the wind flew into the west and so favoured those who had stood to the westward.

This breeze freshened so much that *Firebird* actually rounded Ushant 19 hours after leaving Plymouth, *Trenchemer* being second, *Elizabeth MacCaw* third and *Latifa* fourth, but after passing Ushant the wind veered more northerly and finally fell away to almost a calm, so that the four leaders slowly drifted southward in close company, with the top of *Ortac's* mainsail just visible above the horizon.   *Latifa* arrived first, ten minutes before the *Elizabeth MacCaw*, with *Firebird* third and *Trenchemer* fourth.   The fog came down towards the end, but a gentle breeze took them in and all was well. This same breeze had brought those astern closer up to the leaders, so that the first ten actually finished the 284 mile course within three hours of each other, *Ortac* coming out the winner, as she deserved to, for she had always kept the leaders in sight.

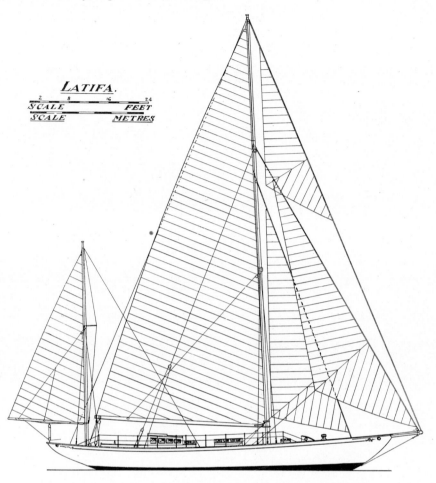

	YACHT	FINISH			CORRECTED TIME	
		H.	M.		H.	M.
1st	*Ortac* - - - -	22	43	(18th)	46	07
2nd	*Maid of Malham* - -	00	11	(19th)	46	48
3rd	*Wi Ki* - - - -	00	16	(19th)	48	26
4th	*Aile Noire* - - -	00	17	(19th)	49	31
	Aralus - - -	00	22	(19th)	51	55
	Tigris - - - -	01	05	(19th)	51	57
	Trenchener - - -	22	13	(18th)	52	40
	Elizabeth MacCaw -	21	44	(18th)	53	22
	Firebird - - -	22	04	(18th)	53	49
	Latifa - - - -	21	34	(18th)	54	07
	Rose - - - -	23	45	(18th)	54	54
	Phryne - - -	12	59	(19th)	55	47
	Sainte Anne III - -	21	44	(19th)	66	32
	May Morn - - -	15	45	(19th)	69	51

LA BAULE, ILE DE YEU, BENODET RACE, 140 MILES

At 5.00 p.m. the racers started on the 140 mile race from St. Nazaire to Benodet, and the first mark on the course, an unlighted buoy off the Ile de Yeu, was troublesome, for it took *Latifa* something like half an hour to find it. However she was first away with a good breeze, just free enough to let her lay her course, but after a while it freed her still more, so that she could set her mizen staysail, and she was soon reeling off knots in grand style, with *Firebird*, and *Elizabeth MacCaw* next astern.

Throughout the night *Latifa* was logging 9 and 10 knots, actually logging $11\frac{1}{4}$ knots in her best hour's run. By dawn she was near Benodet, but did not pick up her buoy, and so lost an hour over this. The wind at dawn dropped away and she drifted into Benodet, leading the *Elizabeth MacCaw* by 1 hour and 20 minutes ; and so *Latifa* won the last ocean race of the season.

	H.	M.	S.
Latifa - - - - - - -	18	14	10
Elizabeth McCaw - - - - -	18	38	07
Maid of Malham - - - - -	18	44	38
Ortac - - - - - - -	18	45	17
Glance - - - - - - -	26	36	27

Firebird being unable to find an unlit buoy being disqualified.

The Royal Ocean Racing Club have a Club championship and this was won by the Royal Naval Sailing Association with 354 points, *Maid of Malham* winning 164 of these, *Stiarna* 66, *Wanda* 41, *Tai-Mo-Shan* 38, *Zoraida* 27, *Chough* 14, *Pam* 4.

	POINTS
1. Royal Naval Sailing Association - - - - -	354
2. Royal Yacht Squadron - - - - - -	249
3. Royal Thames Y.C. - - - - - -	229
4. Royal Artillery Y.C. - - - - - -	191
5. Royal Cinque Ports Y.C. - - - - -	187
6. Yacht Club de France - - - - - -	173
Royal Corinthian Y.C. - - - - -	173
Royal Netherlands Y.C. - - - - -	121
Royal Clyde Y.C. - - - - - -	114
Royal Cruising Club - - - - - -	96
S.K. das Wappen von Bremen - - - - -	80
Marine Regatta Verein - - - - -	75
Royal Engineers Y.C. - - - - -	72
Island Sailing C. - - - - - -	71
The Cruising Assn. - - - - -	68
Hamburger Verein Seefahrt - - - - -	67
Bremen Y.C. - - - - - -	62
Royal Albert Y.C. - - - - -	52
Bournemouth and Hamworthy S.C. - - -	49
Royal Harwich Y.C. - - - - -	37
Royal Southern Y.C. - - - - -	34
Blackwater S.C. - - - - - -	32
Royal Burnham Y.C. - - - - -	21
Royal Yorkshire Y.C. - - - - -	20
Royal Motor Y.C. - - - - - -	18
A.S.V. Danzig - - - - - -	15
Royal Cornwall Y.C. - - - - -	14
Highland Brigade Y.C. - - - - -	12
W.R. Alter Corpsstudenten E.V. - - - -	12
Parkstone S.C. - - - - - -	12
Royal Western Y.C. - - - - -	11
Cercle Nautique La Baule - - - - -	6
Cambridge Univ. Y.C. - - - - -	4

Ortac won the Trenchemer Cup as she scored highest points of all the ocean racers and so won this Cup with 20 points lead of *Maid of Malham*, *Zeearend* being third.

	POINTS
Ortac - - - - - - - - - -	187
Maid of Malham - - - - - - - -	167
Zeearend - - - - - - - - -	121
Latifa - - - - - - - - - -	118
Trenchemer - - - - - - - - -	117

In all these races fostered by the Royal Ocean Racing Club we have travelled 2,500 miles of open sea, and as they have been described from the viewpoint of five different vessels, whose complete plans are shown in this chapter, we see the types of vessel encouraged by the Royal Ocean Racing Club rule, and when we stop to think that such small vessels as *Ortac* and *Maid of Malham*, only 35 ft. on the water-line, have been driven to windward at 7 knots 4½ points off the wind, we realise the good the Royal Ocean Racing Club has done in fostering these races, for only in competition do we get rapid progress.

EVEN WITH ONLY WORKING SAILS SET LATIFA LOOKS LOVELY

A very fine type of vessel has been developed very rapidly, and the seamanlike qualities amongst the owners and crews have also been developed with the same speed, for these seamen have driven their vessels hard to windward when the earlier types of cruising craft would have hove to, calling the weather experienced a gale of wind. The Royal Ocean Racing Club deserves a great deal of credit for all it has done in the short time it has been in existence, and though none of us at the moment can really say how far the Royal Ocean Racing Club will go, we can be sure that it will travel a long way, for the road it has marked out for itself is a first-class road in every sense, for its aim, as we all know, is to develop fast weatherly ships that are also seaworthy to a degree unthought of in the years that are gone, and in the development of these ships it has also developed a very fine type of yachtsman, and as long as it keeps to the road it has planned out it will go forward with ever increasing strength and speed. One imagines that in the years to come, besides containing amongst its members the leading yachtsmen of the world, it will also be a more powerful organisation of the yachting fraternity, for its objects are big hearted and open and will always appeal to the better types of human beings, as any human being who endures the hardships of long distance racing cheerfully must have a great deal of good tucked away inside him. So while we look with pride and pleasure at the work already accomplished by this Club we must also look ahead to ensure that it continues as it should to develop the finest types of seaworthy sailing ships and seamen to man them.

· 9 ·

S'MARIANNE

Length, overall -	42 ft. 2 in.	= 12·855 m.
Beam - -	8 ft. 2⅜ in.	= 2·50 m.
Displacement -	7 tons = 7112 kilos.	

Length, water-line -	31 ft. ⅞ in.	= 9·47 m.
Draught - - -	5 ft. 10⅞ in.	= 1·80 m.
Sail Area - -	645 sq. ft.	= 60 sq. m.

Owner, CARL LIDMANN   *Designer*, F. G. AMEEN

WHEN I look at the clean sweet lines of *S'Marianne*, for everywhere she is as clean as a smelt, the wisdom of giving new designers many chances is brought home to me, for it is difficult to think of a sweeter little vessel

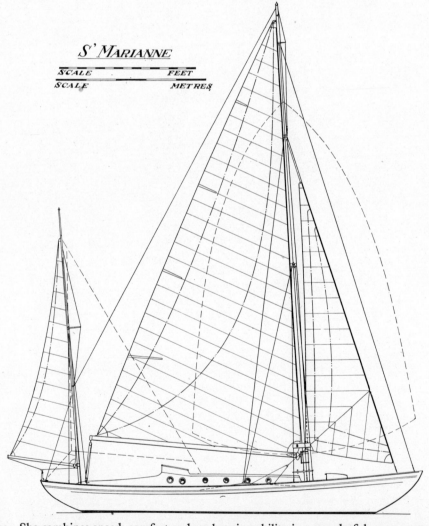

than *S'Marianne*. She combines speed, comfort and sea keeping ability in a wonderful manner, and is a great credit to her designer, F. G. Ameen. Then there come to my mind some of his first designs, which, though showing a great deal of thought, somehow missed the mark. But, as *S'Marianne* shows, he has now arrived at the stage where his work is well nigh perfect. We see an instance of this on the other side of the Atlantic, for a few years ago, when Olin Stephens started to design Sixes, though they had much in them which showed he was not a copyist, but a

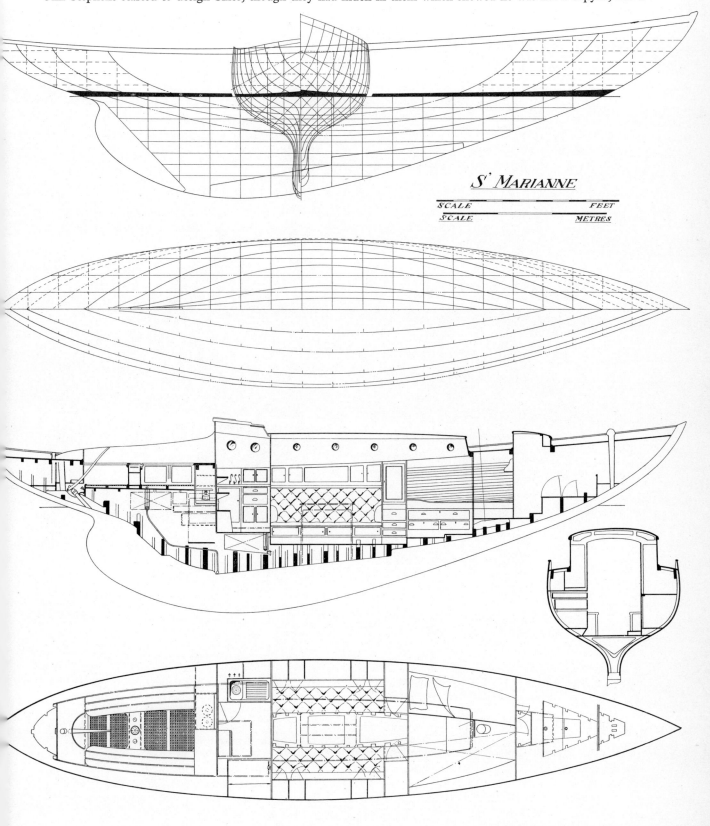

S' MARIANNE

SCALE   FEET

SCALE   METRES

designer trying to express his thoughts in wood and steel, yet his earliest vessels in this class were not successful. But he was given other chances, and now he is one of the foremost yacht designers in the world, although still in his twenties. Indeed, he worked with Burgess and Professor Davidson in the production of *Ranger*, who successfully defended the *America's* Cup this year.

S'MARIANNE WITH HER GENOA SET   AND UNDER HER TRYSAIL

Before looking at the Lines of *S'Marianne* it is as well to look at the bold sweeping profile of the stem, keel, rudder and canoe stern in the accommodation plan below the lines, for here this clean sweeping line stands out, and there is no pause or break in it throughout the length of *S'Marianne*. The impression one gets throughout this design is of bold sweeping lines, for the buttocks are very easy and fair, and one would have difficulty in finding a sweeter set of water-lines and diagonals. If the sections seem a wee bit hard at the bilge, we have to bear in mind that *S'Marianne* has a fairly narrow hull and needs a firm bilge to give her stability and comfort at sea. Those sections remind us somewhat of the best types of hulls to the International rule, though of course these tell of a craft that is easy in a seaway rather than a racer, for the bow sections are sharply V'd, and will cut their way through a head sea without any shock to the vessel while, because she has a canoe stern, the after sections are also well V'd, and take the seas kindly. In fact we can look at these lines for a long time with enjoyment.

From her accommodation plan we see that she has a double berthed cabin immediately abaft her fo'c'sle, and abaft this a cosy little saloon with a settee either side. The galley and pantry are next abaft this, and it will be noticed that the stoves are placed under the bridge deck dividing her cockpit from the cabin.

The cockpit itself is quite large for such a small vessel, and gives her crew room to handle sheets and enjoy watching her sailing the summer seas, for being a Baltic craft she is laid up throughout the winter.

It will be noticed that the cockpit is divided so that the helmsman is separated from the rest by a small bridge deck, in which are placed the compass, clock and barometer, all within his view.

S'Marianne is rigged as a yawl with moderate length masts, and this rig has proved very efficient.

It will be noticed on the sail plan that two different trysails are shown as well as the mainsail. The first of these trysails has a slightly hollow leach, and will be used in strong breezes, while the second one is formed by a very narrow ribbon of sail coming down to the lower crosstree where it then curves out to the boom end ; both reach to the top of her mast, and as there is only 100 ft. in the smaller sail it can be imagined that she will carry this in almost any weather. The idea behind these trysails is that they spread the strain and weight over the entire length of the mast, and keep it all the steadier in a seaway. Such a trysail looks very unusual and wrong to those who have not seen it in action, but it has proved to be very efficient and is being used more and more throughout the Baltic, and having a wire leach it gives no trouble through flapping, for such a narrow ribbon of sail would be useless without efficient control of its leach. It is highly probable that this type of trysail will come into general use as time goes on.

Carl Lidmann found her a pleasant and happy ship, in fact *S'Marianne* has proved to be such a wonderful little vessel that she has formed the basis for several very fine cruisers, notable amongst them being Sigurd Golje's *Diana*, which is a slightly enlarged edition of *S'Marianne*, but with a counter stern instead of the pretty canoe stern we see in these plans. The longer we look at the plans of *S'Marianne* the more we envy Carl Lidmann, and the more we realise that for such a type of craft, it would be very difficult indeed to find a better ship. She has faithfully carried her owner through storm and sunshine, and he is indeed a fortunate man to possess a lovely example of present day tendency in small cruising craft.

F   F.R.C.D.

· IO ·

CORINNE III & IV

Length, overall	-	-	34 ft. 0 in. = 10·35 m.	Length, water-line	-	23 ft. 0 in. = 7·00 m.
Beam	-	-	7 ft. 3 in. = 2·20 m.	Draught	-	4 ft. 8 in. = 1·42 m.
Displacement	-	-	4·10 tons = 4·12 c. m.	Sail Area	-	385 sq. ft. = 35·76 sq. m.

Owner, SVENSKA KRYSSARKLUBBEN   *Designer,* CARL A. ALLBERG   *Builder,* ERIK ERIKSSON

THE Svenska Kryssarklubben (The Swedish Cruising Club) is a remarkably strong and healthy club, full of life and energy. Some idea of its activity and the good it does can be gauged by the fact that every year it builds some type of cruiser, and the various members buy tickets as this cruiser is a lottery boat. This means that a man who probably would otherwise never own a cruiser, is fortunate enough to win and own the vessel which the club has commissioned a designer and builder to produce.

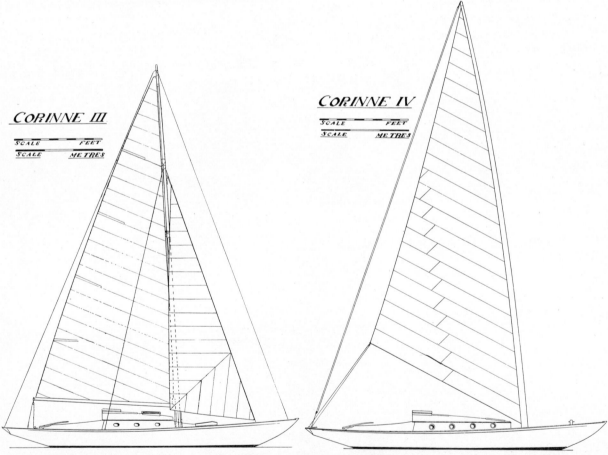

Besides the designer's thoughts going into this craft each year, a great many of the Committees' thoughts are in her too, for they decide the type to be designed and built. In *Corinne III* we see the 1934 lottery boat. In that year the committee chose a design by Carl A. Allberg, and as we look at her lines we realise what a wise choice they made, for *Corinne's* lines are those of a delightful little cruiser, powerful and yet fast and easy in a seaway, while all her buttocks, water-lines and diagonals are very pleasing.

It is the sections and the keel line of this little vessel that please us most when we look at her from a cruising viewpoint, for the bow and stern sections are sharp and easy, as they should be for rough water, and the midship section shows a firm bold bilge, yet one that makes for speed as well as comfort at sea. Her profile shows a keel line that makes for steadiness and ease of handling in a seaway, while above the water the overhangs are moderate and attractive.

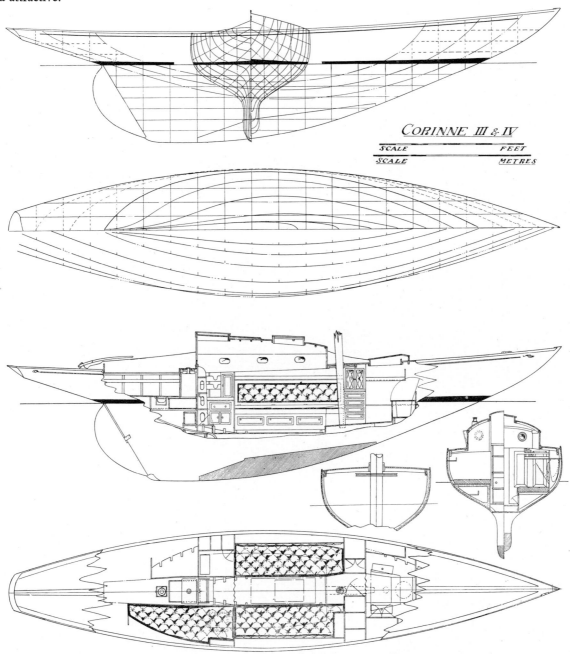

CORINNE III & IV

SCALE ———————————— FEET

SCALE ———————————— METRES

In the accommodation plan we see she has three sleeping berths, one tucked away aft under the cockpit, and one on either side of the main cabin.   Three people cruising in this boat would be happy and comfortable just as long as they wished.

The pantry is arranged under the after end of the coach roof on the port side, and this is probably the best place to put the galley in such small craft, for here there is room to cook and prepare meals.   It is also in a place where the motion is least and the fumes and smell from cooking find their way immediately out through the open hatchway, also hot food can be passed out to the helmsman in bad weather.   Then in good weather, when many meals are taken in the cockpit, they can be handed straight out on to the cockpit table, and at the same time one is within easy reach of the main saloon where, of course, most meals are enjoyed.

Nothing is arranged for the bow and stern overhangs, and one imagines that here they would store their best clothes out of the way and yet in the two driest spots of any small boat, for bilge water never finds its way into these parts, and being free of any deck openings no water can get down from above.

Two sail plans are shown, for as can be imagined *Corinne III*, proved to be such a good little craft that she was again chosen for the 1935 lottery boat, but this time with the Ljungstrom rig. This shows how progressive the Swedish Cruising Club is, for the Ljungstrom rig, as will be seen, is a single sail on a revolving mast without any shrouds or stays at all excepting for the topmast backstay, which runs down to the end of the counter. This rig has proved fairly successful, and it has not only been used in cruisers, but also, as will be seen in another part of this book, by the Aeolus Yacht Club in their 22 square metre B class skerry cruisers. It has much to recommend it, for as there are no shrouds or stays and no headsail, it is very simple to work and handle. Coming alongside or up to a mooring, or for reefing, one simply pulls on a rope pulley, and the mast revolves, and in revolving rolls the sail around itself. While running free, the sail, which is double, opens out and one has double the sail area.

The 1934 rig is a normal Bermudian cutter rig. The base of the sails, being roughly the water-line length of the boat, enables her crew to handle them easily and comfortably, as it is always easier to handle sails that are well inboard because of the extra beam, and this makes for safety at sea on dark nights.

· II ·

ANDRILLOT

Length, overall - - 25 ft. 0 in. = 7·62 m. Length, water-line - 21 ft. 6 in. = 6·55 m.
Beam - - - 7 ft. 2 in. = 2·184 m. Draught - - - 4 ft. 5 in. = 1·34 m.
Displacement - - 4·28 tons = 4348 kilos. Sail Area - - - 366 sq. ft. = 34 sq. m.

Owner, R. A. KINNERSLY   *Designer*, LAURENT GILES   *Builder*, A. H. MOODY AND SON

THIS little cutter made a remarkable cruise this summer, visiting 22 ports in 23 days, her cruise taking her to the Scilly Isles, and amongst other harbours such as Brest, Benodet, Concarneau, Audierne, Lanildut, l'Abervrach, Treguier, Lézardrieux, Ile Brehat, Guernsey and Cherbourg, and when we bear in mind that she has no engine, we realise not only that she had good weather conditions for the cruise, but that she was an exceptionally fine little vessel to be able to take advantage of those conditions.

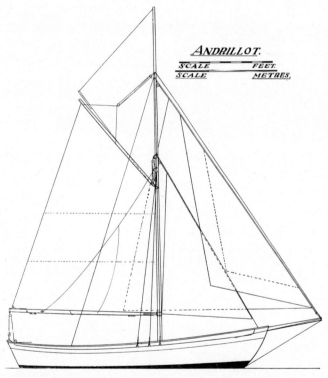

Often, though a vessel meets wonderful sailing conditions she is so slow or clumsy or her owner so lacks seamanship and knowledge, that the benefit of the conditions is lost, and many a vessel lost at sea or hove to in a gale of wind would have been safe in port had she had the ability to get there. Future years will see less damage through heavy weather to vessels as their good sailing qualities will have taken them into port, while a lee shore has also lost its dread because the vessels developed to-day are remarkably weatherly.

All of us remember the fable of the fox and the stork inviting each other out to dinner, and how when the stork asked the fox he had the food in the bottom of a long deep pitcher and was able to eat himself while the poor fox could not get his head into the neck at all, and when the fox asked the stork he had the food in a low flat trough so that he could gobble the food up in large mouthfuls while the stork could only peck at the food bit by bit. We who love sailing the seas must remember this fable when we start thinking and planning out our new ships, for these have to be carefully thought out so that they are suited to the kind of cruising we wish to do, as only then can they take us to the havens where we would be.   With such thoughts in mind we turn to this 25 ft. cutter, short enough and small

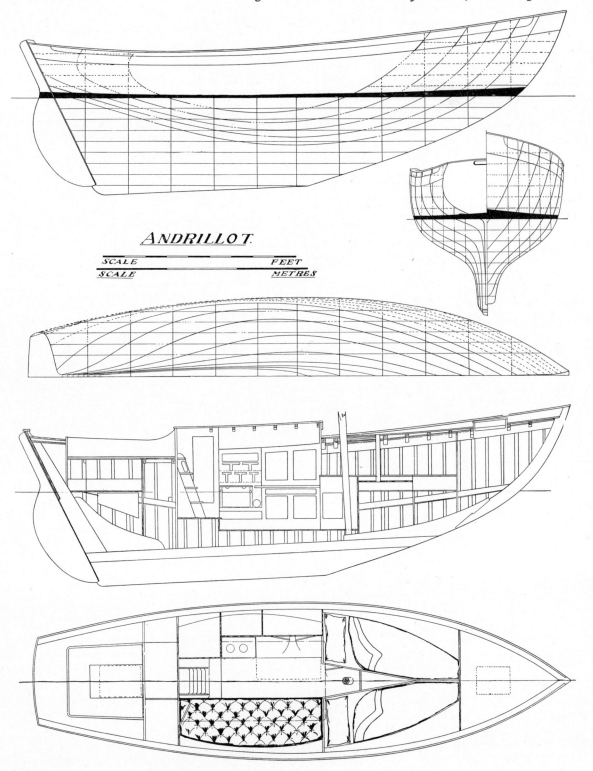

ANDRILLOT.

SCALE _____ FEET
SCALE _____ METRES

enough to take the owner and his wife into all the lovely little harbours they wish to visit, yet large enough to house them comfortably for the voyages they wish to make.

When we meet a transom-sterned boat with very little overhang forward and a gaff rig we expect to find a clumsy hull under water, but as so often happens we are deceived by the outward signs, for under water *Andrillot* has very clean lines indeed. The water-lines and buttocks being very fair, she is really a fine-bottomed boat, though as her sections will show she has been designed to give a great deal of room inside.

In the accommodation plan we see that she has no fo'c'sle as we generally think of such things in small craft, but instead has a double berthed cabin extending just abreast the mast, abaft of which is a cosy cabin with settee to starboard 6 ft. 6 in. in length, and long enough and large enough to be used as a bed in case a third was carried, while to port are the dresser and chart table. At the after end of the cabin the stove, pantry and oilskin locker are arranged. One climbs up the companion way at the after end over the bridge deck and into the cockpit, the floor of which is so low that it cannot very well be self bailing.

Now this bridge deck is a fine and comforting thing in the very worst of weather, but one wonders if the owner will not in years to come abolish it (although it forms a fine sail bin) and instead have two steps up from the cabin straight into the cockpit, for this little vessel, as can be seen, is buoyant, and would very seldom ship water heavy enough into the cockpit to make the need for the bridge deck felt.

Andrillot's rudder, being hung on the stern, makes for simplicity and strength, and if anything should ever happen to such a rudder it is the simplest thing in the world to unship and reship it, and such little vessels have carried out this operation at sea.

The sail plan shows her gaff cutter rig, the well-shaped topsail setting the whole off to perfection. The mast, it will be noticed, is well aft, and as the forestay goes to practically the stem head she has a large staysail, and the jib stay running parallel with this makes for an efficient combination of headsails.

Such a rig only needs a single crosstree, and *Andrillot* is an example of simplicity throughout. But this simplicity has been obtained without any loss of efficiency and we cease to wonder at the 850 miles cruise made by W. Barton and his wife without the aid of an engine, for *Andrillot* is a fine example of a transom-sterned gaff cutter now becoming more and more rare in spite of its low cost and upkeep.

· 12 ·

STOR DRAGON

Length, overall	-	-	35 ft. 3 in. = 10·74 m.	Length, water-line	-	23 ft. 1 in. = 7·03 m.
Beam	-	-	7 ft. 8 in. = 2·33 m.	Draught	-	-	4 ft. 11 in. = 1·50 m.
Displacement	-	-	3 tons = 3048 kilos.	Sail Area. Y.R.A.	-	444 sq. ft. = 32 sq. m.
Lead Keel	-	-	1·67 tons = 1700 kilos.			

SOME four years ago Johan Anker brought out the Dragon One design class and boats to this class proved to be such dear little racers that they found favour in most of the European countries. Wherever a Dragon class has been formed it has increased rapidly in numbers, the reason being that these boats possess all the points a one design class should have, for they are cheap to build, are fast and seaworthy little craft for their size, and are also easy to handle and maintain.

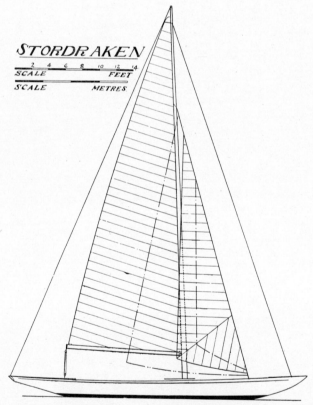

Enlarging this successful design slightly, Johan Anker built himself a small cruiser in which he and his wife have cruised for a fortnight on end, and these plans show the latest developments of that cruiser.

In the lines plan we see the sheer and lines of this cruiser, and rising above it a turtle deck, which would give more room inside, and because the bent frames can be continuous would make for a stronger hull as a whole, and though one would be unable to walk on the side decks when in harbour we have to remember that we do very little walking about on such a small cruiser as this.

The accommodation plan shows Anker's present enlarged Dragon's arrangement, while the solid line drawn above tells us how much more room can be obtained inside with such an arrangement for the deck. So in these plans we see first of all a successful cruising racer developed from the Dragons as well as a third stage of development proposed by Anker for his own use.   So this set of plans gives us food for thought, as we can now share a designer's ideas and problems and have all the fun of wondering just how such a vessel would behave in different states of wind and sea. We must remember that with such a vessel a man can walk through the ship to the fore hatch to

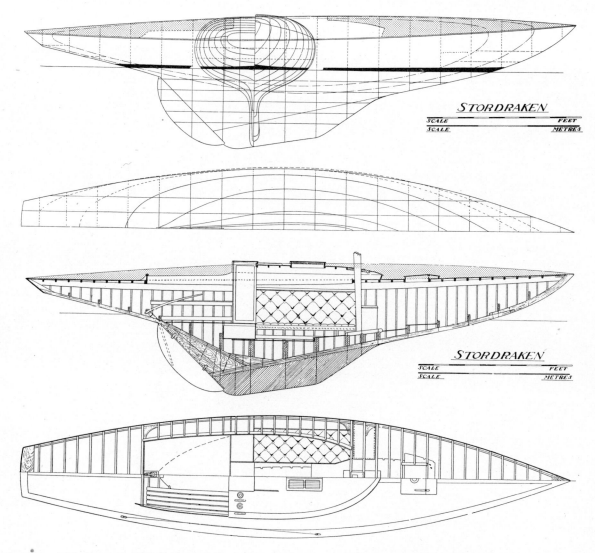

take down and change the headsails, and that with a hatchway immediately abaft the mainmast he can reach through the deck to the tack of the mainsail, while with the boom end within reach of the cockpit there is no need at all for anyone to scramble over her decks to make or shorten sail, and so there is no fear of falling overboard.   Therefore it will be seen that such a deck, if planned and used properly, actually makes for safety at sea, as it keeps people down below all the while.

The sail plan shows a snug Bermudian cutter rig with the sails within the vessel's water-line length where they are easily handled, and though such a proposal as this by Anker is at first strange to our sight it nevertheless opens up a great field of thought as until we have the courage to think out new things there can be no improvement and development in our cruisers.

· 13 ·

WAL BOOT

Length, overall - 27 ft. 10⅝ in. = 8·50 m.   Length, water-line - 23 ft. 7½ in. = 7·20 m.
Beam   -   -   7 ft. 2⅝ in. = 2·20 m.   Draught   -   -   4 ft. 3⅛ in. = 1·30 m.
Displacement - 1·30 tons   = 1320 kilos.   Sail Area   -   -   317 sq. ft. = 29·40 sq. m.

IN our lives there are evenings which we have spent with friends, that are always very pleasant and enjoyable to look back on, and various things bring them very vividly back to us.

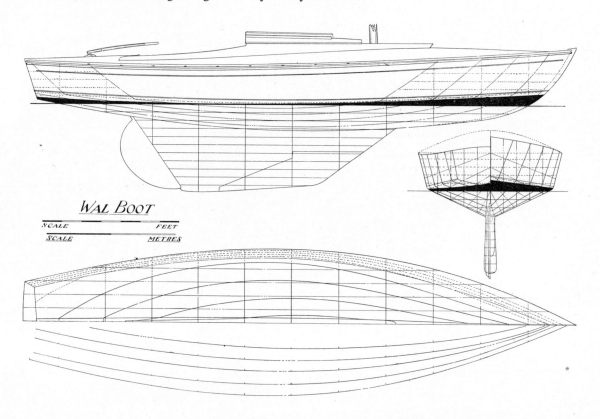

One such evening for me was that spent with Hans Domizlaff at his home, which looks down on the river Elbe, and the constant flow of shipping in and out of Hamburg. My host was a great engineer, a first class seaman and navigator, and above all this a poet and dreamer, so it was not surprising that we suddenly discovered with a shock that it was early morning and time for bed. With us that night, to complete my contentment, was Erich Laeiz, whose friendship I have valued for a great many years. The plans of this Wal Boot (Whaleboat) recall that evening so vividly that it seems but yesterday.

We spent much of the evening in Hans's study, in which we could sit and quietly let our thoughts travel over the seven seas of the world and to every subject under the sun, for there he had paintings, electrical inventions of his own and models of his various ships, from *Dirk III*, the 70-foot cruising yawl designed by Charles Nicholson, to the small Wal Boot. As I looked at this small model I could feel that the idea behind it was that of producing the smallest safe seaworthy one design racing cruiser and as Hans remarked, when you are boxing unless the other man's fist has travelled a certain distance there is no force behind it, and his idea of overhangs follows that thought for he contends that if the boat is at all times in contact with the sea it cannot receive a violent blow from it. So the over-hangs of this boat are so short as to be almost non-existent. This of course means a saving in expense, for the boat

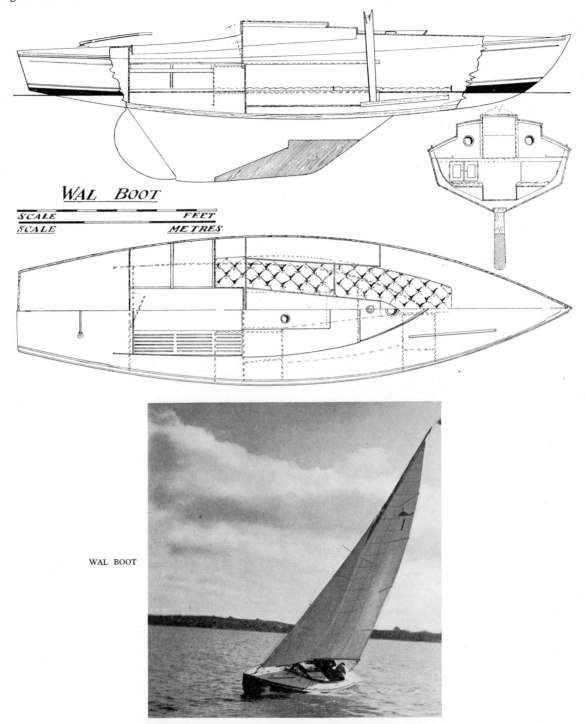

WAL BOOT

WAL BOOT

SCALE   FEET
SCALE   METRES

is cut off once her effective length in smooth water is reached, and these plans show how well the dream of designing and forming a class of small cruising boats for impecunious owners was fulfilled.

The lines show that, though she has a chine, the Wal Boot is very fast indeed, for if we ignore the corners on the buttocks at the chine we see the lines are very easy and sweet, while as we look at the water-lines and diagonals it is difficult to believe that such easy and fair lines can belong to a chine boat until we look at the sections, and then we see that with her rising floor and flaring topsides this boat is a far better proportioned cruiser than many of her round bilged sisters. There is no reason why such a little vessel, in spite of her chine, should not prove fast and seaworthy, and if only all chined boats were designed with so much care and understanding there would not be the prejudice against them there is to-day.

The accommodation plan shows there are bunks for three in this little craft, two to port and one to starboard, while the little galley and pantry is arranged on the starboard side at the after end of the cabin, and immediately abaft

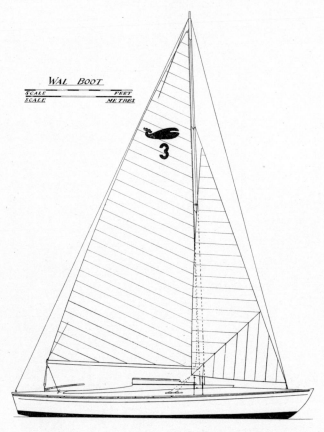

WAL BOOT

this is her cockpit. So she is arranged for sleeping and living aboard without any hardship during summer week-ends.

In the construction plans we see that her keel is one long piece of timber, joining up to the stem with a butt strap on the inside, a strong serviceable yet cheap joint. Bolted to this is the wooden and iron fin keel, two of these keel bolts forming the eyes from which she can be slung on a crane to launch or go aboard a steamer. The construction sections show that the keel and chine are rebated to receive the planking, and so, though the construction is cheap, it is yet very sound.

The sail plan shows the moderate sized mast, which for all its moderation in length gives the mainsail a luff just over twice the length of the main boom. Forward of the mast a well proportioned staysail gives these boats a very efficient rig judged from present day standards. It is not surprising when we look at all this that the class has given such pleasure and joy to a great many people, who otherwise could never have afforded to own their own little ship, for in these wal boots we have fine little racing cruisers in spite of their low cost and chine construction, because Hans Domizlaff who was responsible for the class had a clear view of what they were aiming at, and also a great knowledge of the sea and the ships.

· 14 ·

SKARPSNO (=SPITSGATTER)

Length, overall	- 26 ft. 3 in. = 8·00 m.	Length, water-line	- 21 ft. 6 in. = 6·50 m.
Beam	- 6 ft. 0 in. = 1·80 m.	Draught -	- 4 ft. 3 in. = 1·30 m.
Displacement	- 2·16 tons = 2194 kilos.	Sail Area	- 210 sq. ft. = 19½ sq. m.

Owner, TONY SOMERS   *Designer*, ERLING L. KRISTOFERSEN   *Builder*, NILS T. SCRIVNER

EARLY in May, Tony Somers spoke to me on the telephone and asked if we would like to fit out his 19½ square metre double-ended racer, which was arriving from Norway ; and as Johan Anker had interested me very much in these little boats, we looked after *Skarpsno* from the moment she arrived at Southampton, and towed her to Cowes to step the mast and fit her up.

SKARPSNO OUT TO WINDWARD OF THE FLEET

Skarpsno proved a very interesting little vessel. As will be seen from her lines she has very short overhangs, very V'd sections which make for steep buttocks but an easily driven boat, and very easy and fair diagonals and water-lines. In this boat as in others, we notice that the water-lines once they arrive at the keel develop into almost true streamlines, and one would expect her to slide along in the lightest of airs and at all times without any effort at all, for the sections cut down the wetted surface to a minimum.

From the construction plan we see that the mast is stepped on the deck, and this was the only thing that I could see wrong in this little craft ; for the deck was hardly stiff enough to take the thrust of the mast, and it is probable the owner will stiffen this slightly through the winter, though it has stood all through the summer.

When sailing her one feels that a stiff girder is needed under the mast to take its thrust.

From the construction plan we see the forestay shackled directly into an eye bolt in the deck, and the tension is adjusted by a nut underneath, a method which makes for cleanness above deck, but which makes adjustment rather awkward, as it takes two men to tension that stay, one to watch and the other to work under the deck.

The main framing, stem, fore gripe, keel, sternpost and stern chock are very simple yet strong, and her planking follows the practice of having all its joints glued, there being no caulking whatever, a method which seems to work very well and to keep the sides as smooth as a bottle.

The reason for this 19½ square metre appearing in the cruising section is that she has been used more for cruising than for racing by her owner, and most of the small and fascinating creeks in the Solent have seen *Skarpsno* this summer. Her owner uses an air mattress and takes everything he needs for the week-end, for *Skarpsno* is so arranged

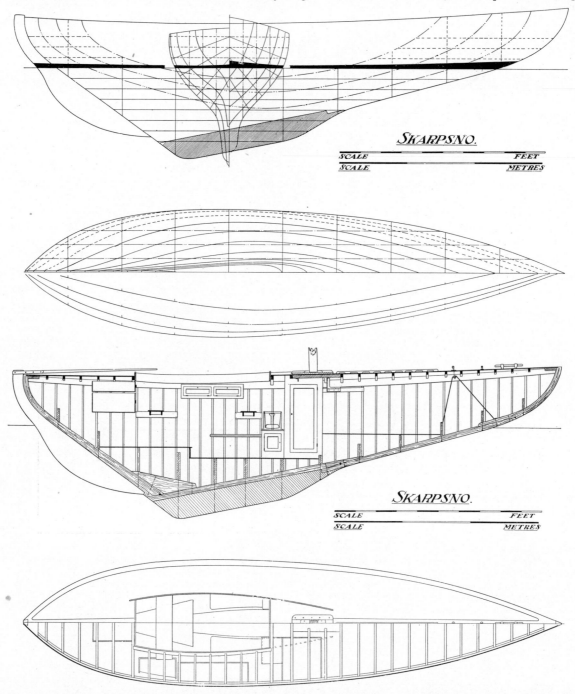

that all of these things stow out of the way, and leave her cockpit free for racing or day sailing, as the after end of the cockpit is formed by a series of very useful drawers in which are stowed charts, blankets, and food all ready to the helmsman's hand yet out of sight and mind until required.

The sail plan shows that though the area is small for such a craft it is very efficient. The top of the mainsail being 32 ft. above the deck gives the mainsail a luff which is three times the length of the main boom, which being 9 ft. 6 in. is no longer than that used on an international 14-footer. The jib halyard being 25 ft. above the deck takes this sail very high, and the rig makes up for its small area by its efficient proportions. This added to the very easily driven and deep hull gives *Skarpsno* a good turn of speed, and also makes her very comfortable for week-end and day cruising, for when standing on her floor which, as will be seen from the plan, is very low, the coaming is shoulder high and this great depth gives one a feeling of comfort and safety.

Tony very kindly loaned her to me for the Review of the Fleet at Spithead by H.M. the King on May 20 this year, and on this day I was a very naughty boy. The Review area was closed at 1.30 p.m. with the firing of the first gun, and we were only just leaving Cowes at the time ; but we wished to see the Review, and, with an easterly wind,

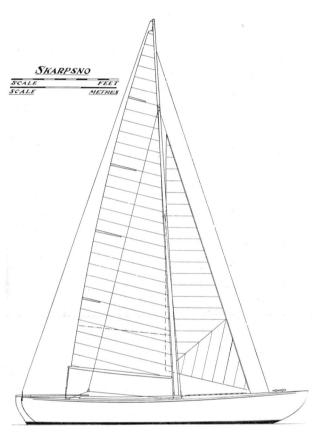

SKARPSNO

started beating towards the centre of the fleet. We tacked through it while the picket boats were out of the way, and directly they approached to shoo us off we would tack outwards, and in this way got half-way through the fleet before we were told to go to our billet. All this time *Skarpsno* sailed extremely well, for though we often lost our wind entirely behind the great ships anchored, yet her hull, with its very easy lines would slide on right through the calm patch and she kept moving all the time.

Early on we had decided to anchor on the Ryde Middle near the *Kaler*, the Esthonian submarine, and help form the Southern border line to the Royal Yacht's passage, where we should be in the orchestra stalls and get a good view of her as she came through, and here we anchored. Soon one of the picket boats came charging up and asked us if we had a berth and we said " Yes! thank you " for we had a lovely berth at the western end of the line of foreign warships. He looked at his chart and saw that no place had been alloted to us, and so he told us we must move. We accordingly started to hoist sail and get the anchor, but as everything should be still, he decided, very kindly we thought, that it would be better if we stayed where we were, and so all was well.

The huge array of our battleships, though not representing the whole of our Navy, filled us with pride as we gazed at them, and one thought that though we were lovers of peace, here was an array of ships and men which would give anyone all the trouble they needed if they provoked us into war. Away to the westward stretched battleships representing nearly every nation in the world, and almost everyone must have hoped that the fleets of all nations would only ever be used for reviews, and that they would never be called upon to fire in anger.

Preceded by the Trinity House steamer, the King steamed through the Fleet, and as we formed one of the line of ships through which he passed we manned *Skarpsno*, though there were only two of us, and cheered our King as he went through, after which the fly past of the Fleet air arm gave us more food for thought. Then we were allowed to get under way, and we sailed through the fleet greeting the various foreign battleships as we passed.

These ships were most interesting, but there is no doubt that the *Admiral Graf von Spee* the German battleship, was the finest looking ship of them all. As the various steamers passed her everyone on board gave her a rousing

GERMAN BATTLESHIP

MOTOR BOAT IN TOW WITH BOWS BASHED IN

cheer, for everyone was stirred to admiration by this very fine looking vessel. Hearing these spontaneous cheers I felt that though we are always decrying our own countrymen, they are still, as always, level headed and fair, and so free from pettyness that they could cheer so fine a ship straight from their hearts though she belonged to another country.

The wind now fell right away, and with hardly a breath we sailed past Ryde to Cowes. Ahead of us we saw the ocean racer *Bloodhound*, and thought what a fine chance for a race, and knowing the run of the tides and where the gentlest of airs would come from, and having such an able little vessel as *Skarpsno* under us, we had caught and passed *Bloodhound* before we reached Ryde. It is not unlikely that those aboard were more taken with the sights around them than with getting the utmost out of their craft, whereas we had seen the fleet and were content to sail and enjoy *Skarpsno's* sailing ability. So we came back to Cowes from where we saw the searchlight and firework display by the fleet, which really looked fine when the whole of it was lit up.

THE FLEET IS ALL LIT UP

· 15 ·

A LAND CRUISE

A LECTURE TOUR THROUGH THE COUNTRIES BORDERING
THE BALTIC

LAST October I received a letter with the Stockholm postmark. It proved to be an invitation from Dr. P. Collinder of the Svenska Kryssarklubben to lecture before them in February; and as I had already been asked to lecture in Holland, Germany and Norway, I decided right away to make a lecture tour of the countries bordering the Baltic, as this would be most interesting, for not only would I meet old friends in these lands, but I would see their countries under winter instead of summer conditions. Though at first sight such a land cruise may seem out of place in this book, it was made amongst people who are bound together in the brotherhood of the sea by such things as the sound of creaking blocks, the patter of reef points on a sail and the wind shrieking through the rigging, the swish of the bow wave and the roar of breaking seas, by low clouds rushing past the moon on stormy nights, and the silvery pathway across the water seeming to lead straight up to the moon and down to the bottom of the ocean on peaceful nights at sea. And as we go through life we find that friendships made on and because of the sea are the most enduring. My land cruise, then, because of all this, has its place in a book on the sea.

My first lecture was arranged for Friday, February 5, in Amsterdam, and as it was impossible for me to leave Cowes until that morning, this meant flying across the North Sea, the plane leaving Croydon at 1 p.m., making an early start from Cowes necessary. It was blowing a gale of wind that morning and raining hard, and low clouds kept visibility on the ground to a very short distance. None of the planes could leave for Paris, as conditions were so bad, and the pilot of our plane said he did not think he would be able to land in Amsterdam, but would go down in Rotterdam instead; but after I had explained to him that Dudok van Heel would be waiting for me in Amsterdam, he, being a true Dutchman, said he would get down in Amsterdam if he possibly could.

I always like to fly soon after a serious accident, for then all the pilots and ground staff are most careful, and only just previously, under similar conditions, one of these air liners had crashed into a house while taking off from Croydon, killing all on board, and I knew that such could not be our fate. With a roar the aeroplane came to life and soon we were in the air with everything blotted out by the thick driving mist and rain. However, our pilot climbed away up clear of all this low driving rain and quite soon we were up in bright sunshine with a flat level floor of grey clouds below us, which here and there had waves on its skyline. The sky was deep blue overhead, so it seemed we were riding along on the top of this rolling layer of cloud. The North Sea crossing was very pleasant indeed, but as we came over the Dutch coast the pilot had to dive down into the rain much below us, and soon visibility was down to less than 100 yards again. However, we went on down until we were just skimming over the sea, and picking up the coastline we once more climbed and made our way to Amsterdam. The pilot having run his distance came down, and we circled round and round the aerodrome for some minutes without finding it though all the bright lights were switched on. So we came into Amsterdam safe and sound, and there was Dudok van Heel looking as cheerful as ever; his smile seemed to disperse the mist and rain, and as we motored along I thought how wonderfully close Holland was to us, as I had only left London two hours before, and was now yarning away to Dudok as we sped along the level roads.

Dudok's lovely estate is within half a mile of Amsterdam, and he with his brothers and sisters have houses on their 25-acre estate, which gives them a great deal of freedom as it is well wooded, and even in the winter birds are singing there. A 50-yard wide stream winds its way through the estate, and with water, trees and green lawns the place gave a feeling of peace and contentment though so close to a great city.

My lecture was to follow a dinner at the Royal Netherland Sailing and Rowing Club, and through the early stages of the dinner, with everyone chatting happily away, I really wondered if they would not be happier continuing their yarning and talking rather than listening to a lecture from me. However, the dinner was so enjoyable that I soon ceased to worry, as I sat between the Commodore, the owner of *Zeearend*, and Dudok, and opposite had de Vries Lentsch Senior and Junior, as well as the editor of *De Waterkampioen*. Eventually we all trooped into the large lecture hall, the lights were turned out, and my talk on sailing across oceans, racing round day courses, and the designing, building and handling of small sailing vessels, started.

Normally a lecturer uses sixty slides for a lecture, taking one hour, but I had double this number, as I think that sight is the greatest of all our senses, for one glance at anything will tell us more than pages of writing and more

DE VRIES LENTSCH SENIOR   AND JUNIOR

THE COMMODORE AND   THE EDITOR OF "WATERKAMPIOEN"

than an hour of descriptive talk. Moreover, I was lecturing in a foreign land, and pictures were of even greater help than they would be normally. So in 1½ hours I had sailed across the Atlantic three different times, in *Typhoon*, a 35-footer, *Diablesse*, a 44-footer, and *Landfall*, which was 60 ft. on the water-line; this, with some coastal cruises, such as sailing down from Norway and to France, balanced up the cruising section of the lecture. Then we raced and won the King's Cup with *Endeavour*, raced in twelve-metres, eights, sixes, 14-footers and canoes, and so covered all sorts of sailing on the sea. Once during the talk I wondered if I ought to be there lecturing on yachting to people who had started the sport in our country by presenting Charles II with his first yacht; for the word " yacht " is of Dutch origin, like the sport itself, and it is only natural that Holland, with its network of inland waterways and seas, should find great pleasure on the water, for in Holland almost every man is a first-class waterman.

The really strange thing is that at the time when Holland presented Charles II with his first yacht, London people were still travelling by water. About 1645 the Thames watermen had appealed to Charles I to restrict the hackney carriages, which were considered to be very noisy and uncomfortable to travel in, but when Cromwell ruled he would not listen to the watermen, and removed all restrictions on hackney carriages, so that by the middle of the eighteenth century Londoners were travelling by land and beginning to desert the water. To-day it would be impossible to get about London by water, as the network of streams which ran through the city is now no more, and one sees the York water-gate an eighth of a mile from the river bank, while, as we all know, the Strand, whose very name tells its story, is now a quarter of a mile away from the river. But thoughts such as these were only flashes of a second, and came when the audience was laughing at a joke, for unless there is something to laugh at every once in a while one cannot expect an audience to last for an hour or more. It is difficult to tell, but almost everyone seemed to enjoy the lecture, and so far as I could see no one went to sleep. Speeches were given afterwards, and then for some strange reason a crowd of us decided to visit a very old flat boat. Before the cabin was filled with smoke and the fumes of gin I had a chance to see the sturdiness of her construction. Built entirely of oak, she was very old and still hard and sound, and one imagined that such a vessel could and did last as long as 200 years.

DUDOK

Being practically a teetotaller, I have always marvelled at the sailing men of all nationalities and their love for smoking, yarning and drinking, and this night was no exception. Pretty soon nearly everyone was talking, and no one seemed to care very much whether any one listened or not. All of this went on for a considerable time, more and more gin bottles and cigars being produced to take the place of those that were nothing but the " empty form of the departed spirit ". In that smoke-filled cabin, cruises and many long voyages were made through gales of wind and over summer seas, vessels were designed and a great number of races sailed again, all the time the fog becoming thicker and thicker within until it was difficult to see a man four feet away. Finally someone suggested opening the hatch, but by now all the cigars were going full blast and it made little difference.

We have a picture of Dutch people being unexcitable, but those hours showed that they are full of life and energy, just as much as we in England are. It seems to me that finally the gin began to run out, otherwise I feel sure we should still be there yarning away, and so eventually we drove to Dudok's home and bed with just another little drink and a quiet yarn before turning in.

Next morning J. Loeff, Holland's representative on the International Yacht Racing Union, called, and drove Dudok and myself at a fearful speed in his car. We travelled so fast that both of us were sick, for Dudok like myself can easily be made sick in a car. However our career finally came to an end at the Amsterdamsche Scheepswerf, and here we met again G. de Vries Lentsch, Jnr., who showed us all round his well-equipped yard. The whole of this yard was extremely interesting to me, for the drawing offices, the machinery and the workshops, slipways and building berths were all carefully planned and laid out. As the yard is at the end of an island it is almost entirely surrounded by water, so that vessels can be launched from a great many slipways, for the whole has been designed to take advantage of its natural surroundings. Here we saw *Zeearend*, which G. de Vries Lentsch had built, and a great many powerful motor yachts being built in steel. The machine for bending frames was of great interest to me. In this country we generally dog the template of the frame on to a slab, the frame is then put into a long furnace and then when red hot bent down round and dogged down to the template, all of which entails a great deal of time and money. But de Vries Lentsch, with his bending machine, bends his frame cold and so saves the expense of the slab, dogs and furnace, and the photograph of him with his son by this machine will explain how it works. A ram is continually driven to and fro between two buffers placed a foot or so apart, these being adjustable while the ram itself drives back and forth. These two buffers can be adjusted with a worm gear, and the ram and its two buffers and two men, quietly and firmly bend frames to their desired shape. It is somewhat after the form of a power hammer.

DE VRIES LENTSCH JNR. AND HIS SON AT THEIR BENDING MACHINE   DE VRIES LENTSCH JNR., UFFA AND DUDOK

Away to the right of this picture can be seen a great wheel, which when swung round by hand works a hand bending machine. The efficiency of this machine is just one detail in a yard full of efficient designing, building and launching methods. It does us all good to see people using their brains, and good methods.

We next visited the yard of his elder brother, and here again a great deal of water flowed around about the yard.

What must be one of the finest laying-up stores in the world is situated here, and in this we saw Dudok's 6-metre amongst a great number of other vessels. Up on the second floor were several of the International Star Class, and standing side by side were a Dutch and a German Star Class yacht, presumably of one design, but as will be seen from the photograph they vary a great deal. I am holding a piece of board on the stern of one, and it will be seen that it stands some 4 inches above the deck, and that is the difference in the depth of the transoms of these two boats. With such variations it is not to be wondered that there is a great deal of difference in sailing different Stars, all of which causes discontent, for they are supposed to be a one-design.

We next went to the building sheds, and here *Tromp II* was half completed. She is Dudok's family cruiser, designed for the shallow waters of the Zuyder Zee, and also with the fact in mind that she might one day take part in the long distance racing at sea. Her plans in an earlier chapter of this book will describe this vessel fully. As always, when building a new ship, there were many problems and points for Dudok to talk over and straighten out with W. de Vries Lentsch, Senior, and so after looking at the other vessels being built we spent an hour or so in his drawing office working out a great many details of *Tromp II*.

We next visited a lovely sailing club, and though it was winter, and all the water had been frozen for several days, the club-house was filled with members, drinking, smoking and yarning over past and future races, rigs, hulls and sails, and though we look upon sailing as a summer sport it nevertheless occupies our time and thoughts throughout the year, for here in the dead of winter were yachtsmen gathering together, visiting their new vessels being built, designing still newer ones and quite happy yarning about sailing and the sea. Once more the evening came round, and Dudok gave a dinner at his home, all of which was very enjoyable, after which we went to a Fancy Dress Ball, and here was a sight of Holland enjoying itself. The ballroom was a place of colour, for the costumes were of every hue and variety, and this again showed that we inhabitants of the colder countries with Northern blood in our veins are every bit as excitable as the Latin races south of us, and are able to enjoy everything that life offers. So another evening came to an end in the early hours of the morning, and on Monday the 7th I said farewell to Amsterdam, and felt sad at parting with its people, especially Dudok and his family, who had been so kind to me.

My aeroplane left at 12.45 noon, and in four hours it arrived at Malmo in the South of Sweden. The weather was fairly clear as we started, but soon low clouds hid the land beneath, which was not visible until we came to the Baltic, where we were some miles to leeward of our course, for we passed to the east of the Island of Fernhern, and looking down on the frozen sea my mind went back to *Vigilant's* cruise and the strong winds she encountered at this point both sailing to Stockholm and on her return trip. The ice was not very thick, and the few steamers could plough their way through it ; we saw one very clearly with a lane of broken ice astern of her, and in front the Baltic frozen completely over, for we were now flying very low in order to keep the land and sea in sight, as we were soon to land in Copenhagen.

Once more we made a safe and perfect landing, and before we left again an interesting thing happened. Some friends were seeing off a young chap who was intoxicated, though it was only the afternoon ; the stewardess, as this chap went by, said to the captain of the plane " Will you take this man? " and he said " No! " and there is no doubt his decision was right, although rather hard on the chap bound for Malmo, for an aeroplane is not the place for a person who is intoxicated, as one never knows what such a man would get up to. So this man crossed by steamer instead of by plane. Malmo is only a few minutes away from Copenhagen by air, so we were soon out of Denmark

THE TRANSOM OF THE WHITE STAR IS 5 INCHES DEEPER THAN THE BLACK STERNED STAR

and into Sweden ; but it is the farthest north the planes work in winter, so that my journey had to be continued by rail. My train did not leave until 10.00 p.m., and I had time for a comfortable dinner.

The weather here was extremely cold. I was told it was 20 degrees below freezing, and the people kept looking and wondering because I did not wear a hat, but as I have never worn one all my life I did not feel the need for one. Another point I discovered was that I was still wearing no underclothes. Dudok had written me a long letter telling me I should wear plenty, as it was much colder in Holland than in the South of England, and I had carefully rehearsed wearing a vest under my shirt for two days before leaving, but I now found that I had forgotten all about it the day I left, and this night was one on which I imagined I should have worn an under vest. The difference in the climate of the Baltic and the South of England, where semi-tropical trees grow in the open all the year round, was most marked. In England, especially the south, we enjoy sailing in the winter as well as in the summer, but this was out of the question in the Baltic, for here the sea was frozen.

My night train to Oslo left at 10.00 p.m. and through the night of February 7 and 8 I travelled from Malmo to Oslo, arriving there at 9.40 a.m. on the morning of the 8th. On the train I met Hans Holter, and as we came off it there was Yngvar Jespersen, Secretary of the Kongelig Norsk Seilforening, to meet us. We drove to my hotel and left my luggage there, after which I went to the headquarters of the Norsk Seilskab Til Skibbrudnes Redning, which like our own Lifeboat Institution is supported entirely by voluntary contributors, who maintain a fleet of a dozen motor and sixteen sailing craft, the service now being 44 years of age. I was most interested in their different models, and noted, for example, that whereas our lifeboats are on the shore and only launched when needed, the Norwegians' cruise about on their station all the while, and so have to be bigger vessels to afford accommodation and the comfort needed, for very sturdy vessels and men are needed to work on the rock-bound coast of Norway, where the thermometer is below freezing and where they have to contend with ice and snow as well as the gales that sweep this coast.

Generally speaking they are double-ended ketch-rigged craft, the overhanging bow being good for breaking thin ice as it runs up over the ice and then pressing down breaks a way through. These bows are raked and are shaped very similar to those on the big ice-breaking steamers. There is a model there of the first lifeboat built in 1892—she is a very round chunky ketch boat; the model of the second built in 1893 has finer bows and cutter rig, but in 1894 they went back to ketch rig, to which they have kept ever since. All the earlier lifeboats had their rudders hung on their pointed sterns, but now the models have a short canoe stern abaft the rudder, and the man to whom this service owes most for its designs was the late Colin Archer, who did so much good work for the lifeboats and fishing craft of Norway. A great many of these however are still much the same as they were 100 years ago, long open double-ended boats somewhat similar to the old Viking ships, and it is amongst this fleet that the life-boats work. There are various pictures round the room, one showing two men clinging to a capsized boat with the

NORWAY NEEDS STURDY LIFEBOATS

lifeboat just coming to their aid, and another of a lifeboat towing in six of these long boats with three men in each, for the off-shore wind was so strong on this occasion that they were being driven out to sea, where they would have been lost had it not been for this powerful vessel towing them back to the coast. The hour spent in this office went all too quickly, for these lifeboats, because they stay at sea with their crews living on board, are near to a cruising man's heart, and it gave me great pleasure to study their hull forms, rigs and accommodation, for here were brave little ships developed for keeping station on a rock-bound relentless coast.

Then Jespersen, Hans Holter and myself journeyed up to the higher lands above Oslo, where after some schnapps to keep the cold out, one for each leg and arm, we had lunch, a meal I thoroughly enjoyed, for I had stupidly for-gotten to eat breakfast on the train, and with the temperature 20 degrees below freezing, the coldest day of the winter there, one enjoyed and needed good food. All round everything was covered with snow, pretty and kindly enough to look upon, for to-day in the sunshine it gave a fairy-like impression to everything; but one felt the crushing power of this falling snow on long dark winter nights.

We arrived back in Oslo before dark (as I was lecturing) and visited Oslo Handelsstands Forening to see the lecture room where everything was arranged and in order. I then went to my hotel to sort the slides out, arriving back in the lecture room at 7.30, half an hour before time, to meet Crown Prince Olaf of Norway, who, it will be recalled, has frequently visited British waters and successfully raced his 6-metre amongst us. We had a most enjoyable yarn, at least it was very enjoyable to me, for the Crown Prince is not only a first-class helmsman but a student of the rules and of the design and build of craft.   Suddenly I looked round and discovered that, while we had been yarning, the great room had filled with people ; there seemed to be some 500 of them, and the sight of this big crowd, and knowing that I had to talk to them for 1½ hours, seemed to sap all my energy, and I suddenly felt very nervous and frightened and made a dive for a table in an ante-room where a man dispensed sunshine in glasses. After several whiskies I once more felt normal and that I could push the side of the house down if need be, and I returned to the lecture room with a large glass of the beautiful amber liquid which raises our spirits.

The Crown Prince made a speech in Norwegian to introduce me, repeating it in English afterwards ; then the lights went out and away we went on the lecture, the slides as before showing pictures varying from square rigged ships, porpoises, whales, birds, seas and all the things we meet when sailing our vessels across oceans, along coasts or racing them.   Then, the talk safely delivered in the 1½ hours, the Crown Prince thanked me both in the Norwegian and the English tongue, after which there was a most enjoyable dinner, which as usual went on and on, for it was so

TO PATROL HER ICY, RELENTLESS, ROCKY COAST

pleasant that no one wished to leave, and the first time I realised it was getting late (for besides not wearing underclothes I never carry a watch), was when a note came to me, for I was sitting next to the Crown Prince, who was in the chair, to say " It is past two, don't you think you should go home? "   But by now the room had a lovely smoke screen across it, and all the world seemed mellow and rosy, and I was quite content to slip the note into my pocket along with the tickets I had just bought for the K.N.S. 10½ square metre lottery boat, Ljungstrom rigged.   For we only go through life once, and mellow moments like these can never be recaptured as time marches on, and we part and are gone, and it is often years before we meet again.   Finally, however, we all went to bed happy and contented and at peace with all the world and life in general.

February 9 dawned, and after breakfast Engineer Oppeguard, Yngvar Jespersen and myself went to the Viking Hall, where the new building when completed will form a cross which will house three vessels, the Gokstaad, Tune and Osberg ships, all of which traversed the seas a thousand years ago.   Standing there one could not help feeling impressed by the fearlessness of the people who travelled in such ships over so many miles of open water.   The plans of two of these and a description of them form the opening chapter of this book.

We next journeyed to Anker's yard, and there met Anker and the Crown Prince.   The four of us wandered round the yard, and as almost everything there was of wood there was a very kindly atmosphere about the whole place, which is lacking in steel buildings, for steel is unsympathetic and lifeless, whereas wood is alive and has faults and virtues and character just as human beings have. In Norway I was constantly reminded of the great part wood plays in our lives. The sweetest music of all comes from wooden instruments, violins and cellos, while the reeds giving some of the loveliest organ notes are also of wood, the tables at which we enjoy our dinners and the chairs upon which we sit are mostly of wood, and finally most of us toddle up a wooden lane to bed; from the cradle to the coffin wood plays a far greater part in our lives than we realise. In Norway even the houses are of wood, as it is such a well wooded country.

One of the first boats we saw was the Crown Prince's 6-metre, which was soon to sail under a British ownership, and whose lines appear in the 6-metre chapter of this book. We then saw his new "six" being built; the hull was complete and the deck beams were being fitted and so there was no doubt as to her being completed before the ice and snow had disappeared. In the middle of this long shop were seen boats of the Dragon class being built, these one-designs coming from Johan Anker's board, and with their low cost, high speed and weatherly qualities these one-designs will go on increasing until finally they become an International class and adopted by most countries of the world. Already there are some seventy of them sailing in British waters, and Johan Anker himself owns an enlarged Dragon in which he and his wife cruise for a fortnight on end. In the far end of this shop was R. G. Perry's blue

THE CROWN PRINCE
AND ANKER

JESPERSON AND HANS HOLTER
IN A SNOW-WHITE SETTING

Noreine having her interior work fitted, so she too was well under way, and it was a pleasure to see such fine examples of the shipwright's art being built. (A description of *Noreine* forms Chapter III in this book.)

We wandered through the blacksmiths' and the fitting shops, and then came to the latest Norwegian lifeboat, which had an amazing amount of timber in her construction. She is double-ended, with the usual raking bow, which will act as icebreaker whenever the occasion arises, and has Bermudian ketch rig, though the wheel house is situated just forward of the mizen mast, for the men handling these ships need all the shelter the designer and builder can give them. Looking at the strength of this vessel one realised that she was intended to be strong enough to go ashore on a rocky coast without coming to a great deal of harm, while her engine is powerful enough to drive her against heavy gales and steep seas. So we had here seen being built, a racing 6-metre and a racing cruiser, both of which would sail the summer seas, and a far sturdier ship made for gales of wind, ice and snow. Now we made our way to Johan Anker's drawing office in which there seemed to be thousands of plans of all sorts of craft from the smallest to the largest. The minutes sped by all too quickly as Johan Anker unfolded and explained the different plans to me, but these moments were some of the happiest I have ever spent or shall ever spend in my life, for here was a master of our craft explaining his different designs and boats. Nowadays people consider it wrong to talk about their trades and call it talking " shop ", but I would far rather hear a man talking about his job than any other subject; a blacksmith, shipwright, watchmaker, or engineer are only on really firm ground when they are talking of their trade and work, and it is far more interesting to hear a man talking of what he so thoroughly understands than to listen to him on subjects on which he has not so great a knowledge. Even now, six months after, I can still recall with pleasure the happy hours spent with Johan Anker in his yard and drawing office, and only hope that fate will take me there again before long.

From Anker's yard we went to see Engineer Oppeguard's new ship being built at the yard belonging to Roberts. This 50-foot cruising schooner was most interesting, for she was built of very heavy timbers and planking, such as are used on the Swedish fishing and coastal boats, and because of this cost far less to build than she would had the scantlings as used for a yacht been employed. There were many unusual things about her: the mainsail was always to stay aloft, brailed up to the gaff and mainmast as the old spankers were in days gone by, and instead of the usual peak halyards a single topping lift from the top of the main topmast head to the outer end of the gaff was used, this enabling the topsail to set equally well on either tack, as there were no halyards for it to press against.

To get head room aft she had a quarter deck, which besides giving room below gave a feeling of superiority, while down below all the details were being developed to make for cosiness and easy work. In the fore end of the dining saloon the drawers containing the knives and plates etc. were double, so that each could be opened either in the saloon or in the galley and pantry forward of it, this enabling the man washing the silver and plates to put them back into the drawer without coming into the saloon. The temperature was still some 20 degrees below zero, and one felt sorry for the men working on this ship, for they had only a roof over them and might therefore be said to be working entirely in the open. However, they were quite happy and contented in their work, and we spoke about them as we were having schnapps back in my hotel before dinner : Jespersen said, " I have always thought that the waiter has the worst job in the world, but to-day I wondered if those shipwrights had not even a harder time." But it was not so : they were creating something with their hands and brain, which is always satisfying in itself. So in the warmth we drank our schnapps, again for each leg and arm, and I forget now if we drank for our head and body and toes and fingers, anyway we were soon warm again and then started our dinner.

In the middle of the dining room was a large table filled with *hors d'œuvres*, and we took our plates and went round this table selecting all the things we fancied. Then having eaten these Jespersen said " What about the second round ? " so round we went once more ; and then Oppeguard said " I suppose we had better complete the course ", and so we once more rounded the table, and now having eaten three great platefuls of tasty morsels we ordered our dinner. 7.15 p.m. came all too soon, for this was the time of my night train for Stockholm, where I should arrive at 7 a.m. Tuesday morning after 12 hours in the train. So I reluctantly said farewell to Oslo, which had created a fairy-like impression upon me with its snow covered trees and hills, and the lights in the various houses which shone brightly through the night.

Once at least during the night the train was held up by snow and ice. It was still dark when we arrived at Stockholm, where I was met by the President of the Svenska Kryssarklubben, Captain K. Nordling, Dr. P. Collinder and Direktor Sigurd Golge and Knud H. Reimers. They handed me, after a very kindly speech of welcome, a programme for their Annual Meeting and for the arrangements in connection with it. From this I saw that I was free until 7.15 p.m. that night, which was the time their Annual Meeting started, and after the transaction I was to give my lecture which was to be followed by a dinner. So it looked like another long evening, and away I went with Knud to his flat for breakfast, after which I sorted out my lantern slides ready for the evening, while Knud read and studied his morning's letters. Soon Bengt Plym was driving us in his car out to his building yard, the Neglingevarv, amongst the Skerries of Stockholm. It is one of the most interesting and famous yards in Sweden ; here hauled out was the 75 square metre *Bacchant* which they had built last year, and one could not help but admire the lovely workmanship and beautiful material put into her construction. At the same time I reflected that here in the Baltic, where the water was fresh and there were no tides, it was far easier to keep a vessel in perfect condition than it is on the sea, for the salt water itself scours varnish severely. When I built *Vigilant* I varnished her, but sailing continually in salt water wore this varnish off, so that we were constantly revarnishing her, but here in the Baltic the upkeep of vessels is as easy as in the fresh water of the Upper Thames.

All around the water was frozen, and fairly soon Bengt Plym and I were sailing around in his ice yacht, which was great fun, for with no resistance the sails drove her along at an astonishing speed. This silent flight over the ice was most enjoyable, after which a little bit of ski-ing gave us a keen appetite for lunch and Knud and Plym no end of amusement, for having planned my life so that I work hard in the winter to be free in the summer, it was my first shot at ski-ing, which I thoroughly enjoyed, and all the time wondered that this form of travel, so swift and easy, was not invented in North America where instead they solemnly plod along with snow shoes. At one part there was a lovely little hill to scoot down, and Knud took a film as I came down over this, but as I had not fallen over this was wasted, so I once more struggled back to the top and then came diagonally across and down the hill to where Knud ground away on his cinema. Between the top and Knud were two patches of bare ice, and at the second patch my feet shot away down the hill sideways and Knud had the picture he wanted of me completely capsized. I have not seen this, but I imagine myself to look like a windmill. After amusing ourselves a little longer we went back to Plym's house, one room of which was filled with models of a great many craft his family had built in the Neglingevarv. The dining room was full of Viking-like carvings, the sideboard, the hanging lamp and all the walls having such carvings and woodcuts on them, all of which made the room most interesting and gave it character. After this we once more went into the shipyard where Bengt showed me the miniature Viking ship his father had built, she being about half the length of the old ships themselves, and not only was the workmanship admirable but also the sweet lovely lines.

We now motored away back to Stockholm for lunch, for the afternoon was well advanced by this time, and after a schnapp for each leg Bengt said, " That's all for me, as in this country the police may take a blood test for alcohol of any motorist, and if there is 2 per cent. of alcohol in the blood we are locked up, and two schnapps is just under the equivalent of 2 per cent. to me." This seems a far more sensible method than asking a man to say " Truly

rural ". After lunch we had to go and change for the evening, and quite soon I was on my way to the Svenska Kryssarklubben's Annual Meeting.

It was interesting to be at this meeting, and entertaining to see the Kryssarklubben conducting its business much as we do in England. Immediately this was over I again inflicted my lecture upon a large audience. Once more before the lecture press people photographed me, and their artists made sketches, and as Collinder said in a letter when he sent me some press cuttings : " In one of them your head seems to have been left to the care of the editorial barber and the result is cosmetic." You know that " cosmos " means " order " as well as " beauty ", and through the lecture this same artist did sketches of some of the slides I had shown, and it is rather wonderful that a chap should be able to sketch so well in the dark.

Through these lectures I wondered if people were understanding what was being said, but as none of the jokes were ever missed it seemed to me they followed everything, and the three talks I had so far given had given me a great deal of pleasure.

A great many attended the dinner ; we had a most enjoyable evening, and once again the cigars and the wine produced that mellowing effect on us all. Enjoyable and interesting speeches were made on all sides, and everyone felt at peace with all the world, and for this reason the night was well gone before we left the dining table.

The next day, Thursday February 11, Dr. Carl Lidman and I visited a great many interesting places in Stockholm. At 4.00 p.m. we went to the New Museum, where Mr. E. Hägg, President of the Pilotage Board, piloted us round the Museum, which was not yet officially open ; but I remember Mr. Hägg more because he is the son of the famous Amiral Hägg of the Swedish Navy, whose wonderful paintings and drawings are found in all the important places of Sweden, illustrating Swedish maritime history. One is amazed that Amiral Jacob Hägg could crowd so much into a lifetime, for many of his paintings are on a very large scale, and all of them have accuracy as well as being able to portray the ship and her surroundings. His painting of the *Fregatten Eugene* in the Magellan Straits gives a vivid idea of the stretch of water and the low clouds flying past the high rocky cliffs, and imparts a wonderful impression of this wild part of the world. All his pictures have the ability to make one feel the weather as well as the seas in which the ships are sailing.

Generally museums tend to be dull, and this is mainly due I think to their being in badly lit rooms, and the subjects not being arranged to make them interesting and at their best, but here all was different, the museum was well lit and cheerful and everything arranged in the best possible way, and this with Eric Hägg's lucid explanations made the voyage round this museum most enjoyable and instructive, for Sweden with its long coastline has a very interesting maritime history. We lingered so long that we had to scuttle and rush away to get our dinner jackets on, for the board of the Svenska Kryssarklubben were giving a dinner to me at the Grand Hotel Royal that night at 7 p.m. After shaving and putting on my dinner jacket I arrived at the hotel, and here were the Board of Directors in the lobby to receive me, and we solemnly shook hands all round, for the Swedish nation is very formal (early in the evening at least). Even Eric Hägg, who had so kindly showed me round the Museum, and in doing so had revealed his kindliness of heart, was now quite formal, and instead of hugging him and thanking him for the afternoon as I would have liked to do, I solemnly shook hands, and all was well, and so we all trooped in to dinner.

The Grand Royal has a magnificent dining-room, and better still a very fine string orchestra, and as we sat round the round table eating and drinking the orchestra charmed our senses. Half way through the dinner I wrote a note requesting the band to play Handel's *Largo*, which, besides being very impressive, is very tuneful and a favourite of mine, but Direktor Golge assured me that he never heard it except at funerals, and that he was doubtful if they would play it. However, he agreed with me as to its beauty, and my note went to the band, who quite soon began to play it, and not only I, but everyone dining there, enjoyed it thoroughly.

| DR. THORAEUS | GOLGE SEEMS VERY THOUGHTFUL | ERIC HÄGG | THE AUTHOR OF THE POEM |

| AT PEACE WITH ALL THE WORLD | ACROSS THE TABLE | CARL TOO IS CONTENTED | DR. P. COLLINDER |

During dinner I was paid the honour of being asked to be a corresponding member of the Svenska Kryssark-lubben, and I was very touched and delighted at this, for always the Club has had a high place in my thoughts. It seemed to me that its blue and white flag, with a compass on the white ground in the centre, guides the Club forward, for a compass is one of the most important details of any cruising craft, and its appearance on the flag is an inspiration to the Club and all its members to steer straight ahead on their course of fostering and encouraging cruising for all craft and all climes. I only hope that I shall live up to the tradition of this splendid Club, and I promised them there and then to write a chapter " On Sea Going Rigs " for their next Year Book, a chapter which with their kind permission is reproduced in this book.

Later in the evening I was presented with a little poem of welcome signed by all the board sitting round the table, and this I still have and shall cherish always as it recalls that happy evening. Once again time passed all too quickly, and after dinner was over Carl Lidman and I went to his flat, where we yarned away happily, and finally I went away home to Knud's flat to bed.

Friday, February 12, at 10.30, Dr. P. Collinder very kindly showed me how the Swedish charts of Sweden are made ; he being one of Sweden's experts at nautical surveying.

It is well known that the land above the water gives a good indication what the bottom of the sea is like, and that we might regard the bottom of the sea as a submerged part of the landscape we are gazing upon, so that high bold land has usually deep water close in, whereas with low flat land the shoals extend out to sea for miles. It follows that the Swedish coast is a particularly difficult one to survey, for all the landscape is of rocks, full of hills and ridges, and this is equally true of the bottom of the sea. And whereas on mud banks a few soundings enable a chart to be made, for the sea wears them smooth and even, it is not so with the underwater part of Sweden's coastline. The surveying steamer, besides sounding, is fitted with two long poles down under water and a cross bar stayed fore and

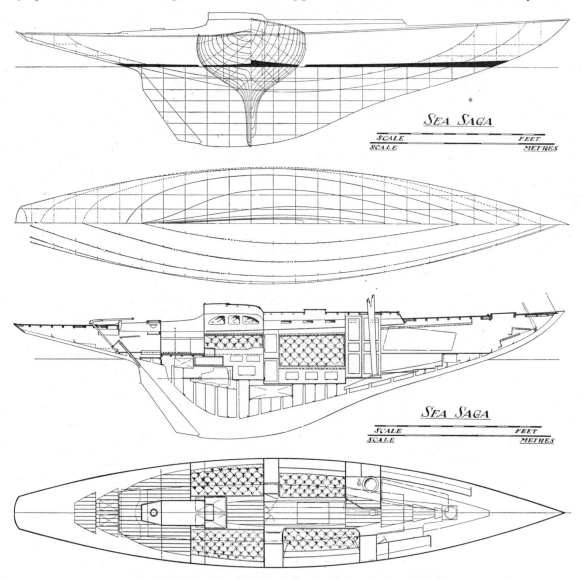

SEA SAGA

SCALE   FEET.
SCALE   METRES

SEA SAGA

SCALE   FEET
SCALE   METRES

aft with which she sweeps for the rocky hills and ridges. This arrangement is very similar to the horizontal bar we use at gymnasium, but inverted under the bottom, and channels are swept thus as it is the only way they can be sure that such a channel is free from a hill or ridge of rock, for several soundings of the lead might easily drop into a crevice or valley and not on the projecting points and spurs.

When we buy a chart we seldom stop to realise all the work that has gone into the making of it, but here this morning I had a vivid picture of it all. There were the surveyors and the ship and their existing charts first of all, and from these expert draughtsmen drew the new charts. These were then etched on copper plates, and finally printed, and after every chart has been printed the plate is taken out, wiped and polished absolutely clean and clear. Then ink is worked into the plate carefully and evenly and another print is made, so that every chart is really a copper-plate etching and a work of art, and when we think that the average chart takes ten months and costs something like £10,000 to produce the first copy, we realise how cheap they really are. Here in Sweden the taxes help to pay for the cost of surveying and making charts, for Sweden, like so many of us, owes her prosperity to the sea and her seamen, and it is therefore only fitting that those living in Sweden and benefiting from this should help to pay for the making of charts for seamen, and this is but another example of the wonderful times in which we live. Here was I travelling round Europe by aeroplane and train, and could not afford to buy even an engine of one train, and yet at my service were not only the trains and the aeroplanes, but all the organisation at the back of it, the thousands of miles of laid track, all of which is only possible because we pool all our resources and money, so the poorest are able to make long journeys in comfort.

Dr. Collinder has been surveying round the North Cape and over most of Sweden's waters, where as well as the depths of the sea and the contours of the sea bed, there are many problems connected with the compass because of the iron ore in that part of the world. The two hours spent with him were happy and interesting ones for me, and all the while he was telling little anecdotes of the people of the North, who after a winter of darkness reckon they can go throughout the summer months without any sleep at all, and the picture I got from him was, that where we have

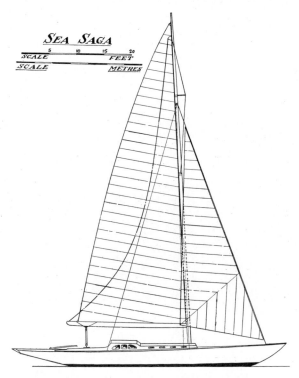

SEA SAGA

SCALE   5   10   15   20   FEET
SCALE   METRES

365 days in our year, each with so many hours of darkness and light, they live their year as though it were one day, the winter being the night and the summer the day. I hope one of these days to visit the people who live under such conditions.

At 12.30 there was a lunch with the Svenska Kryssarklubben, a most enjoyable meal, after which Dr. Thoraeus, the chairman of the Boat Committee, very kindly took me over the Technical College of Sweden, which proved to be very interesting indeed. As can be imagined with so many miles of sheltered waters between the Skerries, the people of Stockholm spend a great deal of time travelling by water, not only for the pleasure of it but because it is the easiest and best way as well as the cheapest (for there are no rails or roads to keep up) to travel around. At this College many models were tested before they were built to carry passengers in the Stockholm Skargard, and I was very pleased indeed to see that a boat to carry 250 passengers was of the V-bottomed hard chined design, for the years to come will see this design used more and more in big ships, as the weight of the propulsive machinery is decreased through the metallurgist giving us lighter and more enduring metals and the engine makers producing lighter engines ; these vessels can reach higher speeds, and plane, making little wash, as they ply between the Skerries of Stockholm, and I imagine that in the future this will apply to the largest liners of the world, though of course they will often meet conditions under which they must slow right down.

As well as the testing tank there was also a very fine wind tunnel, and I would like to have spent days instead of hours here. After this Dr. Thoraeus took me to the archives of the Svenska Kryssarklubben, and here again there is much to see and enjoy, for the Club has a large membership. It prints a monthly magazine and a Year Book, and every year it commissions a designer and builder to produce a cruiser to the Club's ideas, which is disposed of by lottery, a member thus getting a new ship for a krona or so. A great deal of knowledge is put into the design of this vessel, for as can be imagined the Committee are all men with a great knowledge of the sea and its ways, and the Svenska Kryssarklubben is able to pool all its thoughts and pass them on to a designer to be incorporated into the vessel, so each year the lottery boat represents not only the thought and skill of the designer and builder, but also all the experience and thoughts of the Svenska Kryssarklubben's Committee. Three of these vessels appear in this book, *Corinne III* and *IV* and the 1937 lottery boat.

Next I went to see Erick Lundberg, *Bacchant's* owner, who is a great collector of rare rugs and carpets. It will be remembered that he took his 30 square metre *Bacchant* to America and won eleven races out of eleven starts. Then came my last dinner in Stockholm, for I was leaving on the midnight train for Gothenburg at the other side of Sweden, and I felt sad at leaving behind so many good friends, and the capital of Sweden, which was so full of interest to any lover of the sea.

Our train was again delayed by snow and ice, and the wonder is that Sweden is able to keep up such a good service through her long winters, for we were not very late in arriving at Gothenburg, Knud was on the train with me coming down to Gothenburg to see Tommy Adams' cruiser being built.

We made straight for the Palace Hotel across the road where we booked rooms and had breakfast, and quite soon Axel Karlander, Commodore of the Aeolus Yacht Club came along. After a yarn Knud and I motored out to

THE MUSEUM AT GOTHENBURG WAS LIGHT AND CHEERFUL. THE PAINTINGS ON THE WALLS ARE BY AMIRAL HÄGG

A. B. Sverr's yard, where cruisers and racers were being built. The boat we had come to see was the one Knud had designed for Tommy Adams; as her lines show she has a light displacement and an easily driven hull. She was planked and being sheered down before her deck beams were fitted across, and looked a very fast piece of wood, that was still large enough to have comfortable quarters aboard. Here again wood was used for the construction of the workshops and building sheds, and even now in the dead of winter new hauling-out sheds were being built.

Besides building yachts of all types, A. B. Sverr also makes nautical intruments, compasses, lamps, and what were more interesting than even these were the lovely models being made for the different museums, ranging from old sailing ships to the modern steamers and aeroplanes. Meanwhile the Göta Älv was all the time running fast down to the sea, carrying ice with it. Beyond the river there is a steep rocky hill of brown rocks with enough trees on it to take away any barren look, and as we drove back to Gothenburg, which takes its name from this river, I was impressed by the loveliness of the scene, for the bright sunlight picked out the trees and rocks, which were showing through the snow, and also brought up all the different colours in the houses we passed as our level road wound its way round the foot of the hills to our right, while on our left the river Gote was bearing its ice down to the sea, and beyond the river the hill stood up bold and clear.

That afternoon I visited the Gothenburg Maritime Museum, and here met Ivan Petersen, who very kindly explained many of the details connected with the old Viking ships. This Museum was again well lit and cheerful, and most enjoyable as there were many things of interest there. Models of the ice-breaking steamers, which Sweden needs to keep her ports clear for the winter, have slightly overhanging bows, which riding up on the ice bear down on it and crush it, but as well as this some of them now use a propeller, which sucking the water away from under the the ice takes away its support, often causing the ice to break from its own weight before the bow of the ice breaker has climbed up over it.

There were models of their fishing fleet and the methods employed for fishing, models of the harbour and its construction, and many wonderful paintings by Amiral Hägg, giving an outline of Sweden's naval history. There were models and photographs of old Viking ships and all the sailing ships that have come since, and the time went very swiftly here.

Back at the hotel I met Ture Rinman, one of the editors of Sweden's leading yachting paper, *Segel & Motor*, and the editor of *Morgontidningen*, who very kindly invited Knud and me to his house. Ture, or as he was nicknamed in England, " Pure ", has done a great deal of sailing in all countries in vessels from square rigged ships down to the little 22 square metre racers fostered by the Aeolus Yacht Club, and his home had the tang of the sea everywhere in it. The pictures, the arrangement of the rooms, all told of a seaman's instinct. The tablecloth was roped like a sail, and at one end of the room port and starboard lamps shed their red and green lights. Knud and I felt at home right away, so much so that though our visit was only supposed to last ten minutes and consist of schnapps, we were soon settled down for the evening and cigars, and another mellow and enjoyable evening passed all too quickly, for Ture's home was one which encouraged dreaming of days at sea. One thing that kept holding my attention was the carved stern of an old sailing ship with its high pooped lanterns fitted to the wall, for from the interior a gentle glow made it seem very real.

I FOUND AXEL'S DOG A HOME IN MY POCKET

Sweden is a very formal country, and people may know each other for years without becoming close friends, but Ture's room with its warmth and cheer broke down artificial barriers right away, and very soon Knud and I raised our glasses and said " Du ", and Ture's face lightened up with pleasure, for from then on this meant that we were brothers, strangers to each other no more. But all too soon another night had fled and the early morning hours saw Knud and me back at our hotel.

The following morning was Sunday and members of the Aeolus Yacht Club were going off to their Island home, and they had kindly invited Knud and myself, so we made our way down to the double-ended Diesel motor boat that was to take us out through the ice to the Island.

Gothenburg was in the grip of winter, and the only channels which vessels could use were those kept open by the ice breakers and the steamers in and out of the port. Even here the ice was two inches thick, for it froze again immediately after a vessel had passed through, and to me it was very interesting to watch this short overhanging bow, common to all Norwegian and Swedish pilot and fishing craft, for this would ride up over the ice till the ice would crack, and so our bow was continually rising and falling as we made our way through the ice-bound water, and small pieces would fly out on either side sometimes 100 yards across the ice, while ahead cracks appeared before it finally broke, looking for all the world like cracks in a window pane when you have thrown a stone at it. All of this happened without any difference in the speed of our craft, for the very fact that her Diesel engine shook her seemed to help to break the ice and enabled us to go steadily on through.

We could not go direct to the Island as the water was too heavily frozen ; instead we had to go two sides of a triangle before making our way to the short pier from Aeolus Island. Here we landed a few members while the rest of us went round some of the other Islands or Skerries, and this to me was a voyage full of interest, for as we passed one channel and a fishing village, Ture told me of the German square rigged ship that had run in there during a winter's gale, and thinking she was in another channel, had struck a rock and foundered. When he told me of the seventeen Swedish fishermen who had lost their lives endeavouring to save the crew, I could not help thinking of the depth there is in the brotherhood of the sea, for here was the whole village at the risk of their own lives endeavouring to save those of perfect strangers, people whom they had not known existed a few hours ago. There is no doubt the sea brings out the finest qualities in human beings, and it is because of this that the friendships we make on the sea are the most enduring of all.

LOWERING THE FLAG ON AEOLUS ISLAND

Ture also showed me his small cottage on one of the small Islands, and I thought how fortunate he was to live such a pleasant life, writing of the sea he loved with a cosy home in Gothenburg for the winter when all around was ice and snow, while his summer months were spent in his cottage on the Island.

After our tour of the Islands we once more came back in sight of Aeolus Island, and now the Aeolus flag was flying bravely in the breeze, and the Island seemed greatly improved because the Aeolus people were now occupying it on shore. Once alongside the pier we were soon in the warmth of the clubhouse, and after a schnapp for each leg we had a wonderful drink which warmed us up no end ; then we sat down to our midday meal.

During the meal and the morning Dag Lindscrand and Axel had explained to me the B class Skerry cruiser which the Aeolus Yacht Club was forming, and here before us was a model of their boat for the following summer. Here was another active and energetic Club, whose aim was to foster and produce a more normal and a cheaper boat to the 22 square metre rule. Their idea was to keep the length down to more normal limits and to use only home-grown timbers and Swedish-made sails, and to have an iron instead of a lead keel. The boat this Club was building, as it was a lottery boat, was a very interesting craft, designed by Berti Bothén ; the Club were fitting her with the Ljungstrom rig, and as they very kindly said I could reproduce her in this book, her plans will be found in the racing section, illustrating the 22 square metre chapter.

Besides talking boats at this meal we had a sing song, and those there quite enjoyed the sea song *Australia* which I sang and which has such a swinging tune, for they soon got hold of the chorus and nearly lifted the roof when singing. At the end of this meal Axel Karlander in a very kind speech presented me with the blue and white flag of the Aeolus Yacht Club for my dining table at home, and in my reply I said that while the flag would always remind me of this pleasant day in the Aeolus Yacht Club, the blue seemed to me to stand for the blue skies and sea, with its white waves, and the sea, while it divided, also united the countries of the world, and when we sailed on the sea we became part of a great brotherhood, and we all sailed on the same level sea, and so came to one level, for while man can own parts of the solid earth he cannot own any of the sea, which is free and treats everyone exactly alike, and when on it we all feel the same wind, seas and sunshine. We all used the same sun for navigation and finding our position, and so we were all part of one large family, and this flag would remind me of the brethren of Gothenburg, the white would remind me of the ice and snow covered skerries, while the blue would remind me of the blue skies and seas we all loved. So the flag was a symbol of winter and summer, and I wondered if the reason so many Swedish flags were blue and white was this great contrast they had in their seasons, for in the winter everything is snow clad and white, and in the summer the skies seem almost always to be blue in their waters.

It was now getting late, so after a short ramble over the Island we fired a salute, lowered the flag and returned to Gothenburg once more, and I still have the empty cartridge cases which fired the salute that day.

COPENHAGEN'S MERMAID LOOKS SIDEWAYS AT THE SHIPYARD ACROSS THE WATER

Back at our hotel that night Ivan Petersen of the Maritime Museum and I spent an evening yarning about old ships and customs, and we finished the evening in the home of Pontus Lundquist. The double windows of this house are of the latest and best type. In winter when the window is shut it folds together like a book and there is a double thickness of glass with an insulating air space between, but when needed this can open as an ordinary window, or it can open in the form of a V so that the wind will strike either side and not come in, and the air flows in and out of the room above and below the window. Before we knew it, it was early morning and time for bed.

Monday morning I spent in a farewell visit to the Maritime Museum, and after lunch caught the train for Copenhagen where we arrived at about 10.00 p.m. Here I looked forward to seeing E. Gundestrupp, Overingenior, and his family, whom I had not seen for several years. There are two stations in Copenhagen, and as we stopped at the first he came on board looking as fit and cheerful as ever, and we both went along to my hotel, the Astorias, a hotel which was very interesting. It was long and narrow and every room had outside windows, for a passage way ran the full length through the centre dividing the different bedrooms, while on the ground floors the dining rooms took the full width of the building. My bedroom was only 12 ft. × 12 ft., had a bed, wardrobe, sofa, coat rack and its own bathroom, W.C. and basin. It is the first time I have seen ship practice carried out on shore, and the wonder is that it is not more frequently done.

We yarned away happily until bedtime, and the next morning I visited the yard at which he was Overingenior, and here they were building a great many different vessels. We next called on the Yacht Club, and our walk to his home took us past the Copenhagen Mermaid, still sitting contentedly on that cold rock. Soon we were at the Gundestrupp's home, and here in the years that had passed there had come about a change; the son and elder daughter were both married and had children, so that Mr. and Mrs. Gundestrupp were now Grandpa and Grandma; the other daughter had grown up, and I was very touched by the fact that all the children had made a special effort to come in from different parts for this mid-day meal, at which I was present. All too soon the meal came to an end, and we all had to go our different ways. The last time I had seen that family was in a tiny harbour of Denmark, as we lay near each other when I was cruising in *Vigilant*, and I wondered how long it would be before we should all meet again.

In the afternoon I visited the museum in the dockyard, and there as usual found a great deal of interest, and met the wonderful craftsmen who had made a great many of the lovely models in this museum. Amongst others

AT THE GUNDESTRUPPS' HOME

were working models of the early propellers used in the old battleships. When the sailing ships first took to steam, they still did a great deal of sailing, and between the sternpost and the rudder post there was a parallel aperture, in which a frame fitted snugly. This frame carried the propeller, and as the propeller was keyed on its fore side and the after end of the propeller shaft had a key way cut in it it meant that the propeller in its frame could be lifted out clear of the water when the slot in the shaft and the key way in the propeller were up and down; all of which shows the lengths to which those earlier people went not to alter or interfere with the sailing efficiency of their craft more than could be helped.

That evening E. Gundestrupp and his wife had kindly consented to have dinner with me, and it was a meal I really enjoyed, for though my guests were grandparents and older than I, age is not a barrier to enjoyment in this world, for every age has its charms, and this night I quoted them the Chinese poem of which I am very fond:

ON BEING SIXTY

" Between thirty and forty, one is distracted by the Five Lusts;
Between seventy and eighty, one is a prey to a hundred diseases,
But from fifty to sixty one is free from all ills;
Calm and still—the heart enjoys rest.
I have put behind me Love and Greed; I have done with Profit and Fame;
I am still short of illness and decay and far from decrepit age,
Strength of limb I still possess to seek the rivers and hills;
Still my heart has spirit enough to listen to flutes and strings,
At leisure I open new wine and taste several cups;
Drunken I recall old poems, and sing a whole volume."

Every human being is rather like a fortress with a deep moat around him, which forms him into an island, and we can only enjoy other people's company when we lower the drawbridge and ask them inside. The more interests we have in life the more drawbridges we have that we can lower, for a different bridge must be used for different people; the bridges over which we ran to and from each other that night with our thoughts and words were mainly bridges connected with sailing and seafaring matters, and I once more thought of the truth that friendships made on the sea are the most enduring of all. The reason for this is, that when we play games such as tennis we can stop immediately it rains or the weather becomes unpleasant, but when we play on the sea we must take whatever the Lord sends in the way of weather, and often we find, that though we have started out to play at sailing and navigating the sea, before we have gone very far it is all in deadly earnest, for with the wind and sea increasing to a gale our play game of yachting has taken on a new aspect, and unless we have wisdom and strength and courage, and our vessel proves herself to be seaworthy, manly and sturdy, we shall not arrive. Thus all sailing people below their laughter and song are very earnest and have good qualities, for the man who endures the hardships the sea imposes upon him must have a great deal of good in him, and it was for that reason that this land cruise of mine had been so pleasant.

As I left on the midnight train my greatest wish was to see Gundestrupp and Copenhagen again soon. The train faithfully carried me through the night, and so I came south to Berlin and to Herr Gudowinis, and away we went for lunch. During our luncheon interval I asked him if I should salute and say " Heil Hitler " at the beginning and the end of my lecture that night, for all around, the people and waiters greeted each other with that salute ;

HERR GUDOWINIS

Herr Gudowinis asked me just what I thought about this ; and to try and explain my views on life I said to him, that when I go into a beer house with a cheerful crowd who want to sing I drink and sing with them and enjoy it, and when I go to a church then I am as quiet and timid as a mouse except during the singing of the psalms and hymns, which I enjoy aloud, and pointed out to him that I should be delighted for him to salute our King if he were with me in England, and that as Hitler was their equivalent of our King I should be only too pleased to salute him in their way. He said : " If you feel that way about it, it would be very nice indeed for us if you said ' Heil Hitler ' at the beginning and end of your lecture," and so that was agreed upon and I followed the customs of Berlin.

The lecture that night was at their Maritime Museum, and the lantern itself was well arranged underneath the seats of the audience, all of whom went up at an angle of 45 degrees from the speaker on the floor, and while I could see the lanternist and the lantern the audience were unable to. R. Andriano Korvettenkapitan a. D. introduced me in German and perfect English and thanked me at the end in both languages again.

Amongst those present were many naval officers, for the German Navy encourages the art of sailing amongst its officers and men, and in so doing undoubtedly increases their knowledge of the sea, winds and weather. There were speeches after the lecture and then a crowd of us trooped away to a dinner or supper in a large and very well laid out restaurant, where each room represented the different parts of Germany, the different costumes worn and the different dishes and beers sold there, and this country atmosphere in the middle of Berlin was very refreshing, for it seemed to bring a breath of fresh air into a large city and as our naval friends left I saw for the first time the Nazi salute to Hitler given with perfect understanding and balance, conveying a great many things at once. There was the open hand of friendship, and one saw that no weapons of any sort were in it, for all our salutes come from a very old sign, where a man held his right hand up to show it contained no weapon in the treacherous days that we hope are hundreds of years behind us ; nor was this salute stiff and irritating, but rather a friendly kindly gesture of a man saying goodnight to a friend. So another evening came to a close, or almost, for Henry Scheel a young American designer, who was studying in Berlin, came along to my hotel for a nightcap, and we sat and yarned a while longer before it was finally bedtime.

In Berlin I had the pleasure of meeting Harold Tapken, and two examples of his work are to be found in the Power Craft section of this book. In his outboard motor boat with the engine fitted amidships we see the keynote of his endeavours, all of which are directed towards efficiency, and there is no doubt the arrangement he has planned, as seen in this 16-footer, should prove a great boon to all who use an outboard engine, for it enables them to use it inboard in the middle of the ship where the boat is perfectly balanced at all times.

He very kindly came to yarn to me the morning after the lecture, and I spent the afternoon in the Maritime Museum of Berlin where there was a great deal to see, for not only were there very old ships, but one part was given over to their naval history of the 1914 War, and I was able to see and understand the war from their viewpoint easily and clearly. Wandering amongst these museum pieces on this afternoon when all over the world there were rumours of war, I hoped there would be no more wars, for no matter where one wanders and what country one is in, there one finds kindly hospitable people, and war destroys all this kindliness and brings out the vices in all mankind, and does no good but a great deal of harm, as any country who wins a war has spent so much of her best blood in the winning of it that she has lost more than she has won.

Leaving the museum I collected my bag and made for the station, to catch the " Flying Hamburger " to Hamburg. This train does the journey in two hours, so I was quite soon in Hamburg under the care of Hans Petersen and driven out to his pleasant old world house where I was to spend the night.

Here it was pleasant and peaceful, for the house was entirely surrounded by trees; we had a most enjoyable evening.

Amongst Hans's guests that night was a timber merchant, and we got to talking of the difficulties of the English system of measuring; he told me that though on the continent the metric system was universal, our English system was still used a great deal in the timber trades where old methods still prevailed. Then in the early hours of morning when we would normally be going to bed, someone suggested a good cabaret show, so off we dashed, and it was very late before we finally turned in after a very happy evening.

The next day there was a Sailing Club meeting, and here I met Admiral Goetting, who has done so much for sailing in the German Navy, and many other notable German yachtsmen. Amongst them was Dietrich Fischer, now married, and as I shook hands with him it came home to me that we were all getting older, as it was some years since I had seen Dietrich, years in which he had become married. Eric Laeiz, with whom I was to stay, was there, as can be imagined, for he is Germany's representative in the International Yacht Racing Union, having often visited our country in that capacity. For the rest of my stay I was to be his guest, and as his family are the owners of the famous German Flying " P " line, which goes back to the early sailing days, I was looking forward to my stay at his home, which I knew was full of lovely things collected by him. So after we had all dined together and visited several places at which to drink we came to his home for a nightcap, and when the rest were gone the two of us had a quiet yarn before toddling up to our rooms and sleep.

Next day was the meeting and dinner of the Deutfdeher Seglerverband in the afternoon, so I spent the morning in the museum, and while studying some old German books in a quiet room, I suddenly heard the click of two heels, and the words " Heil Hitler ". I was deeply engrossed in these old books, so I looked up expecting to see Hitler himself in the room, and was most disappointed to find it was only a chap saying good morning to me.

In the museum there were some lovely lanterns that once were hung on the quarter galleries of old ships, and pictures of old sailing vessels belonging to the ancestors of Herr Laeiz, and many other interesting things, so the time soon came for me to go to the meeting and the Labskanassen supper, all of which was interesting and instructive. Heavy clouds of smoke slowly drifted across the room in which the meeting was held, and through this thick fog I could dimly see a picture on the other side of the room, a square rigged ship sailing along a rock bound coast on a misty day, with the sun shining and breaking through, giving the scene and the seas a brighter look and catching the edges of the sails, the crests of the seas, and the rocks, so that the picture, which would otherwise have been dreary became light and cheerful; and between this seascape and myself was a room full of people drinking, smoking and trying to hammer out the racing rules and programme for next summer. It was all very entertaining, and so like our own scenes at home, yet different. Here in a room were people like Hans Petersen, Herr Laeiz, Henry Gruber, Dietrich Fischer, Dr. Pullitzer, in fact all the notable sailing people in Germany, for they had come in from all parts of the country, Kiel, Bremen, and Henry Gruber from Flensburg way up on the Danish border; and whenever bits that did not interest any particular one came along he drifted out to the bar where he could get down to more serious drinking. Great arguments and speeches were made, and the whole meeting went on for hours, as one could imagine, for it was all a lot of fun, and with a drink and a smoke to make us feel contented there was no reason to hurry the meeting through. Finally it came to an end, as all things do, and we sat down to our one course meal, which was most enjoyable. Then once again we all sat round yarning and drinking, as I had not seen Henry Gruber for a long time there were a great many things for us to talk over, so we two, with interruptions, had a quiet yarn. There were many others there with whom to talk, and so the early morning and bedtime came too soon for all, for as the evening went on we got more and more contented and mellow, but finally we drifted off to our various sleeping quarters and peace descended on the city for the night.

The next day there was an early luncheon, after which I inflicted my lecture on this interesting gathering of sailing people, for it had been arranged to fit in with the Annual Meeting, so that the people from all parts could be present. After the lecture we all sat down to coffee and cognac and more talking. The great thing about sailing is that there is so much to discuss about it that one never reaches the end of the subject ; with cricket there is only the game to talk about, for all stumps and pitches are very much alike and the same applies to the ball and bat, but with the sea and ships there are thousands of variations of hull shapes and rigs, and the sea is never the same, while the pitch upon which we go yachting is no less than three parts of the earth's surface, and takes us to all lands and the utmost parts of the earth, and ships, the sea and the way of a ship at sea form a never ending topic. The only thing that I have ever found that stops it is when the bottles have run dry, and that evening, my last in Germany, gives

ERICH LAEIZ AND HANS DOMIZLAFF

an idea of how wide and varied the subject of sailing is, for after our coffee and cognac, when I had said goodbye to everyone I could see, Herr Laeiz and I went off to call on Hans Domizlaff, a great engineer and the author of *Dirk III*, a book which describes the various cruises he has made in this yacht to the Faroes, Shetlands, Norway, Heligoland, the Baltic, etc.

When we arrived it was our intention to say good afternoon and perhaps stay half an hour, and then leave, but soon we had settled down in comfortable chairs with a full glass and a feeling of contented peacefulness, and it seemed only natural that we should stay to dinner and that our afternoon should take us well on through the early morning hours, for we soon got to talking of the sea and ships ; before dinner my host presented me with a copy of his book, and I treasure the inscription there very much, as it says :

"Uffa Fox with much love to my famous countryman on the sea.

HANS DOMIZLAFF."

For the sentiment expressed is one I have always felt, that is, that the sea, because it enables us to travel from one country to another, really unites instead of dividing the countries of the world.

This book had just been translated into English, and the translators had left out a chapter in which Hans describes the weather at sea as a great piece of orchestral music. I wrote a note to the translators there and then, and asked if it was too late for them to translate and put this part of the book in, for those who love the sea in all its moods have often been inspired by the various changes in the weather, just as we have been by a wonderful piece of music, and it seemed to me that one of the finest chapters of the book was being left out. We dined by the light of old candles, which was so soothing, whereas most electric and gas lighting is irritating, and after dinner wended our way down to Domizlaff's study and there fell to talking about all types of craft. In a glass case was a model with full sail of the Nicholson boat *Dirk III*, which had carried Hans over so many miles of calm and stormy sea, and there were other models of craft which he had owned ; and finally we came to the model of the Wal boat, of which he was the father, and which was his effort to bring the pleasure of sailing and cruising to people who could not afford an expensive type of craft. Then, as our conversation went from ships to navigation, he produced his Dirklogbuch, which is so arranged that one can write as little or as much as one wishes without hurting the book in any way, for, as we know, in some watches there is a great deal to write about, and often ten minutes will give one a page of writing, while perhaps ten hours of sailing will not call for any comments in the log book.

We then came to navigational instruments, and I explained to Hans the parallel ruler which I had made and used but had not perfected or patented, this of mine consisting of an ordinary rule working between the square or true compass at the bottom, and a round or magnetic compass above. The top compass being adjustable can be swung round and clamped down, so that at one glance one had a true bearing and also the compass bearing on the parallel rule, and the true compass, being the square bottomed one, can be placed on any part of the chart, as its straight side can be kept parallel with the nearest latitude line when a course is laid off. Then the magnetic course can be read on the upper compass, and the true course on the lower. Thus one eliminates a great deal of work in

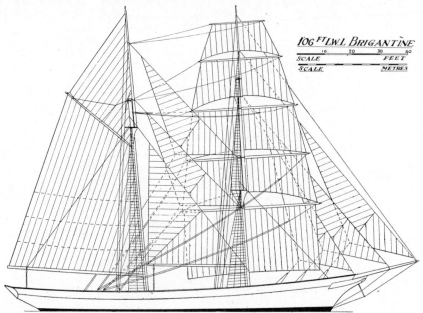

106 FT LWL BRIGANTINE

laying off a course. After my explanation Hans produced a dear little box in which was a far, far better arrangement than the one I used. He, too, had a square compass for the true compass, and above it was a circular adjustable compass, which could be adjusted to the magnetic North, and swinging round this was a straight edge of glass, but only the magnetic compass had points and bearings on it, so one could not read off the true compass, only the magnetic ; but then, besides the variation this parallel rule had an extra refinement, for on the straight edge arm, was a little screw on which adjustment for the deviation could be made. It was the finest thing for laying off a course that I have ever met with, for though extremely simple it enables a man to lay off his course in one second, and know that what is read is right (see *Gadget* chapter). The night being cold we drank hot rum, and as there was no sign of this or our subject giving out, for there are more angles and phases in sailing than beams of light from a good diamond, I could see with delight that we were in for another long evening. And so we were, for next our mutual friend Henry Rasmussen with whom I have sailed hundreds of miles came into our talk, and no sooner had we drunk to his health than Hans produced plans of a new vessel he was proposing to build with Abeking and Rasmussen ; and so the evening went on, for with any new plan there is a great deal of interest and enjoyment, and my argument for the order being placed at once was that we were all getting older and each year went by quicker than the preceding one, as we had more interests in life, and each succeeding year was a smaller fraction of the total life we had lived and so became a smaller and ever decreasing amount of time in our lives, and that we should therefore do the things we wished to, as to delay meant that we should never do them, or if we did we should be too old to enjoy the doing of them ; and I have lived my life this way.

With the firm of Abeking and Rasmussen there came to my mind their design for a 133 ft. brigantine, a vessel with a great deal of accommodation and room aboard ; as the lines will show she is a roomy and yet sweet-lined craft, and for all her size has only 12 ft. draught, which would enable her to go into most harbours and even quite small creeks and havens.

From this lovely ship we came to talking of the various countries of the world, then to the way they were managed. It was only natural, too, that from the brigantine we should go back through history to the earlier seafarers, and soon we were back amongst the old Vikings, and with this came up the Nydam ship dug out of the

North German marshes some years ago. We almost always think of the Vikings as originating in the Scandinavian countries only, but they came from the whole of Northern Europe, and as the lines show, this ship was very long with the easy and sweet lines used so long ago.

It so happened that a German cinematograph company wanted a true model of this German ship, and as it was well known that our friend Henry Rasmussen was greatly interested in the early history of shipbuilding, it followed

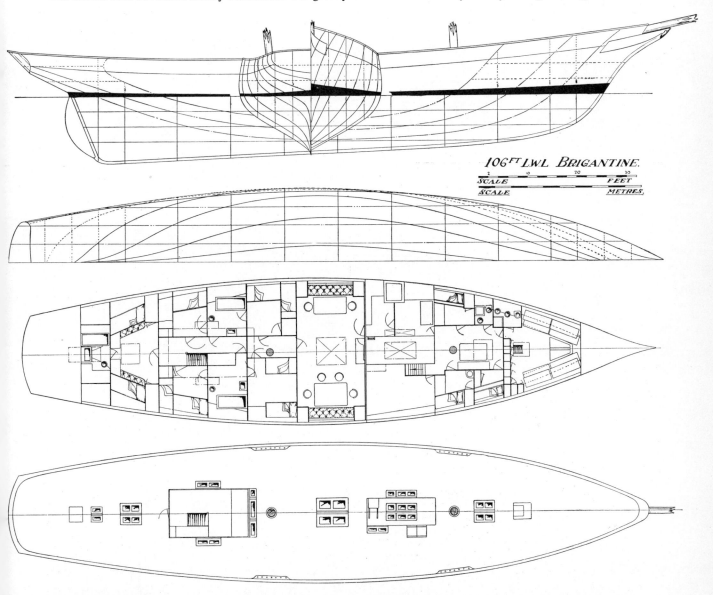

106FT LWL BRIGANTINE.
SCALE   FEET
SCALE   METRES.

that the picture company naturally went to the firm of Abeking and Rasmussen to build an exact replica of the Nydam ship. They copied the vessel so well, that it could stand the criticisms of any historical authority, which meant a great deal of intensive study.

The age of the ship was determined by the coins and arms found in it, which proved they had originated at the time of the founding of the Anglo-Saxon Kingdom.

She is 23·38 metres or 70 ft. overall, with a beam of 3·13 metres or 10 ft. 3 in. and she was rowed with 30 oars each side ; as can be seen her lines are sweet and fair, and one would find difficulty in improving upon them for such a vessel to-day.

The construction is also extremely good when we consider the materials to hand in those far distant times. Though the planks are riveted together, which shows that metal fastenings were well known in those times, yet the planking is lashed to the solid frames, and not bolted, so it would seem that the idea behind this was to ease the strains upon the hull caused in a seaway or when the boat was swelling or drying due to the changes in the weather, for there is a great deal of give and take in these lashings, which enable the boat to work without splitting or tearing her wide planks.   The result of this method of construction was an exceptionally elastic hull.

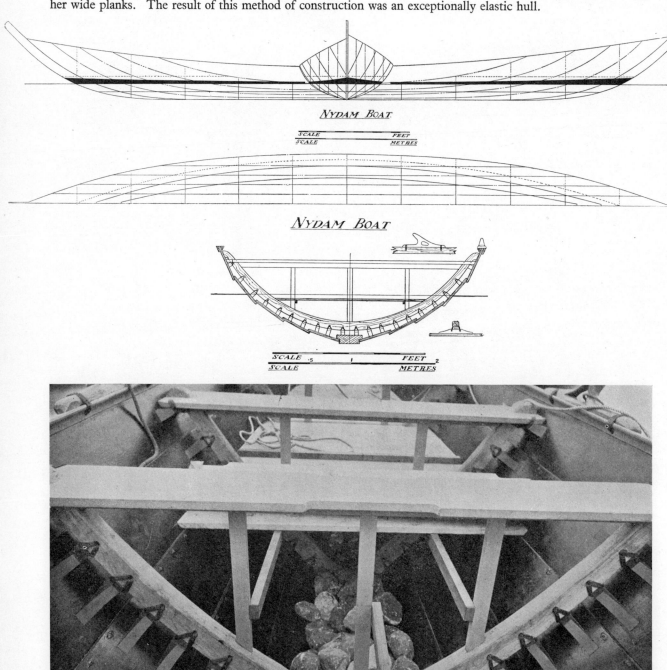

NYDAM BOAT

NYDAM BOAT

CONSTRUCTIONAL DETAILS

All these constructional details were carefully developed and worked out by Abeking and Rasmussen, but then the problem of colour came in.   The old sagas said the boats were tarred under water and the topsides painted white or red and sometimes both and the coloured copy of the Bayeux tapestry, which shows ships of the Viking type in its story of the Conquest of England by William, was also studied, and so everything possible was done to ensure accuracy in all respects.   Finally it was known that small rough stones were laid along the keel inside to give stability (the amount used of course varying from time to time, as they could be thrown overboard when such a craft had cargo), but who could tell now, 1500 years after, just how many of these were used at different times?   So one of the

PARTLY PLANKED

EVEN TO-DAY IT WOULD BE DIFFICULT TO IMPROVE UPON HER LINES

THE NYDAM SHIP

pleasantest evenings of my life ended in talking of the old sea rovers, for though not yet light the evening had gone well into the morning, and so with a final glass of cheering grog Herr Laeiz and I went to his home and to bed.

The next day I flew to England and home, and so ended a land cruise through Holland, Norway, Sweden, Denmark and Germany, and as it was a winter's cruise it had given me a better understanding of the old Norse mythology, for knowing these northern countries in the splendour of summer I was struck by the great difference in the season of winter, for the silent snow falling heavily and relentlessly had made a deep impression upon me, and for the first time I understood the dark tragic thread running through the old tales of the Northmen.   But more even than this understanding, I brought away many lovely memories, of friends round their firesides while winter held the whole countryside in the grip of its icy hand, and therefore end this winter's tale with the warm-hearted poem presented to me by the Svenska Kryssarklubben, my greatest wish being that perhaps once again I'll be able to sojourn amongst the kindly people in the countries bordering the Baltic.

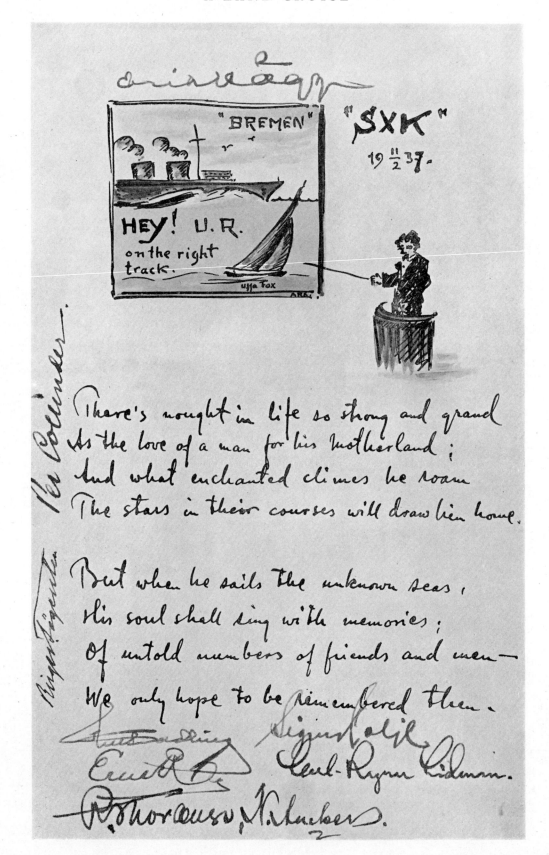

There's nought in life so strong and grand
As the love of a man for his motherland;
And what enchanted climes he roam
The stars in their courses will draw him home.

But when he sails the unknown seas,
His soul shall sing with memories;
Of untold numbers of friends and men—
We only hope to be remembered then.

PART II
POWER CRAFT

IN this section the vessels are arranged according to length, *Piet Hein*, a royal yacht, leading the fleet. Amongst the cruisers we find full powered craft for use on inland waters and on the open sea, also motor sailers, vessels which are good whether considered as power craft or sailing vessels, and then the hard chined or express cruiser type of craft. The latter begins with two work boats, one for the Navy and one for the Trinity House. The reason for these two leading is that, being designed and built for work, they are called upon to endure more than their sisters designed for pleasure, as they have to carry out their duties in all weathers, winter or summer. The smallest in this section is a 16-foot boat designed to take the outboard engine amidships; and finally we come to Sir Malcolm Campbell's *Bluebird*, which holds the world's record for speed on water, and which was designed by Fred Cooper; and though her complete plans do not appear in this book, the sketches give a very good idea of this remarkable little vessel. Her complete plans are not included because Freddy is writing a book for next spring in which they will appear. And so once more we have every type of power craft to study at our leisure.

· I ·

PIET HEIN

Length, overall -	101 ft. 8 in. = 31 m.		Length, water-line -	96 ft. 2 in. = 29·28 m.
Beam - -	18 ft. 8 in. = 5·70 m.		Draught - -	5 ft. 1 in. = 1·54 m.
Displacement -	114 tons = 115,824 kilos.		Engines - -	Two Stork-Ganz Diesels.
Speed - -	10·50 knots.		Total Power - -	320 h.p.

Owner, PRINCESS JULIANA and PRINCE BERNHARDT.   *Designer*, H. W. DE VOOGT.

Builder, G. DE VRIES LENTSCH, JNR.

BECAUSE of the present-day means of travelling by land, sea and air, which make voyaging a matter of hours instead of days, the telephone, which enables us to talk to people in any part of the world, and the newspapers

PIET HEIN IN THE LOCKS

and wireless, countries are more closely connected than ever before in the history of the world, so that we not only have friends in all countries, but also we visit and receive visits from them frequently. We talk to them by 'phone when not able to visit them, and on the wedding day of Princess Juliana of Holland we in England were able to

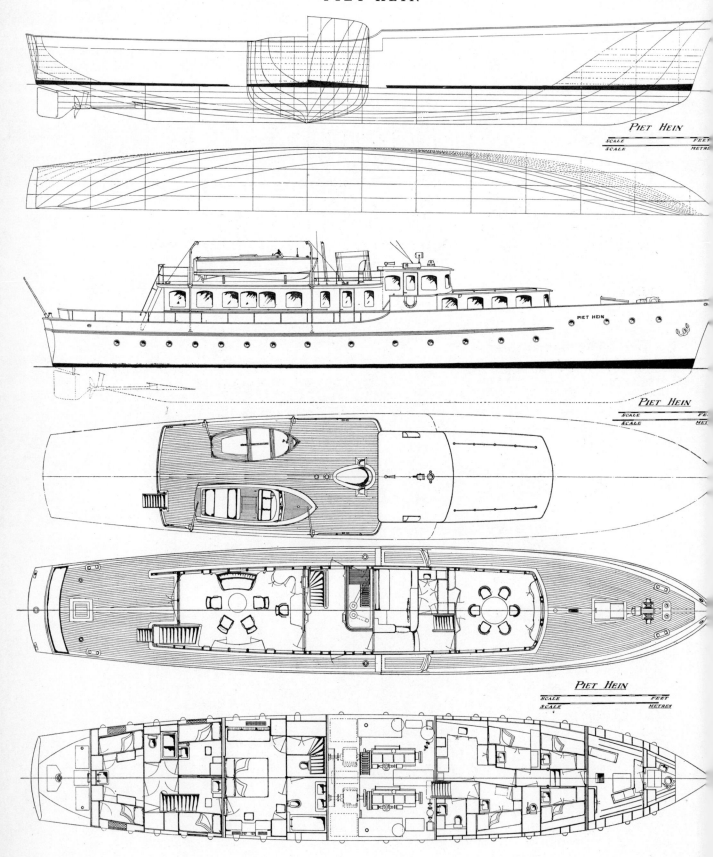

PIET HEIN

SCALE   FEET
SCALE   METRE

PIET HEIN

SCALE   FE
SCALE   ME

PIET HEIN

SCALE   FEET
SCALE   METRES

listen to and vizualize the whole ceremony because of the perfection of wireless to-day. I was greatly impressed by this ceremony, but more even by the kindly wisdom in the speech by the Chief Priest after the ceremony was over. Though Holland is separated from us by the cold North Sea, she is closer then ever before in history, and we take a

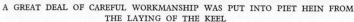

A GREAT DEAL OF CAREFUL WORKMANSHIP WAS PUT INTO PIET HEIN FROM THE LAYING OF THE KEEL

TILL FINALLY SHE WAS LAUNCHED

great interest in the fortunes of her people, so that when the people of Holland decided to present their Princess and Prince Bernhardt with a Royal yacht it seemed almost as personal as though we were presenting a yacht to members of our own Royal family. It is because of all this that *Piet Hein* is so interesting to us, and heads the Power Craft section of this book.

AT THE LAUNCH: PRINCESS JULIANA, PRINCE BERNHARDT, MR. TRIP, PRESIDENT OF THE COMMITTEE AND J. DE VRIES LENTSCH JNR., THE BUILDER

The Committee appointed to deal with all the problems that were bound to arise chose H. W. de Voogt of Haarlem as designer and G. de Vries Lentsch, Jnr., of the Amsetdramsche Scheepswerf to build her, and although the choice might seem a difficult problem to some, to those of us who know and understand it was really a simple matter, for these two stand out as being the best to design and build such a vessel.

Holland is a land with vast inland seas and an elaborate network of canals, and to navigate these there are a great many problems to be surmounted by the designer of such a large vessel, for *Piet Hein* is over 100 feet in length. When we think of such a vessel entering and leaving narrow locks and steaming over shallow seas such as the Zuyder Zee we realise the difficulties, but looking at the lines we see that H. W. de Voogt has given a great deal of thought to the overcoming of them.

PRINCESS JULIANA AND THE BUILDER

BEAUTIFUL VENEERS IN RESTFUL TONES ARE USED IN
THE OWNER'S STATEROOM

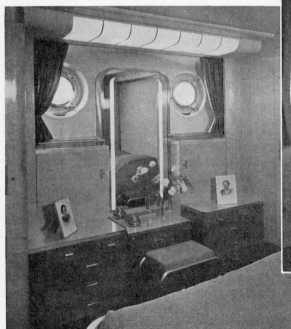

IN THE MAIN DECK SALOON, LOOKING FORWAR

The sections show that she has no outside keel at all ; instead she has a bilge keel either side to steady her, while the profile shows that the keel line is cut up fore and aft to enable her to manœuvre. The sections also show the firm bilge of *Piet Hein*, which makes for stability, while the long buttocks and easy water-lines make for a very easily driven hull and one that will disturb the water very little when under way, a point very important in shallow water, for we all know that when vessels are driven hard in such conditions they pull up great quarter waves astern and become unmanageable. It is therefore important in such a vessel to have a very clean sweet-lined bottom, and we cannot help admiring this design.

We see that the deckhouse is arranged so that aft there is a cosy and comfortable lounge, forward of which is what might be termed the entrance hall, with a winding stairway leading below, immediately forward of which is the wheel house, raised slightly above the rest of the deckhouse to give a clear view all round. Forward of this is the dining saloon with its round table and curved sideboard at the fore end, while fore and aft of this deckhouse there is a good clear deck space. Below decks the crew, galley, engineer and engines take the fore half of *Piet Hein*, and

THE DECK SALOON

abaft of this we have the owner's accommodation. There is a double berthed cabin aft, which is divided from two single cabins by a bathroom to port and the after companion way. Forward of this is the owner's cabin with bathroom and companion way to the deckhouse at the fore end, and so we see that the accommodation aft, like the dining table, is arranged for six people, and one imagines that Princess Juliana and Prince Bernhardt will have many pleasant voyages in *Piet Hein* with four of their closest friends around them, and that she will afford them a peaceful retreat from all the worries of state affairs. There is no doubt that the people of Holland have chosen the best way they could of expressing their kindly thoughts to Princess Juliana and Prince Bernhardt.

· 17 ·

HIGH SPEED MOTOR CRUISER

Length, overall -   104 ft. 6 in. = 31·90 m.   Length, water-line - 103 ft. 2 in. = 31·50 m.
Beam   -   -   15 ft. 5 in. = 4·70 m.   Draught   -   -   5 ft. 7 in. = 1·70 m.
Displacement -   54·8 tons. = 55,676 kilos.   Engines -   -   - Three Maybach Diesels.
Speed   -   -   35 knots.

Designer, ABEKING & RASMUSSEN   *Builder*, ABEKING & RASMUSSEN

THOSE of us, who have seen the New York business man going to work, and returning in the evening to his lovely home on Long Island, have thought that such a man lives a very pleasant life. He enjoys his country home through the late afternoon, evening, night and early morning, and then has all the pleasure a yachting cruise can give as he makes his way down Long Island Sound, in which he is surrounded by the country and pleasure craft,

THE MODEL GIVES AN IDEA OF THIS VESSEL

then down the East River, where he sees working boats of all sorts from small motor boats up to the largest liners, and has on either side of him town and city life. And all of this time he can contemplate the problems he is likely to meet during the day, for there is no doubt that the sea tends to make one meditate and reflect. His motor cruiser will land him at a pier and a short drive or walk through the city takes him to his office where he works, and the labours of the day being ended in the early afternoon he once more boards his fast cruiser and sails away. As we look at the plans of this high speed motor cruiser by Abeking and Rasmussen, all of this rises up before us, for she was designed with this in view ; and looking at her lines we see that while she is a very easily driven hull with a flaring bow forward to throw away the sea, she is at the same time capable of a high speed with very little wash, and the plan showing her as she lies afloat gives an idea of the grace of these speedy motor cruisers, for her sheer, deckhouse, and streamlined chart room and wheel house all have the long unbroken lines that make power vessels graceful.

As we look at the accommodation plan we have to bear in mind that this vessel is large enough to have two decks and so give double the accommodation.

Forward we have the foc's'le with four folding berths in it, abaft of which is a double stateroom, while coming farther aft is a single stateroom to port and a wireless room to starboard. Separating these from the engine room is a galley and pantry taking the full width of the ship, her 750 gallon water tanks dividing the galley from the engine room.

In the engine room we have three 60·5 400 P.S. Maybach Diesels, for this vessel is driven by three propellers, one on a centre line and one to port and starboard.

Immediately abaft the engine room is the owner's cabin with a bathroom to port and a washroom to starboard,

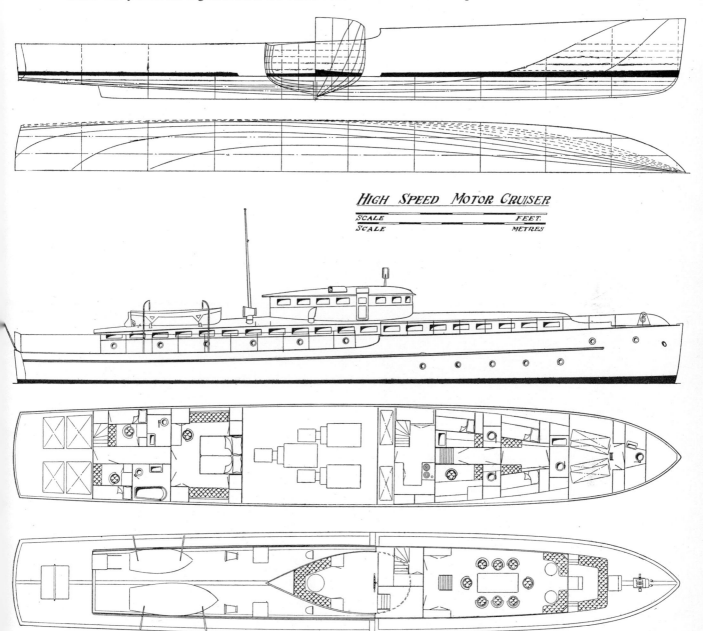

and aft of this we have the captain's and the engineer's cabins. Her four fuel tanks holding 2,400 galls. are housed in the stern, where they are fairly free from fire risks.

On deck we have a forward cockpit with a hatchway leading down into the foc's'le forward of it, and abaft this is the dining saloon with a table to seat eight people, and with its L-shaped settees in the two forward corners we can easily imagine the comfort in this saloon, for with windows all round one has a clear view. Abaft this is the streamlined wheel and chart house, the after end of which is arranged with a table placed around settees, so the wheel and chart house is also a smoke room. These plans give an idea of the state of perfection reached by these high speed motor cruisers, which while being large enough for comfort are still small enough to be used to run an owner in and out of New York water ways.

· 18 ·

SULARA

Length, overall -	90 ft. 3 in. = 27·5 m.		Length, water-line -	86 ft. 5 in. = 26·34 m.
Beam - -	16 ft. 0 in. = 4·88 m.		Draught - -	7 ft. 0 in. = 2·13 m.
Displacement -	68·30 tons = 69,400 kilos.		Sail Area - -	1085 sq. ft. = 101·00 sq. m.

Owner, BILL HORBURY.   *Designer*, CAMPER & NICHOLSON.   *Builder*, CAMPER & NICHOLSON, LTD.

DESIGNED and built by Camper & Nicholson fourteen years ago, *Sulara* has a great deal to recommend her to our notice, for as we see from her lines she requires very little power to drive her, the buttocks and water-lines being very easy and sweet, while the sections show that wetted surface has been considered, and it is wetted surface

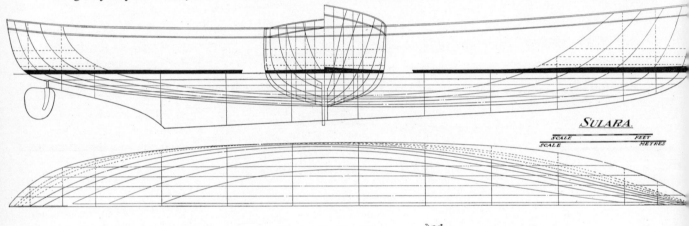

SULARA.

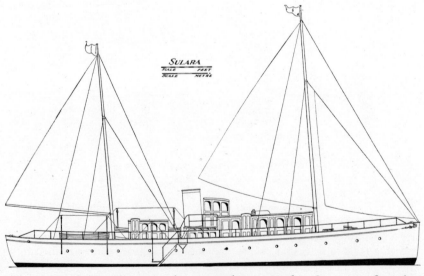

SULARA

that creates the greater part of the resistance at low to moderate speeds. So we see from her lines that *Sulara* is very economical to run, provided one is not driving her to the utmost.

Sulara's owner, Bill Horbury, was using her as a tender to his six-metre *Coima* when I first met her, and there is no doubt she made an excellent mother ship for a " six ", being large enough to house the crew of five aboard in comfort, and yet small enough for the racer to lie alongside or astern, and whether anchored off Cowes or moored in Torquay Harbour the two vessels seemed exactly suited to each other.

SULARA HARDLY DISTURBS THE WATER AS SHE STEAMS ALONG

The afloat plan shows *Sulara's* unbroken sheer line and the teak deckhouse above the deck level. At the fore end is her saloon, immediately abaft of which is the galley, then we have the wheel house and the funnel, while further

THE SIX-METRE COIMA ALONGSIDE SULARA IN TORQUAY HARBOUR

aft is the after deckhouse, and this arrangement enables those on board to have a clear view all around, whether at meals in the saloon or yarning in the after deckhouse, while there is plenty of open deck space to walk upon and give a sense of freedom.

Below decks we see that there are four folding cots in the fo'c'sle, abaft of which the captain has his cabin to starboard, while the engineer and steward share a cabin abreast him to port. Next aft we see there are two single staterooms, abaft of which is the engine room taking the full width of the ship for a length of 18 feet, giving a great deal of space round the engines.

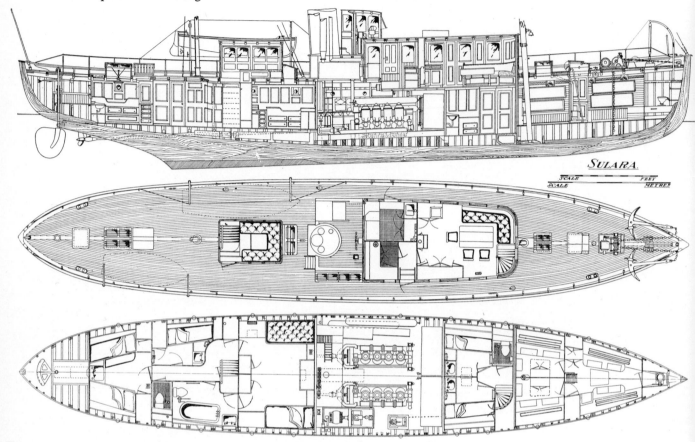

Immediately abaft the engine room we have the owner's stateroom, with his sleeping berth to starboard and a sofa on the port side. A door on the port side leads through into the bathroom which can also be reached from the passage, so that those occupying the single berthed cabin on the port side abreast the bathroom or the double berthed cabin aft can use this bathroom if they wish. *Sulara*, in fact, is laid out for six or seven people.

She has four tons of lead on her keel, and this with her proportions and lines make for a very fine sea boat, for such an easily driven hull disturbs the sea very little. Used as a parent ship *Sulara* impressed me as being a very suitable vessel for such a job, as not only could she take the owner, his friends and *Coima* to the different harbours from which the races were held, but once they had arrived she provided them with a perfect home, one where they were free from all the worries of shore life, and where they could be as quiet or as noisy as they wished, and at the same time be in close touch with the sea and its ways, so that they were able to feel what the weather was doing and was likely to do.

· 19 ·

THE GERMAN COASTGUARD BOAT

Length, overall -	77 ft. 1$\frac{5}{8}$ in. =23·50 m.	Length, water-line -	75 ft. 8 in. = 23·05 m.
Beam - -	13 ft. 9$\frac{3}{8}$ in.= 4·20 m.	Draught - -	3 ft. 5 in. = 1·041 m.
Displacement -	26 tons = 26,416 kilos.	Engines - - -	Two Maybachs 550 h.p.
Speed - -	20 knots.		and one Maybach 100 h.p.

Owner, THE GERMAN GOVERNMENT   *Designer*, ABEKING & RASMUSSEN   *Builder*, ABEKING & RASMUSSEN

THOUGH designed and built as a coastguard cruiser, or rather because she was designed for this purpose, this vessel is most interesting to us, for being a work boat she has to be more efficient than she would be were she

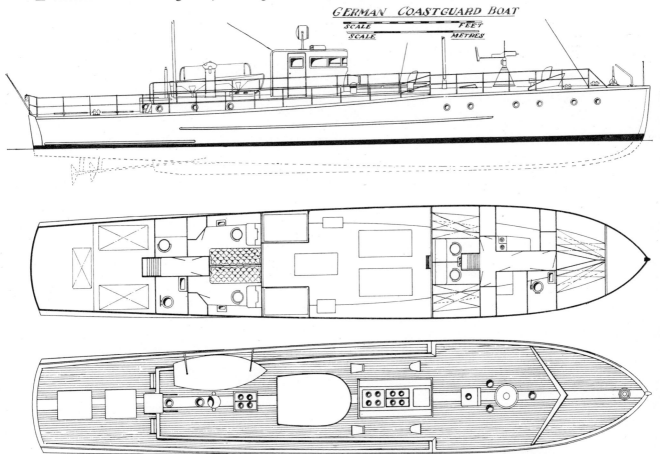

only a pleasure boat, as she must carry out her job no matter what the weather. Such a vessel must be good in a sea-way and at the same time must have a good turn of speed, and in the lines we see that her designers have combined these qualities.

The bow has been designed to carve its way through the seas without any shock, while we see the bow sections

135

flare off at the top and throw the sea and spray clear of her decks. Amidships the bilge is easy and yet firm enough, when combined with the hard turn in the bilge right aft, to give steadiness at sea.

We notice that the line immediately below the water-line has an unusual curve in its after end. This is due to the flattening of the stern before bringing it down to the keel, but at this point the water is running clear aft under

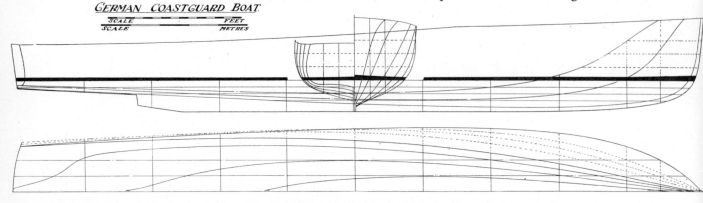

GERMAN COASTGUARD BOAT.

the bottom of the boat, for the bow has parted it and now the hull is running over the water just as skis run over snow, and so we have to pay more attention to the buttock lines at this point than to the water-lines, and the buttocks as we see are very easy and fair throughout the run.

The construction plan shows that she is a composite hull of steel and wood, her planking being of two thicknesses. The inner skin, of Honduras mahogany 10 mm. thick, is laid diagonally, while the outer, of 20 mm., is laid fore and aft, and as this construction makes for a very strong hull these vessels have stood up to sea work as one would expect them to

Outside she has a long keel running practically the whole length, and this, while steadying her in a seaway, is cut away aft so that she can manœuvre easily and quickly.

THE COMFORTABLE MESS ROOM

AT FULL SPEED

Her engine room amidships takes one-third of her length, and in this her three engines which drive her three propellers are installed. Forward of her engine room we have two double berthed cabins, a galley, washroom and a fo'c'sle with four berths in it, while abaft we have the captain's and telegraphist's quarters, the stern being given over to fuel and water tanks, as while she has two large fuel tanks in the engine room these extra tanks aft increase her range of action.

Her deck is quite clear and simple, the wheel house being situated immediately over the engine room so that the helmsman and engineers are in close touch with each other all the while, and with its windows this wheel house and chart room gives a clear view all round. The searchlight and the port and starboard lights are arranged on top of the wheel house.

The breakwater on the fore end tells us that in spite of her flaring bows this vessel expects to have water on her fore deck at times, for as she is a worker she cannot choose her weather. Immediately abaft this breakwater her small gun is mounted, and we hope that this gun is worn by her much as our policemen wear their truncheons and seldom if ever called into action.

Though not developed for the cruising yachtsman, he will find these plans interesting and instructive, as work boats, though developed for special purposes, are often driven hard at sea when pleasure boats would be in harbour waiting for the weather to change for the better.

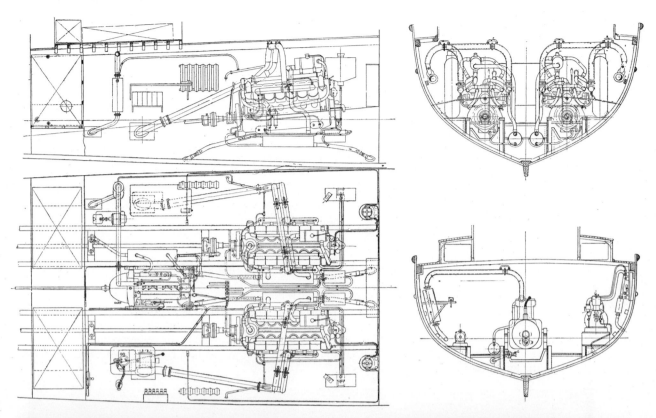

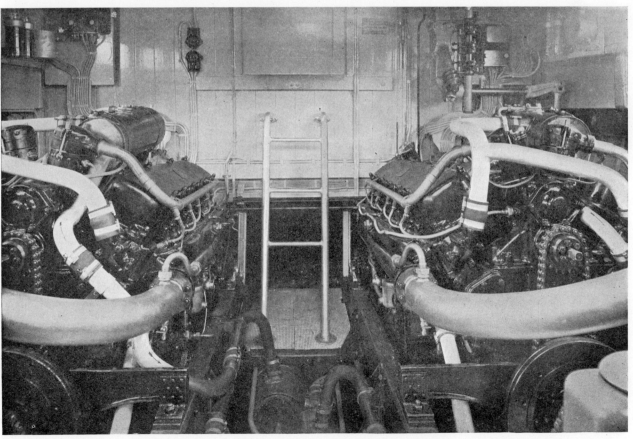

THE ENGINE ROOM PLAN AND THE ENGINE ROOM

· 20 ·

L A H L O O

Length, overall -	70 ft. 0 in. = 21·336 m.		Length, water-line -	65 ft. 6¾ in. = 19·98 m.
Beam - -	14 ft. 0 in. = 4·267 m.		Draught - -	5 ft. 10½ in. = 1·79 m.
Displacement -	55 tons = 55,880 kilos.		Engines -	Two 72 h.p. Gleniffers.
		Speed - - - - 10½ knots.		

Owner, ROBERT STEELE.   *Designer,* G. DE VRIES LENTSCH, JNR.   *Builder,* G. DE VRIES LENTSCH, JNR.

WHETHER she is twisting and worming her way through a fleet of closely moored yachts in harbour or out at sea, *Lahloo* creates an impression of great ability, for while she is able even at low speeds in confined waters to turn about as her owner wishes, she is also a fine and powerful sea boat. *Lahloo* has been watched with interest this summer wherever she has been, for she is a very fine type of the modern full powered cruiser, and her bold sides and sheer line give her a seamanlike appearance often lacking in this style of power craft, for *Lahloo* gives the impression of having very little top hamper.

LAHLOO

When we look at the lines we see that her stem runs almost plumb down to her long straight keel line which is practically as deep forward as it is aft, where it lifts very slightly to keep the rudder free from damage when grounding.

The water-lines are very fine indeed, and when we look at the sections we see enormous flare forward, which makes for a dry deck in a seaway. Throughout she has a rising floor, which makes for an easily driven ship, while the after sections are very V'd and so very suitable for sea work.

The accommodation plan shows the crew's quarters forward, abaft of which is the galley leading into the saloon with its three square ports either side, which give a good view all round to those inside whether sitting or standing. Immediately abaft this we have the engine room, in which her two 72 h.p. Gleniffers, which drive her at 10½ knots, are installed in such a way that there is full head room all round, and this room together with the ventilation makes

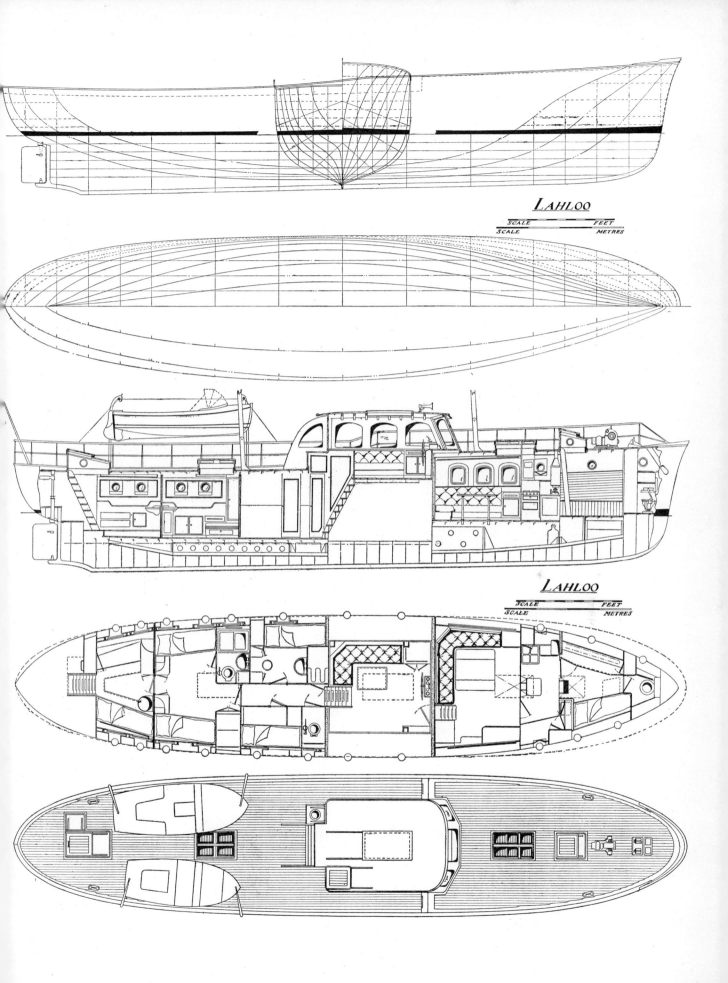

for an engine room in which the engineer can get at any part of his engines whenever he wishes without being cramped or suffocated. One is apt to cramp the engineer and his engines into too small a space, which is a mistake, for a full powered ship such as *Lahloo* depends entirely upon her engine beat as a man does upon his heart beat.

Above the engine room is the deckhouse, which with its sliding sunshine roof and its windows all round is a very fine place in which to be no matter what the weather. In this deckhouse, which is really the wheel house and chart room combined, we have the steering wheel forward and to port a settee and a chart table, while over to starboard is the flag locker, and from the plan we see that the fore and aft bulkheads separating the engine room from the rest of the ship are insulated and padded, these being no less than 12 inches in thickness.

THE DECKHOUSE IS OF TEAK—

THE DINING ROOM OF OAK—

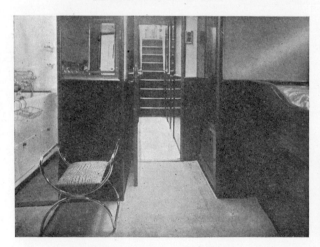

THE OWNER'S CABIN OF WALNUT—

BUT THE ENGINE ROOM IS MAINLY REVOLVING STEEL

The whole of the after end of the accommodation is given over to staterooms, there being two single staterooms immediately abaft the deckhouse. Separating these from the owner's double berthed cabin, which takes the full width of the ship, is the bathroom to port and the linen locker and wardrobe to starboard ; abaft the owner's cabin there is yet another stateroom with a sleeping berth to starboard and a sofa to port, a companion way leading out from this on to the deck. Back here her 14 foot motor launch and the 12 ft. 6 in. dinghy are slung to port and starboard in the davits, and so we see this 70 footer is very compact.

Throughout the summer *Lahloo* has been used as a tender by her owner to his Eight-metre *Saskia*, towing her from port to port and providing a wonderful floating home for the owner.

She is the latest development of a long line of vessels by G. de Vries Lentsch, and so it is not surprising that she is such a perfect little ship in every way, and that *Lahloo* has two sisters whose only difference is that their accommodation aft is slightly different.

One of the charms found aboard all ships is in the workmanship and materials used to panel out the various cabins and staterooms, for the sea is such an exacting mistress that flimsy stuff like the plaster and wall paper as used ashore in houses will not endure ; and on board *Lahloo*, besides having the pleasure of being afloat we have all the charm that the best of woods can give to cosy cabins and staterooms. The deckhouse is furnished throughout in teak, while the dining room is panelled out and furnished in oak, which fills us with delight, for the flowery grain of oak soothes and charms us as very few other woods are able to. Walnut is used to panel out the cabins, and

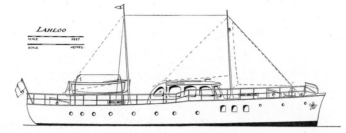

whenever I have been aboard I have enjoyed the cosiness and restfulness only found afloat and I have always thought it a great pity that more houses are not panelled and lined out entirely with wood.

There is another point about *Lahloo* that makes for contentment and rest, and that is her three sails, for though they are small for such a ship, they nevertheless give one a feeling of comfort, for they would steady her in a beam sea and damp out any tendency to roll, and to have them aboard gives one a sense of security otherwise missing aboard a power vessel.

· 21 ·

VALDORA

Length, overall	-	70 ft. 0 in. = 21·336 m.	Length, water-line	- 52 ft. 0 in. = 15·85 m.
Beam	-	15 ft. 0 in. = 4·572 m.	Draught	- - 7 ft. 0 in. = 2·134 m.
Displacement	-	34·70 tons. = 35,255 kilos.	Sail Area	- 1333 sq. ft. = 123 sq. m.
Speed	-	9 knots.	Engine	- 72 h.p. Gleniffer Diesel.

Owner, R. H. TURNER.   *Designer*, A. M. DICKIE & SON.   *Builder*, A. M. DICKIE & SON.

IMMEDIATELY we look at *Valdora* we realise that she is a motor sailer, and a fine example of this type of craft at that. Her lines are those of a sailing vessel, and at the same time are very suitable for being driven either by

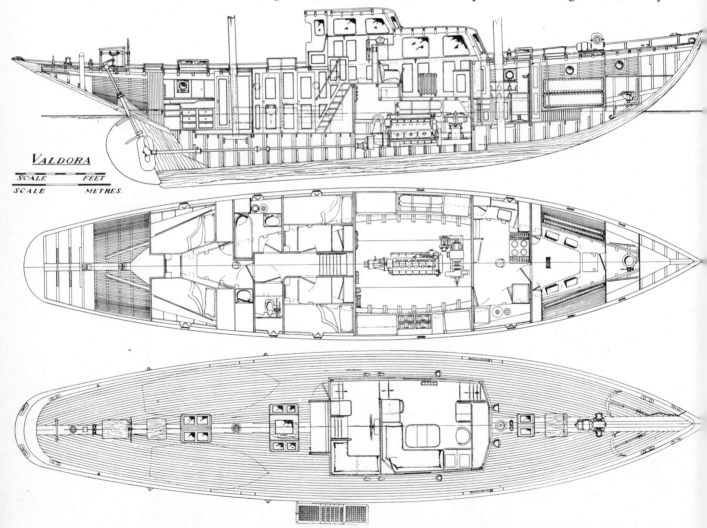

sail or power, as her water-lines and buttocks are very clean, easy and sweet, and were she given more draught the purist, who loves sailing vessels only, could not but help admire her as a sailing vessel; but because she has an engine the draught has been kept easy.

From the construction plan we see that she is well and truly built, her frame work being arranged to take every strain it is conceivable for her to meet at sea or ashore or in harbour ; and with her $7\frac{1}{4}$ ton lead keel and her 72 h.p. Gleniffer well amidships she is able to lift her bow and stern to the seas, and as one would expect is a very fine sea boat.

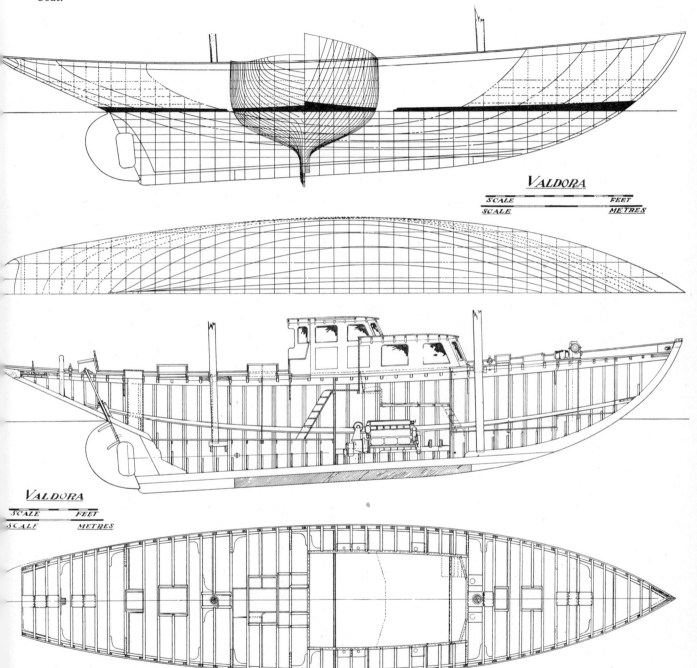

She has four pipe cots in the fo'c'sle and a galley taking the full width of the ship.

Next we have the sunk deckhouse over the engine room, the fore part of this deckhouse being her dining saloon and the after part a very comfortable wheel and chart house.

Abaft the engine room are her sleeping quarters, and here we have four single berthed cabins with bathrooms and wash basins, etc. in their midst, so that they are accessible to all four cabins. As can be seen from the deck plan when her boats are hung outboard in the davits she has a wonderfully clear deck.

The sail plan shows her two boats hung in davits, and we see that the main and mizen booms are arranged so that they clear these boats and the davits, a point often lost sight of, for unless they clear it means that as long as the davits are rigged the sails cannot be eased away for a free wind.

VALDORA LOOKS GOOD WHETHER UNDER POWER   OR SAIL

The sail plan is that of a high peaked gaff yawl and for a vessel of this type such a rig is probably the best that can be devised, as it is very efficient and yet most seamanlike, and as can be imagined when she is under way

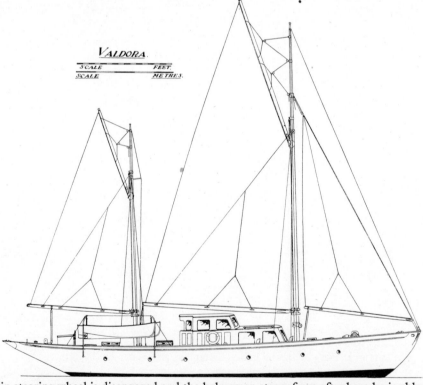

sailing the midship steering wheel is disengaged and the helmsman steers from aft where he is able to watch his sails and get the utmost out of *Valdora*. Those of us who have seen her under sail in a smart breeze have been so impressed that we have always looked for her ever after, and as *Valdora* has proved such a fine sea boat in her cruises in British and foreign waters we often have our wish granted.

· 22 ·

GLENGOUR

Length, overall - 39 ft. 3 in. = 11·96 m.   Length, water-line - 35 ft. 0 in. = 10·67 m.
Beam   -   - 10 ft. 0 in. = 3·048 m.   Draught   -   - 4 ft. 11 in. = 1·50 m.
Displacement - 12·3 tons = 12,500 Kilos.   Sail Area   -   - 671 sq. ft. = 62·30 sq. m.

Owner, CUTHBERT GRASEMANN.   *Designer*, W. G. McBRYDE.   *Builder*, JAS. ADAM & SONS.

GLENGOUR is a remarkable little ship; her owner and his wife can, and do, handle her alone, their cruising taking them into small harbours where even such a short vessel has to turn in her own length. Though she is a full-powered motor boat she is also very able under sail, and strangely enough is as fast as a 23-ton Bristol Pilot

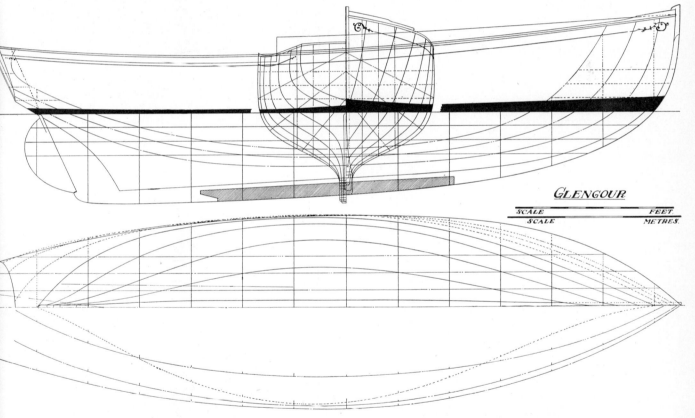

Cutter to windward in a good breeze, all of which we wonder at until we look at the lines, and then we see that her designer has given her a remarkably clean under water bottom, and if only her keel were a little deeper and her free-board a little less we should say she was of the Itchen Ferry type, a type which for many years has been recognised as fast and weatherly in spite of its shallow draught, this partly because of the firm bilges, which keep the vessel upright, maintaining her full draught.

Glengour's lines show great understanding and as one can imagine are the result of a great deal of thought, for seldom do we see such a good bottom in power craft which sail.

As her accommodation shows she is very comfortable below, and since no paid hands are carried the fo'c'sle becomes a single berthed cabin with six feet of headroom. Immediately abaft of this is her cosy saloon, while next aft we have the washroom to starboard and the galley to port, so arranged that the food can be placed right on the saloon table or up into the deckhouse, for as can be imagined meals are taken in both places according to the weather and mood of those aboard. Underneath the deckhouse the engines are installed together with their fuel tanks and work benches. They take the full width of the ship, but very little room, as the floor of the deckhouse forms the roof to the engine room, while abaft the engine room is a double berthed stateroom.

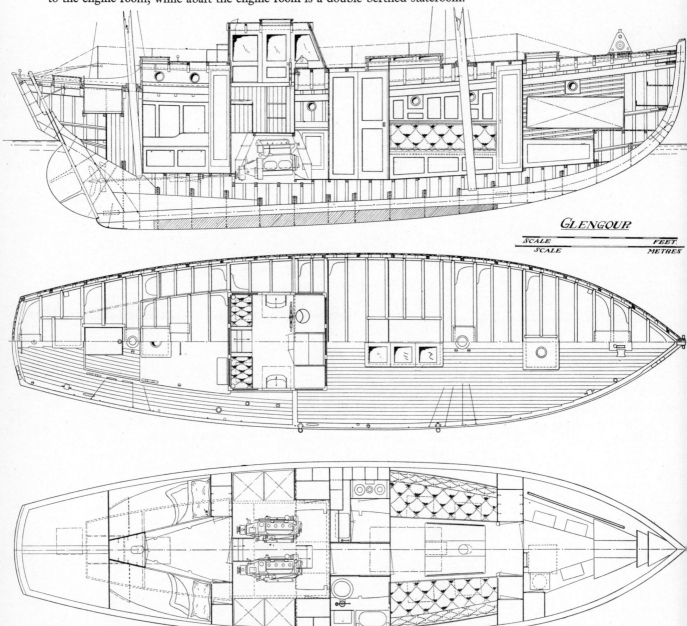

GLENGOUR

SCALE   FEET
SCALE   METRES

One good point in the engine and galley being amidships is that, in case of fire, those aboard can escape either through the fore hatch or through the after hatch. This summer, while on the Norfolk Broads, I saw a motor boat which had burnt out, those aboard being trapped in one end by the flames through which they had to rush to save themselves being roasted alive, after which they were taken to hospital all badly burned. Had they not been on the Broads with help around, but at sea, it is probable they would have perished, all for the want of an exit away from the fire ; and so it would seem that all power craft should have hatchways arranged to enable those aboard to leave any part of the ship without going through another. *Glengour* is a good example of this arrangement, for she has a hatch forward, skylights over the saloon, hatchways to port and starboard immediately over the engine and galley, and a hatchway out of the after cabin, while right aft there is yet another leading in and out of the sail locker, this being placed slightly to port so that it clears the tiller ; for *Glengour* when sailed is generally steered by the tiller

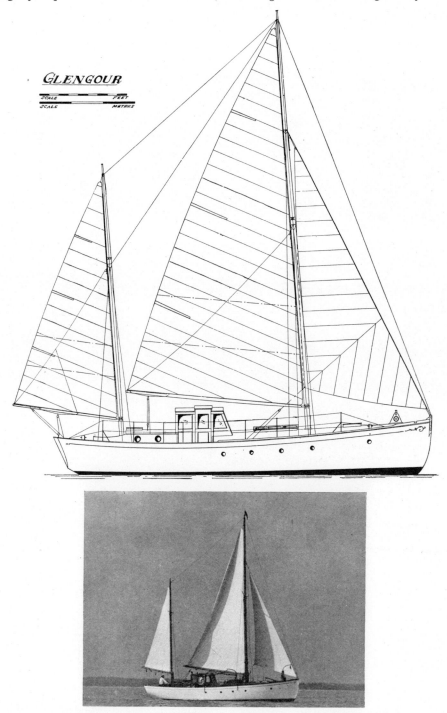

GLENGOUR UNDER SAIL

from the after cockpit, which has been used a great deal this summer, because the weather has been so warm for this country.

It will be seen that *Glengour* has twin screws, and these enable her to turn round on her heel, a valuable point in small harbours when sailing shorthanded, for it saves all the trouble of running out warps and warping round. In

Yarmouth this September *Glengour* turned with one engine ahead and the other astern in $2\frac{1}{4}$ minutes on her heel, while another power cruiser with hands aboard took 14 minutes to warp round.   An owner and his wife would find it hard work warping round.

GLENGOUR IN LOCH KEILLS

Another point that makes for easier handling aboard *Glengour* is the Reed power windlass forward, while as will be seen from her sail plan the sails are easily set, stowed and handled, for her mainsail is only 377 sq. feet in area. Her total area of 671 sq. feet enables her to sail so well on all points of sailing that we are amazed until we see her out of the water, for one seldom suspects that power craft have underwater lines so suitable for sailing, and there is no doubt that McBryde has produced a wonderful little vessel in *Glengour*.   We have to bear in mind that the owner's last vessel was an ex 10-metre, and the fact that *Glengour* pleases him under sail tells us that as well as being a full-powered motor boat she sails remarkably well, so well that after the day's sail and the haven reached and one is in the saloon with the owner and his wife, one feels that the contentment and rest not only comes from the comfort found on board, but also from the fact that *Glengour* has made her harbour under sail, and her all-round ability makes one feel that the owner is happy and contented with his ship.

· 23 ·

S. K. S. LOTTERY BOAT

Length, overall - 32 ft. 1⅜ in. = 9·79 m.   Length water-line - 26 ft. 10⅞ in. = 8·20 m.
Beam - - 9 ft. 4¼ in. = 2·85 m.   Draught - - 3 ft. 11¼ in. = 1·20 m.
Displacement - 4·23 tons = 4299 Kilos.   Sail Area - - 350 sq. ft. = 32·8 sq. m.

Owner, SVENSKA KRYSSARKLUBBEN.   *Designer*, J. LINDBLOM.   *Builder*, CARL WESTIN.

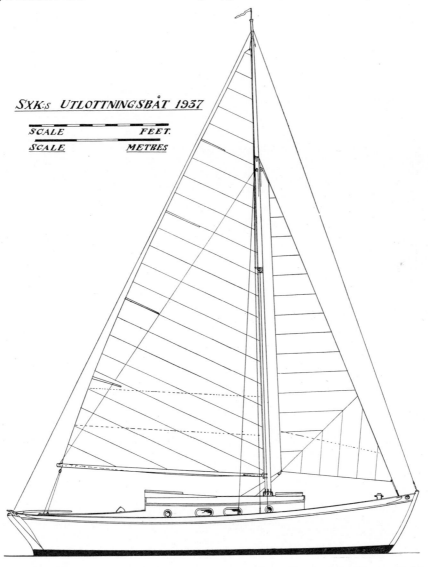

SXK:s UTLOTTNINGSBÅT 1937

SCALE   FEET.
SCALE   METRES

SWEDEN is fortunate in having so strong and energetic a Club as the Svenska Kryssarklubben, which covers every branch of cruising, from designing, building and sailing until the laying up·season is on them, and even then it continues its activities, for its members meet and lectures are arranged throughout the winter months.   Also every year this Club commissions a designer and builder to produce a cruiser for them, amd many notable craft have been produced in this way. When built, a lottery is held and one member finds himself the owner of a fine cruiser.

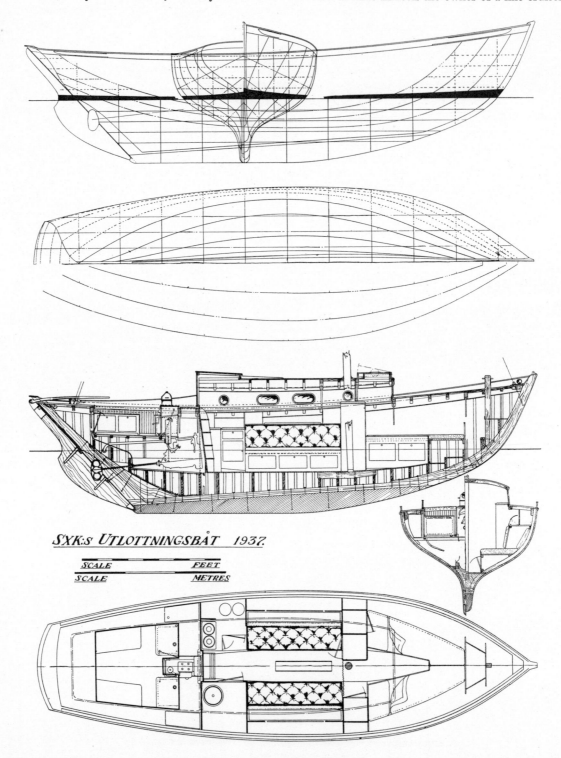

SXK:s UTLOTTNINGSBÅT 1937.

SCALE —————— FEET

SCALE —————— METRES

In the past these have been sailing craft, but in 1937 the Club decided upon a vessel which, while being a good sailing boat, would also give a first-class performance under power ; the Committee rightly considered that the two could be combined to produce a first-class vessel whether considered from a sailing cruiser's viewpoint or from the power cruiser's point of view. As we study them, we see that J. Lindblom has produced a set of lines that would make this little vessel sail remarkably well. She has moreover a very efficient rig, as the luff of her mainsail is more than twice as long as the main boom, and she has not been starved of sail but has quite a good spread, enough to please the man who loves to cruise under sail.

We next look at these lines from a power point of view, and we see that the hull is very easily driven, those V'd sections and easy water-lines needing very little power to drive them. She is a fine sturdy power vessel.

Whether a man is a sailing or a motor boat man his ideas on accommodation must be very similar, and that for this vessel is well laid out. Forward she has a double berthed sleeping cabin with lockers at the after end, immediately abaft of which is her saloon where two men can sleep in comfort if need be. At the after end of this we have the galley and pantry. The whole layout being very roomy and complete for such a vessel.

Four steps take us out of the saloon on to the bridge deck and into the cockpit, under which is situated the engine and its tanks, partitioned off from the accommodation by a bulkhead, an arrangement which keeps the smells of an engine clear of the interior, and because of this has much to recommend it. In fact the engine situated this way is ideal for such a sized vessel, for it is entirely clear of the accommodation, and this makes for happiness and safety aboard a small ship. Future years will see more and more of this type of vessel, aiming at perfection under sail or power, and the Swedish Cruising Club are to be congratulated on their effort to forward the motor sailer.

· 24 ·

SAUNDERS' SEAPLANE TENDER

Length, overall -	35 ft. 0 in. = 10·67 m.	Length, water-line -	35 ft. 0 in. = 10·67 m.
Beam - -	6 ft. 6 in. = 1·98 m.	Draught - -	2 ft. 5 in. = 0·736 m.
Displacement -	2·43 tons = 2468 Kilos.	Engine - -	71 h.p. Grey.
Speed - -	15 knots.	Propellor - -	16 in. diameter.
			13 in. pitch.

Owner, SAUNDERS-ROE, LTD.   *Designer*, S. E. SAUNDERS, LTD.   *Builder*, S. E. SAUNDERS, LTD.

A QUARTER of a century is a long time for a man to admire one motor boat and its work, yet this seaplane tender is close on twenty-five years old, and still gives perfect service to Saunders-Roe's flying boats. She still

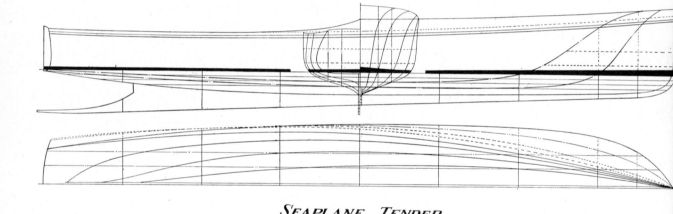

SEAPLANE TENDER

SCALE — FEET
SCALE — METRES

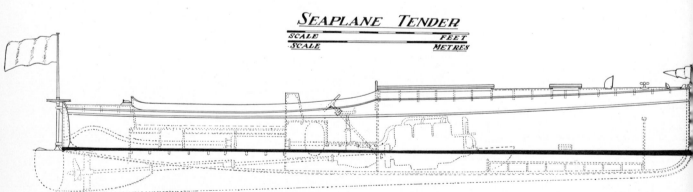

seems up to date to our eyes, for she is a thoroughbred of the round bilge type, creating little wash as she streaks along at 15 knots, and she finds her way into this book on two very important points :

(1) Her design, which is seaworthy, speedy and yet creates little wash or fuss, and

(2) Because of her construction, for she has stood up to a great deal of hard work bravely, and one would have difficulty in improving upon this design for similar work to-day, for we see in the long easy water-lines and buttocks, a vessel that while capable of a good speed requires very little driving, and the sections while making for a stiff steady sea boat are also those of an easily driven craft. The flare off forward, throwing the sea away from her decks, is

washed out amidships, where her side is plumb, while aft the tumble home takes any heavy look away from her transom, and besides this cuts down the wind suction from the stern by that much.

From her arrangement plan we see from midships forward she is decked in, the engine room being completely housed, and with the fore hatch closed this launch is able to stand a good deal of sea, for we have to remember that summer and winter she is operating in the Medina and the Solent, and that the Solent seas are very steep and break-

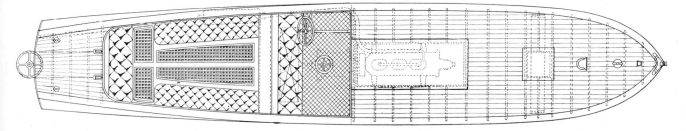

ing when the wind is against the tide. Because of this the deck adds greatly to her seaworthiness, while the long keel and skeg, stiffening the hull throughout and carrying the propellor bracket and the rudder, also tell of a craft used in a seaway and one that has to take the ground and hard knocks at times. As we study these plans we see a great deal to admire and appreciate, and looking at them we can picture this launch dashing along cleanly at 14 to 15 knots.

Her construction of $\frac{3}{4}$ in. $\times \frac{1}{2}$ in. timbers, spaced 6 in. centres, and $\frac{7}{8}$ in. Honduras mahogany planking, and her 3 in. wide keel of American elm, has enabled her to stand up to hard wear for just on quarter of a century, even after which time she still seems fresh and new not only in her condition but also her design for the sea has never changed and as it is difficult to think of a prettier launch for sea work it might be said that she will be up to date in appearances for many years to come.

· 25 ·

AN ADMIRAL'S BARGE

Length, overall -   30 ft. 0 in. = 9·144 m.   Length, water-line -   29 ft. 9 in. = 9·067 m.
Beam   -   -   7 ft. 10 in. = 2·387 m.   Draught   -   -   2 ft. 2 in. = 0·66 m.
Displacement -   3·52 tons = 3576 Kilos.   Engines -   -   -   100 h.p. Birmal.
                                Speed   -   -   -   - 21 knots.

Owner, H.M. NAVY   *Designer*, GROVES & GUTTRIDGE   *Builder*, GROVES & GUTTRIDGE

BECAUSE working boats have to perform in all kinds of weather, two work boats designed and built by Groves & Guttridge of East Cowes are the first of the V'd bottom boats described in this book.

A few years ago all the boats of all the navies of the world were of the round bilged type, but now all are building V-bottomed chined boats, and the reason is not far to seek. We all know that up to a certain speed the round bilged type of craft offers less resistance, but once certain speeds are reached and the vessel begins to plane, then the V-bottomed hard chined boat is the more efficient. The navies of the world are now concentrating on the building of small wooden motor torpedo-boats ranging in speed from 30 to 50 knots, these vessels being from 60 ft. up to 100 ft. in overall length. Their duty is to launch torpedo attacks on battleships, relying on their speed to enable them to get within striking distance, and to escape after their torpedoes have been fired. In a way these vessels have put the clock back a great number of years to the days of the old torpedo-boats, which were very small, and which were finally outclassed by the torpedo-boat destroyer, which now is only called a destroyer, and seldom does anyone think or realise that these came into being simply to destroy the small torpedo boats of 50 years ago.

Now though the speeds at which these new torpedo boats can travel are higher than before, guns have also improved, but an attack by one of these boats could be aided if a bombing attack was simultaneously carried out from the air, so the aeroplane has helped to bring into being the torpedo-boat once more.

Though these hard chined V-bottomed boats are good sea boats in that they can travel through and survive heavy seas, they cannot yet be regarded as being able to work independent of the shore or parent ship, for as we all know giant liners, and all ships at sea at some time or another, meet conditions in which they must slow down, and when we remember that these vessels are only steaming along at normal speeds such as the square root of their water-line length, and that planing vessels travel at double and treble the square root of their water-line length, then we can see that times must often come when they have to slow right down. Even when driven along at their high speeds in normal weather they are putting heavy strains upon themselves, and upon the people on board, and the success of these vessels must rely largely upon the understanding and the knowledge of their limitations by those in charge, for though not fair weather ships they must have ideal conditions in which to travel at their remarkably high speeds.

Side by side with this development we have the speeding up of all naval craft, and the boat illustrating this theme is a 30 ft. admiral's barge capable of 21 knots when loaded with her full equipment on board.

The lines plan shows that she is a V-bottomed hard chined boat, but the V'd sections forward are filled out at the bottom, the forward sections revealing this fulness, which gives fore and aft stability ; and as we look at her sections and buttocks we can imagine this vessel's bow parting a sea and then as the sections flatten we can imagine her running over the water as cleanly as skates over ice.

Her 100 h.p. Birmal engine is situated just abaft of midships, and as can be seen from the arrangement plan it is housed very low in this barge, a point which makes for stability and steadiness as well as giving room on board.

The construction is of double-skinned mahogany on mahogany frames with Canadian rock elm timbers in between, the stem and keel being of English oak, while all the interior decoration and panelling is carried out in mahogany.

It will be seen that the helmsman occupies the forward cockpit, the compass being situated just forward of him, and he is connected to the midship cockpit by voice tubes. Between these two is situated the officers' cabin, there

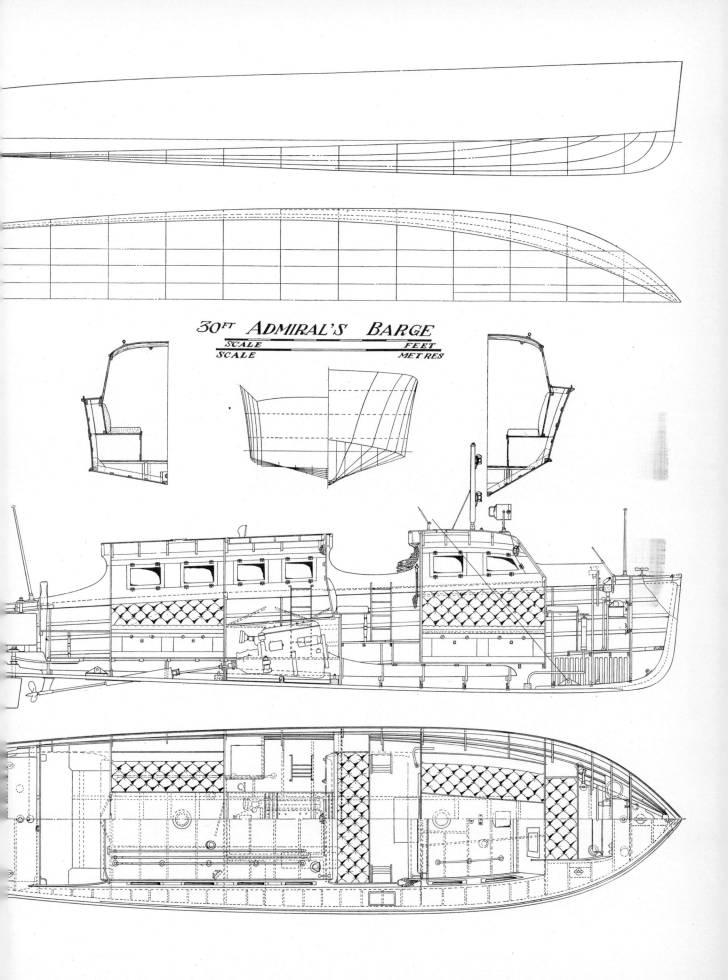

30^{FT} ADMIRAL'S BARGE
SCALE   FEET
SCALE   MET RES

being another cabin abaft the engine room and a third cockpit right aft, so though only 30 ft. long this admiral's barge has three cockpits and two cabins, and when we consider all the room aboard her and the weight put into her

SOMEWHAT SIMILAR TO THE ADMIRAL'S BARGE THIS 30-FOOTER BY THE SAME FIRM ATTAINED A SPEED OF 28 MILES PER HOUR

construction, which is of the very best of materials, we realise how well suited the lines and design are for the job for which she is intended.

25-FT. COMMITTEE BOAT FOR TRINITY HOUSE

Length, overall -	25 ft. 0 in. = 7·62 m.		Length, water-line -	24 ft. 9 in. = 7·543 m.
Beam - -	6 ft. 3 in. = 1·905 m.		Draught - -	2 ft. 0 in. = 0·61 m.
Displacement -	2·4 tons = 2438 Kilos.		Engine - -	50 h.p. Birmal.
		Speed - - -	16¼ knots.	

Owner, TRINITY HOUSE   *Designer*, GROVES & GUTTRIDGE, LTD.   *Builder*, GROVES & GUTTRIDGE, LTD.

This 25-footer was designed and built by Messrs. Groves & Guttridge, Ltd., as a committee boat for the new Diesel electric motor vessel *Patricia*. So, though the name of " The Elder Brethren ", given to those at the head of the Trinity House, creates an impression of sedateness, we see that they are up to date in every way, as indeed they always have been throughout the long years in which they have cared for our seafaring affairs. In this committee boat we see a very efficient fast running launch, for this 25-footer, loaded and with fuel tank full, has a speed of 16¼ knots ; and when we think of the strength of her construction, and the weight in such things as her

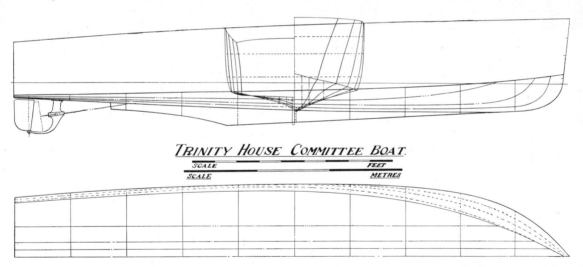

TRINITY HOUSE COMMITTEE BOAT.

sling plates and her strong outside keel, we realise what a fine performance this is. She is built of double-skinned mahogany on sawn mahogany frames with Canadian rock elm timbers between, while the stem, keel and main framing is of oak, the interior being panelled with mahogany. When we bear in mind her robustness (and she has to be strongly built to withstand the wear she is bound to meet in service), we realise that such a speed with her 50 h.p. engine is only obtained through a great understanding on the part of her designer and builders. The lines show that her hollowed V'd sections are slightly round in the fore foot to give greater fore and aft stability, and the V'd sections of the forebody gradually flatten as they go aft to the transom where she is almost flat : while from the arrangement plan we see that forward she has a hatch for the bowman which normally is kept shut at sea, abaft of which is a 7 ft. cabin. The steering wheel and helmsman are at the after end of this, on the starboard side, abreast of the 50 h.p. Birmal motor, where the helmsman is in close touch with the engine, an arrangement that makes for short and thus very serviceable gearing levers.

Abaft this midship cockpit, in which the engine and helmsman are situated, is the after cockpit with its spray hood for bad weather, and under the after deck, well out of the way, is her petrol tank, so though only 25 ft. in length this committee boat has a great deal of room and a good turn of speed, all of which is not surprising, for S. E. Porter, M.I.N.A., the designer to Groves & Guttridge, has been designing successful hydroplanes and fast motor craft since they came into being. He was chief designer to S. E. Saunders, Ltd., throughout that firm's

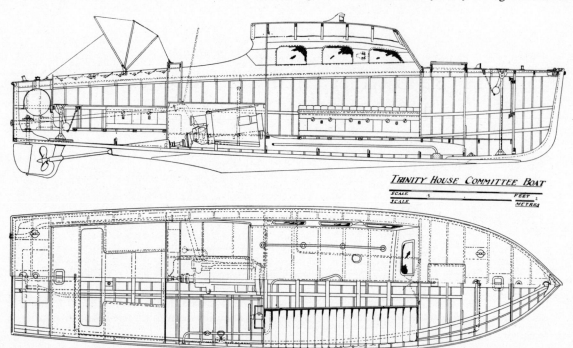

TRINITY HOUSE COMMITTEE BOAT

successful career, and now with the son of S. E. Saunders he is part of the firm of Groves & Guttridge, Ltd., and just as a good band relies upon the composer for the wonderful symphony it plays, so does a firm of good workmen rely upon their chief designer, and the chief designer is the beginning and the end of any firm, as without him no matter how good the workmanship and materials, they must fail, a simple fact often lost sight of.

· 27 ·

AVRIL

Length, overall -	36 ft. 0 in. = 10·97 m.		Length, water-line -	34 ft. 10½ in. = 10·63 m.
Beam - -	11 ft. 0 in. = 3·35 m.		Draught - -	2 ft. 4½ in. = 0·72 m.
Displacement -	6·52 tons. = 6624 Kilos.		Engines - - -	Two 90 h.p. Chrysler.
Diameter of propeller	13 in.		Pitch of propeller -	10 in.
Speed - -	20 m.p.h.		Prop. revs. per min.	3200.

Owner, C. H. KEARLEY, ESQ.   *Designer*, FRED COOPER   *Builder*, GROVES & GUTTRIDGE, LTD.

WHENEVER we look at a set of plans of any vessel, we should always keep the job for which she is intended foremost in our minds, for it is by her suitability for and ability in that job that she stands or falls. A tug boat built with engines and tanks for towing vessels and supplying water to them, while being extremely suitable for her job, would be useless as a cruising vessel, for with practically all her space taken by her very powerful

THIS QUARTER VIEW OF AVRIL SHOWS HOW CLEANLY SHE RUNS

machinery and water tanks there is little left for accommodation. In the case of *Avril* we must bear in mind that her owner wanted a small fast cruiser which besides being speedy would house the owner and two or three friends in comfort and enable them to make long week-end cruises along our coasts or cross the Channel in good weather and visit French ports. The fact that, in her first season, practically every port between Dover and Land's End saw her, and that she crossed the Channel several times, shows that *Avril* amply fulfilled her owner's requirements.

The lines plan shows her to be of the hollow V'd hard chined section type of craft so efficient when planing speeds are reached, for in spite of all her comfort and accommodation *Avril* bustles along at 20 m.p.h., and when we consider that she has only a pair of 90 h.p. engines we realise that her lines are ideal for such a vessel, a fact borne out by the three photographs, two at speed and the third showing her floating to her exact trim immediately after launching.

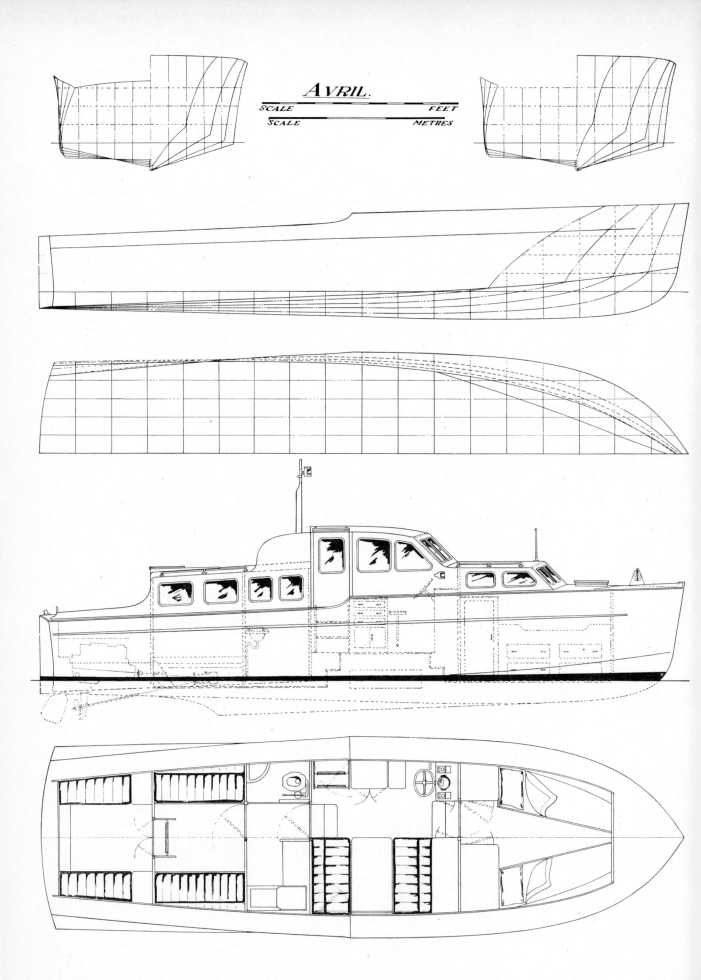

AVRIL.

SCALE   FEET

SCALE   METRES

In this type of vessel light weight is an important factor, and strength is of even more importance, and these two are combined remarkably well in this hull, for as her voyages show the hull is strong and seaworthy while her high speed shows at the same time that she is lightly built.

AVRIL AT 24 KNOTS

THE RAKING FORE END
OF HER DECKHOUSE

Diagonal and fore and aft planking, which has proved the strongest method, is fastened to mahogany frames, while the chine, gunwales, keel, etc., are of Canadian rock elm.   Only by using the best of materials can strength and lightness be combined.

L   F.R.C.D.

The wonderful accommodation on this vessel is made possible by the arrangement of her twin engines under the after cockpit seats in each quarter, where though they are entirely out of the way they are yet easily accessible. This installation, moreover, proved remarkably quiet, as the V drives used were silent and vibrationless.

Forward of the wheel house we have the owner's stateroom with a berth to port and starboard, and from the plans we see that he has any amount of wardrobe space in this cabin.

Abaft this is a wheel house and saloon combined, her water tank being arranged under its raised floor. The helmsman's position is to port, and he takes little room away from the deckhouse, for a car type wheel with all

AVRIL FLOATED EXACTLY TO HER MARKS WHEN LAUNCHED

controls and instruments within easy reach makes the handling of this vessel easy for one man. Immediately abaft him is the chart table, while to starboard, in this bridge saloon, which is without doubt a very pleasant feature of the vessel, is arranged the dining room with accommodation for six people. After a meal is over the table, being hinged, can be folded out of the way, while the settee backs are so made that the two settees can be formed into a double bed for the night if needed.

Abaft the bridge saloon is the galley and washroom, and next aft this we have the after stateroom, with a port leading out into the after cockpit. Seldom do we see such ample accommodation on a boat only 36 ft. overall, all made possible by the arrangement of her twin engines, and a glance at the photographs tells us that she is wonderfully light and airy below. The large windows are a particularly attractive feature, as not only do they light the interior and make it cheerful, but also they enable everyone below to see everything that is happening outside. As we study these plans we realise that the owner is a fortunate man to have thought of such a vessel, and then to have taken his ideas to a man like Fred Cooper, who was able to transfer these thoughts into such a wonderful little ship.

· 28 ·

DREAMTOO

Length, overall -	35 ft. 0 in. = 10·668 m.	Length, water-line -	34 ft. 0 in. = 10·363 m.
Beam - - -	8 ft. 9 in. = 2·667 m.	Draught - - -	2 ft. 6 in. = 0·762 m.
Displacement - -	11,000 lb. = 4·92 tons.	Engines - -	Two 60 h.p. Chrysler.
Diameter of propeller	24 in. = 0·609 m.	Pitch of propeller -	28 in. = 0·711 m.
Speed - - -	20 m.p.h.	Propeller revs. -	900 per min.

Owner, SIDNEY HILL, ESQ., J.P.   *Designer*, FRED COOPER

Builder, SOUTHAMPTON LAUNCH & BOAT CO.

THOUGH similar in design to *Avril*, and from the same designer's board, *Dreamtoo* is designed for a different job. Her owner wanted a vessel that, while wholesome enough to make long coastal passages at a good turn of speed, could be used quite often at low speeds when her owner was spinning for mackerel ; and it speaks well for this little vessel's design and engine installation, that not only is she able to make fast coastal passages, but also she is able to cruise along at 3 m.p.h. for hours on end without fuss or vibration or any oiling up of plugs, etc.

ALL CONTROLS ARE GROUPED HANDY TO THE HELMSMAN

The lines show that, while generally speaking she might be termed a hollow V'd hard chined boat, in the forward sections her forefoot has been swollen out to give greater stability here. This is the chief difference between her set of lines and ideas and those employed in *Avril*.

The owner, Sidney Hill, had first of all commissioned Freddy to design a 27 foot day fishing boat with 50 h.p. engines and a speed of 12 knots. But quite by chance the building had to be postponed, and in the meantime Sidney Hill, who had been studying the various V-bottomed cruisers from Fred Cooper's board, decided that he

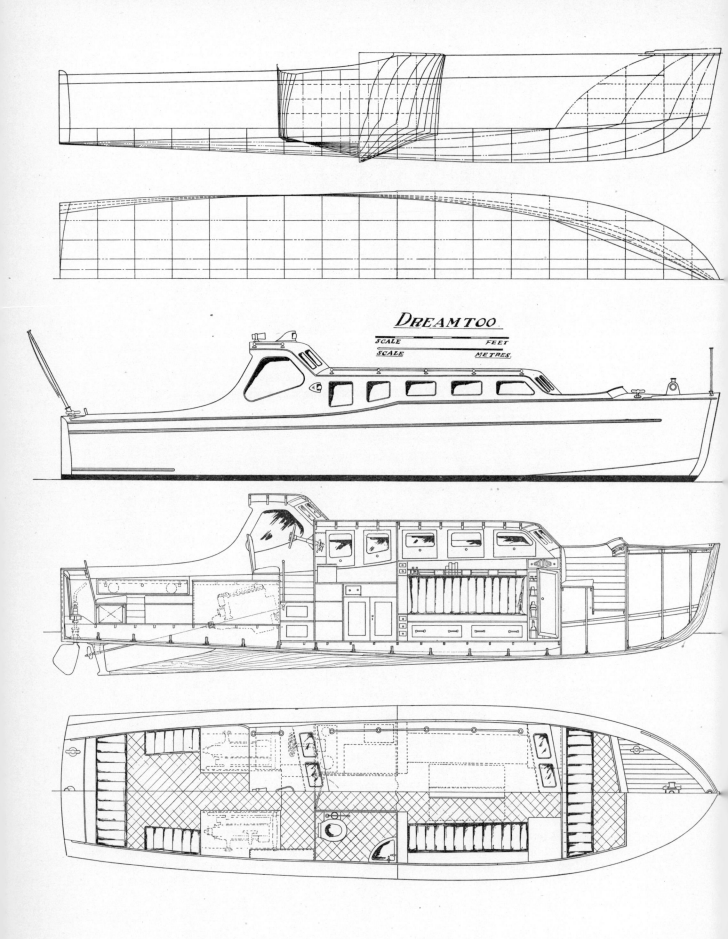

DREAMTOO

SCALE ———————— FEET
SCALE ———————— METRES.

THE ROOMY SALOON LOOKING FORWARD—

AND AFT

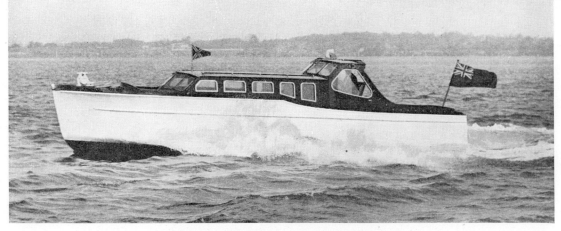

DREAMTOO IS GOOD FOR 17½ KNOTS WITH 120 H.P.

would go for a larger and faster type of craft that would plane.   These plans, and the vessel herself, bear out the fact known to most of us that second thoughts are often best, for there is no doubt that *Dreamtoo* has fulfilled all her owner's requirements.

In the bow she has a forward cockpit, and immediately abaft this is a comfortable saloon where six or eight people can enjoy meals prepared in the galley immediately abaft it on the port side.   To starboard of the galley the washroom

DREAMTOO AT SPEED

is arranged with a sliding door, which takes up little room, and next aft is the wheel shelter and after cockpit, her twin engines being arranged under the two sliding car type seats in the wheel shelter.   The latter affords excellent protection to the after cockpit and is high enough to give a good clear view over the bow ; and as all controls lead on to the steering wheel she is as easily controlled and handled as a car.   As the fishing is done from the cockpit, the fishermen and helmsman are all close together, which enables them to work in perfect harmony, and her dead beat compass and navigational instruments are within view of all, immediately forward of the helmsman.   It is not surprising that she has given perfect satisfaction, for with her sprung settees, cocktail bar, galley and cosy dining saloon, lockers for fishing tackle and her seaworthiness, she fulfils all the requirements of her owner and has given him a great deal of pleasure in the past two years.

· 29 ·

9 METRE RUNABOUT

Length, overall -	29 ft. 6 in.	=9 m.	Length, water-line -	27 ft. 5 in.	=8·35 m.
Beam - -	6 ft. 6¾ in.	=2 m.	Draught - -	1 ft. 11½ in.	=0·60 m.
Displacement -	1·8 tons	=1828 kilos.	Engine - - -	100 h.p. Maybach.

Speed - - - - 23 m.p.h.

Owner, R. STUTTGART   *Designer*, HAROLD TAPKEN

DESIGNED for use on Lake Constance (Bodensee), where the water is very rough at times, this runabout is heavily built with a double bottom and weighs two tons with her fuel on board. The 95 to 100 h.p. Mayback motor, weighing half a ton, also follows out this idea of robustness, and when we think that this runabout is capable of a speed of 23 miles an hour we see she is a good example of her type.

THE TAPKEN 9 METRE RUNABOUT AT 23 MILES PER HOUR

As the owner intended using her on the Rhine as well as Lake Constance for cruising purposes, the draught was restricted, but even so she has a good outside keel which, as can be seen, is deep enough to protect the propeller and its skeg from hard knocks. It will be noticed that there is a passage way down the starboard side of the engine connecting both cockpits together. This is an important feature, for as we all know when several children are together they immediately get into mischief and have to be looked after, and if father had to climb all the way over the usual midship deck, which extends right across the boat, he would arrive amongst the children too late. The very fact of his having easy access to the fore cockpit and the children acts as a restraint on them, for they feel at all times they are within reach of his long arm, and it would seem that though arranged this way for children, most runabouts would be the better for having a passage way, so that one could walk the whole way fore and aft.

Her lines tell us that she is of the hard chined V'd bottom type of craft, which is so efficient at high speeds. It is only of late years that outside keels have come into favour with this type of craft, for generally speaking, until recently they have been used for speed work only, but now they are coming into more general use, and so we see more and more features that have given so much service to their older round bilged sisters being incorporated.   The outside keel is a case in point, this strengthens the hull and shields it from hard knocks and protects the propeller as well as enabling the boat to be grounded without damage to her bottom.   At the same time the keel gives such a boat as this a great deal of steadiness fore and aft at all speeds, so though the outside keel seems wrong to those of us

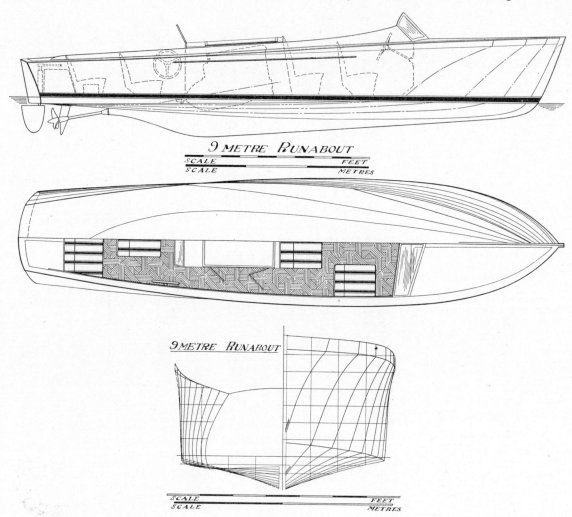

9 METRE RUNABOUT

who have built and watched this type of craft grow for some 30 years, it is only because the earlier vessels of this type were designed for speed and racing only.   Having proved their ability they are now adopted and used as fast utility boats all over the world, and in consequence such things as outside keels and heavier construction are rightfully used on them, for not speed but usefulness is the first consideration.   So once again we see that the racing brethren have developed and perfected a type which, with modifications making it slower, has now a wide appeal to cruising people, and this vessel should be looked upon therefore as a racing cruiser, and as such she would be difficult to improve upon.

· 30 ·

BONZO

Length, overall -	16 ft. 0 in. = 4·87 m.		Length, water-line -	14 ft. 9 in. = 4·49 m.
Beam - -	5 ft. 0 in. = 1·50 m.		Draught - -	1 ft. 9 in. = 0·53 m.
Displacement -	0·45 tons = 457 kilos.		Engine - -	25 h.p. outboard.
		Speed - - - - 28 m.p.h.		

Owner, HAROLD TAPKEN   *Designer*, HAROLD TAPKEN

THE outboard motor boat has a great deal to recommend her. The engine can be taken out in a few moments and another shipped to take its place, so repairs and adjustments are easily made, and in addition to this, outboard boats can be put on trailers and taken all over the country without any fear of upsetting their shaft lines. They will always therefore hold their place in the sun.

BONZO AT REST

One of the drawbacks of the outboard, however, is that the engine hung over the stern is difficult to ship and unship, as not only does the weight of the engine pull the stern down but also that of the man shipping it ; then, too, it is constantly getting water over it, which is bad for any engine. Another disadvantage is that the driver of an outboard boat has to sit well forward to counteract the heavy weight on the stern, and so he has only very remote control of the engine. But Harold Tapken of Berlin designed this little speedboat to take the outboard inboard, and as can be seen from the plans the outboard engine slots down through the hatchway amidships immediately abaft the step, an arrangement which has much to recommend it. First of all it can be easily shipped and unshipped, for one can get all round the engine, and besides this it is in the middle of the boat where she is more able to carry it. The third reason for it being good is that it is easily reached and adjustments can be made even at full speed, whereas in the normal outboard the helmsman is a long way away from his engine. Besides all this it is well protected from flying spray. So this little craft has a great deal to recommend her to the outboard enthusiast, for with the engine unshipped she is light and easily portable, so that she could be taken to various parts of the country by car and trailer.

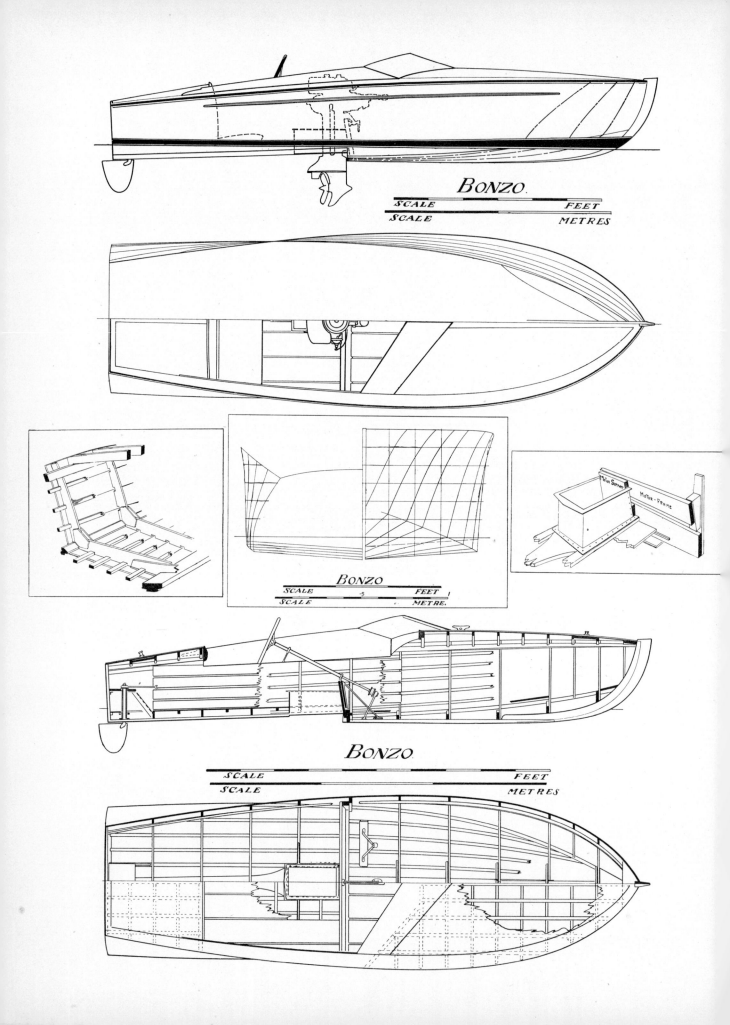

BONZO.

SCALE ⸺⸺⸺⸺⸺⸺⸺ FEET

SCALE ⸺⸺⸺⸺⸺⸺⸺ METRES

BONZO

SCALE ⸺⸺⸺ ·5 ⸺⸺⸺ FEET

SCALE ⸺⸺⸺⸺⸺⸺⸺ METRE.

BONZO.

SCALE ⸺⸺⸺⸺⸺⸺⸺ FEET

SCALE ⸺⸺⸺⸺⸺⸺⸺ METRES

This boat weighed just on half a ton because she was heavily built in order to last a long time, for she is designed as a touring boat. With an outboard motor developing 14 h.p. she streaked along at 20 m.p.h., while when a 25 h.p. motor was installed her speed went up to 28 m.p.h. These speeds as well as being good for such a heavily built hydroplane, also tell of another advantage the outboard boat has over the normal hull, for in five minutes one can change this boat from a 14 to a 25 h.p. craft, the speed at the same time going from 20 to 28 m.p.h.

BONZO AT SPEED

Bonzo is now 10 years old, but even so she still looks fresh to our eyes, and is still giving good service to her owner, and is a reminder to people who look upon outboards as boats capable of lasting a summer only, that providing they are well and truly built and well designed, they will probably last a life time ; they have thus a choice between a fast and flimsy hull with a short life or a stronger slower hull that will last many years. Engines cannot be expected to last like hulls, for they are built of metals which are not enduring, but this is not as bad as it seems at first for engines have improved faster than hulls, and so do not need to be so lasting.

There is no doubt that Harold Tapken in developing and designing *Bonzo* has done a great service for the outboard enthusiasts, all of whom would do well to study and ponder over this set of plans, for there is a great deal to be learnt from them. One hopes that outboard racers will make rules calling for more robust and seaworthy hulls, for until such rules are formed outboard boating and racing cannot flourish as it easily might, for the outboard boat is the poor man's racing motor boat, but as developed to-day this racing is very costly.

· 31 ·

BLUEBIRD

HOLDER OF THE WORLD'S WATER SPEED RECORD

Length, overall - 23 ft. 0 in. = 7·01 m.	Length, water-line - 22 ft. 3 in. = 6·782 m.
Beam - - - 9 ft. 6 in. = 2·895 m.	Draught - - - 1 ft. 9 in. = 0·533 m.
Displacement - 4945 lb. = 2240 kilos.	Engine - - - Rolls-Royce 2150 h.p.
Speed - - - 129·5 knots.	Propeller revs. - - 9000 per min.

Owner, SIR MALCOLM CAMPBELL   *Designer*, FRED COOPER   *Builder*, SAUNDERS-ROE, LTD.

FOR many years we have thought of Fred Cooper when we think of record-breaking hydroplanes, for he has designed so many of them. Therefore it is not surprising that when Sir Malcolm Campbell, the holder of the

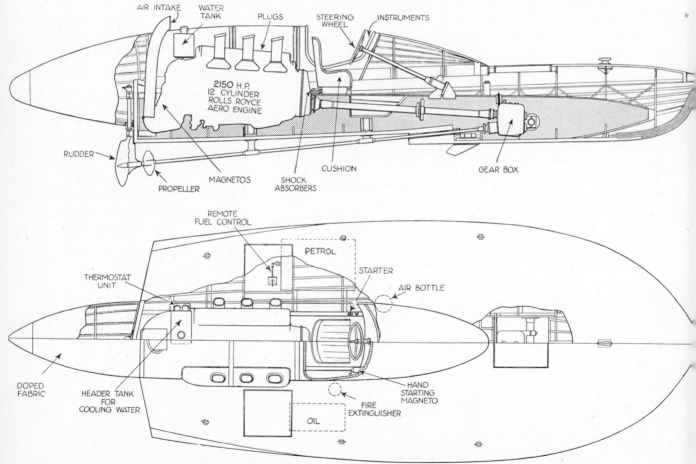

land speed record, went for the water speed record, he came to Fred Cooper for the design, for in the design of those other craft a great deal had been learnt which could be applied to this new vessel.

Freddy's idea was that for record breaking a very small hull with a single engine was the type of craft to go for, and he decided upon a 23 ft. overall length with 9 ft. 6 in. beam, calculating that this would make the hull, capable of 130 m.p.h. with the 2150 h.p. Rolls-Royce Engine. After seven weeks spent in tank testing with no fewer than

22 different models, Freddy's first ideas were confirmed, for his first model was the one which came out best. The tank tests enabled him to go ahead with the constructional details with great confidence.

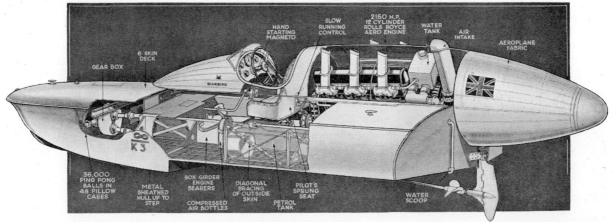

As we all know, weight is a most important factor when it comes to planing over the water, and accordingly *Bluebird* was built by Saunders-Roe of sea-resisting ply. Over this part of the job Freddy had the help of my old foreman, Fred Goatley, who as a foreman has probably built more hydroplanes than any other man.

NINE ON A DECK NEVER INTENDED TO CARRY MORE THAN ONE MAN

After a great many tests on samples the ideal ply was arrived at for each part of the hull, which is almost entirely built of this material in varying laminations and thicknesses. The bottom ply is of five different skins, while the frames of the boat are of seven ply, cut from one sheet eliminating all joints at the gunwales, chines and keel, which not only are a source of weakness but increase the weight.

The long engine bearers are box girders of ply, while the deck of six skins is not an eighth of an inch in total thickness. Duralumin and alclad were used in the construction, and so we see that throughout weight was saved as much as possible, and that the hull was very strong is borne out not only by the fact that she broke the world's water record, but also by the photograph of Sir Malcolm Campbell being congratulated by Albert Schmidt at the conclusion of his trials, for this picture shows nine men concentrated on a very small part of her deck, a load which the designer never intended it to stand.

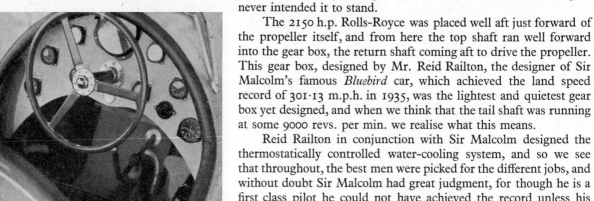

THE COCKPIT SHOWING THE GREAT NUMBER OF INSTRUMENTS REQUIRED IN A BOAT OF THIS SORT

The 2150 h.p. Rolls-Royce was placed well aft just forward of the propeller itself, and from here the top shaft ran well forward into the gear box, the return shaft coming aft to drive the propeller. This gear box, designed by Mr. Reid Railton, the designer of Sir Malcolm's famous *Bluebird* car, which achieved the land speed record of 301·13 m.p.h. in 1935, was the lightest and quietest gear box yet designed, and when we think that the tail shaft was running at some 9000 revs. per min. we realise what this means.

Reid Railton in conjunction with Sir Malcolm designed the thermostatically controlled water-cooling system, and so we see that throughout, the best men were picked for the different jobs, and without doubt Sir Malcolm had great judgment, for though he is a first class pilot he could not have achieved the record unless his merry men had put the instrument into his hands with which to do it. So throughout, from the first line on the designer's board, to the day when in September *Bluebird* broke the world's record, the best men that could be found were putting forth their best, and it is only in this way that such performances are put up.

The sketch with the side broken away gives a very good idea of the construction of this vessel, while her arrangement is more easily seen in the block drawing, and a study of these two blocks will teach us a great deal about this wonderful little hydroplane. Her full plans are not included, for Freddy is writing a book on hydroplanes, and we both agreed it would be better for him to keep her complete plans for that book, which without doubt will be interesting and instructive, as it comes from one of the greatest of experts in fast power craft design.

BLUEBIRD AT SPEED. THIS PICTURE SHOWS THE CLEAN WAY SHE RAN THE WHOLE MILE, THERE BEING NO FLUFF OR FUSS AT ALL FROM HER FORWARD STEP

PART III

RACING

ONCE again our Racing Section is filled with the best designs by the best designers, and we have in it racers of all types to the I.Y.R.U. metre rule, to the Scandinavian Skerry Cruiser rule made International in 1928, and a design with additional restrictions known as the " B " class Aeolus 22-square metre. Then we have in contrast to these seaworthy racers the 20-square metre Rennejolle *Ferret* from the lakes of Central Europe, and the light lively dinghies and canoes. This Racing Section finishes with a chapter on one-design classes, and I sincerely hope that this last chapter will lead towards International Racing in one-design classes, for it seems that if only the National Sailing Authorities or, better still, the International Y.R.U. itself, could give a lead in one-design classes by selecting and making, say, a design National or International, they would be doing a great service to those who from choice or necessity race in the one-design classes. The twelve designs which illustrate this chapter are by the leading designers of the world, and so a careful study of them and the chapter will, I hope, do a great deal of good.

· 32 ·
"J" CLASS
ASTRA

Length, overall -	115 ft. 0 in.	= 35·05 m.		Length, water-line -	75 ft. 0 in. =	22·86 m.
Beam - -	20·2 ft.	= 6·16 m.		Draught - -	13·8 ft. =	4·216 m.
Displacement -	140 tons.	= 115,824 kilos.		Sail Area - -	7500 sq. ft. =	665·2 sq. m.

Owner, HUGH F. PAUL   *Designer*, CHARLES E. NICHOLSON   *Builder*, CAMPER & NICHOLSON

A S we look back at the various vessels developed to the different rating rules, we generally find that the last to a rule has been a type of craft that no one ever dreamt the rule would produce ; with the passing of years and the straining of designers for speed at all costs, they have produced undesirable types of vessels, in which everything

ASTRA, THE LAST OF THE LARGE CUTTERS TO THE I.Y.R.U. RULE

was sacrificed to speed, till finally in desperation the owners have cried out for a new rule. But this is not true of the I.Y.R.U. rule, which was dropped in favour of the American "J" class rule, for in *Astra* we see one of the loveliest vessels it is possible to think of. Her lovely rounded midship sections and the sections of her bow and stern all tell of a vessel which the rule makers hope to encourage, for whether looked upon as a cruiser or as a racer *Astra* is certainly a beautiful ship. Her profile is one that would be fine in a seaway and give no anxiety to those on board,

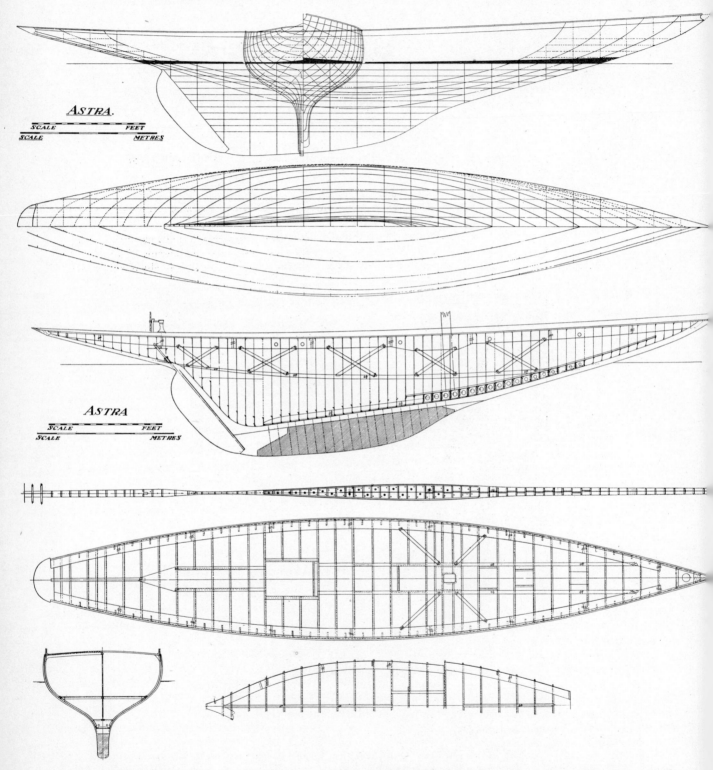

ASTRA.

SCALE   FEET
SCALE   METRES

ASTRA

SCALE   FEET
SCALE   METRES

as the keel is long enough to give steadiness, and every one of her lines tells of a good sea boat, with a fine turn of speed; looking at these lines it is difficult for us to decide whether such a wonderful hull and set of lines were produced because of the rule or in spite of it. But one thing is certain, that when the sun went down on the I.Y.R.U. rule for the large class, it sank on some of the loveliest hulls yet designed. *Astra's* speed and seaworthiness come from one of the loveliest sets of lines I have ever seen, for without doubt, in her Charlie Nicholson created a masterpiece, and her lines will serve as an inspiration for all time.

Astra is of composite construction, her $2\frac{7}{32}$ in. Honduras mahogany planking being fastened to steel frames, and a glance at her construction plan shows that she has five sets of double diagonal bracing in her length, and that she has an exceptionally strong mast step to take the thrust of this spar, while in the deck plan we see the diagonal bracing in way of the mast, and that though the $2\frac{3}{32}$ in. thickness deck would tie all her frames together fore and aft, these are already tied throughout her length by fore and aft plates.

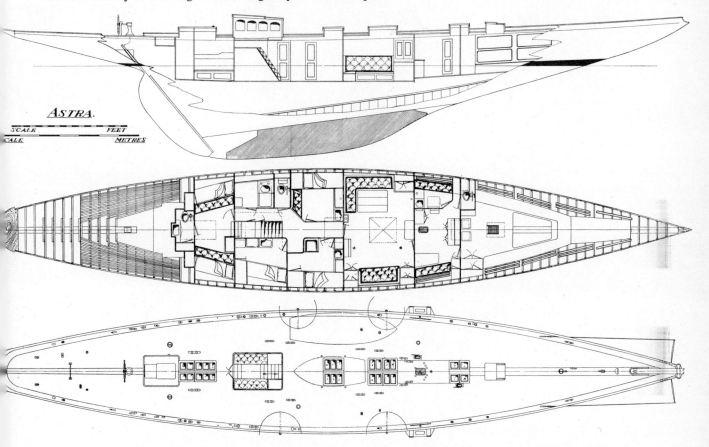

ASTRA.

SCALE FEET
CALE METRES

From the mast forward *Astra* is given over to her crew. On the port side of the mast is the Captain's cabin, while to starboard is the pantry and messroom, and the whole fore end is given over to the fo'c'sle, in which are situated the stoves. Immediately abaft the mast is the saloon, with an L-shaped settee round the swing table to port and a sofa set to starboard, and from here aft a passage way leads to the deck companion. To starboard of the passage are two staterooms, while to port is a bathroom and a third stateroom. The deckhouse itself with its settee either side is very cosy, and abaft this is a double stateroom with a washroom at its after end, the entire counter being given over to sails and stores.

Astra is so comfortable that her owner, his family and guests can live aboard her throughout the summer; and though there were no other large cutters to race against in British waters this season, she was fitted out as a floating home, for her owner was racing his new Twelve *Little Astra* round the coast, and *Astra* became the mother ship. Whether she was anchored in Torbay or close to the rocks off Cowes Green, she gave one a feeling of contentment and rest, for here one felt was a man who was enjoying to the full the peace only to be found on the sea in a sailing ship, free from all the disturbances inseparable from power craft, where generally there are engines of some sort running, charging dynamos, etc. But for all her peaceful appearance when at anchor, under way she has throughout her life caused those racing against her many a restless moment; she has many prizes to her credit and looking back at her lines we can see that she is capable of winning many more, for no matter what rating rules come along the sea and wind remain exactly the same.

Her sail plan shows the old three-headsail rig, for *Astra* came out in 1928, before the double-headsail rig was adopted by the " J " class. She has, however, this great advantage, that she can change from a three-headsail to a

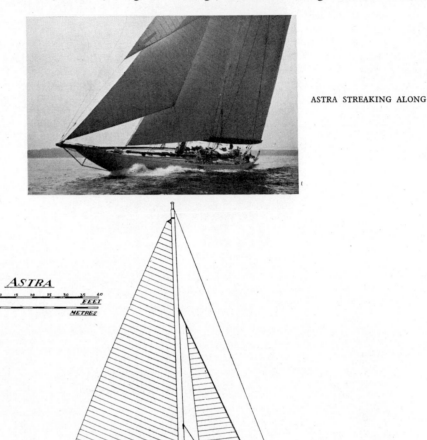

ASTRA STREAKING ALONG

double-headsail rig in a few minutes by taking in her jib and its stay and setting a large quadrilateral jib on the jib topsail stay, for her owner has kept *Astra* up to date and any improvements in rig and sails have been quickly brought into use. It is because of this she is still able to race with a fair chance of success against her more modern sisters.

AMERICA'S CUP, 1937

The Americans having accepted T. O. M. Sopwith's challenge for the *America's* Cup and acceded to his request that the races should be held in July, there were no " J " class races in British waters for the summer of 1937. H. Andreae had lent *Endeavour I* to T. O. M. Sopwith as a trial horse, and if she proved to be faster under American conditions than *Endeavour II*, then she was to be the challenger for the contest; and so with our two best " J's " away in America it was felt that there was no point in racing the class this year on our side of the Atlantic.

May 1 was the day chosen for *Endeavour I* and *Endeavour II* to start on their voyage across the Atlantic in quest of the Cup, and a great many of us journeyed to Gosport to see them depart. It was a perfect day with a light easterly wind and sunshine, so that the two racers looked their best. We could not help admiring the way in which they were prepared for their 3000 mile voyage. As we all know, while the hulls of the " J's " are perfectly seaworthy, and quite strong enough to stand up to an Atlantic gale, they are cursed with a rule which produces a weak maidenly rig, and so while no change had been made to the hulls, the spars and rigs were far different from those under which they would be racing. For, although they were being towed, if the weather really became bad they would have to let go their parent ships and fight for themselves.

T. O. M. SOPWITH WITH HIS DESIGNER CHARLIE
NICHOLSON AND HIS SAILMAKERS COLIN RATSEY
AND STANLEY LAPTHORN

GIVING CAPTAIN WILLIAMS TINS OF HIS
FAVOURITE TOBACCO

Both vessels were rigged as yawls, with their mainmasts shortened so that the old jib halyard height became the top of the mast.

Lifeboats were stowed on their decks, and teak protecting-covers made to cover the various hatchways, while round their sides stanchions and life lines were rigged almost shoulder high. In fact everything possible was done to ensure that both vessels and their crews would arrive at the other side in perfect safety.

One of the finest trawlers that I have ever seen, the *John*, a Belgian, had been chartered to tow *Endeavour II* across. She impressed me not only as a perfect looking sea boat, but because she was so up to date that her skipper could talk by wireless telephone to his office all the while he was at sea. It was difficult to think of a better craft for the job in hand.

On board her were stowed the topmasts and both masts, spars, booms, spinnaker booms, etc., of the two racers, and with all this aboard she struck one as being a fine parent ship for *Endeavour II*, her measurements being 127 ft. overall with 22 ft. beam and 12 ft. draught, and her two 500 h.p. Diesels giving her a speed of 12 knots.

At noon the two *Endeavours* left Camper & Nicholson's Yard, and slowly towed out of Portsmouth Harbour, their crews taking the last look round as they got under way. Over in the Dockyard the sun shone brilliantly on the old *Victory* and the Royal Yacht, while H.M.S. *Hood*, just home from the Mediterranean, reflected back the sunlight from her light grey topsides. All around whistles and sirens were blowing to wish the *Endeavours* a happy voyage, and during their passage out of the harbour mouth, flags were waved and more sirens blown, and everything paused to wish the pair godspeed.

The battlements of Portsmouth were crowded with cheering people, for Britain's two best " J's " were going out to cross the Atlantic in order to race against the best America could produce. And so the voyage down the harbour was very stirring, but once outside calmer thoughts prevailed.

We felt then that the two *Endeavours* were better than any "J" class yachts America possessed. Everyone knew that *Endeavour I* was faster than *Rainbow*, whose speed was practically the same as that of *Yankee*, who last year, racing in our waters, had not shown up at all well ; the fate of the Cup, therefore, largely depended upon how good or bad the new yacht they were building would be, for if *Ranger* proved no better than their last defender, then it was almost certain that one of these two *Endeavours* would bring the Cup back in her locker. After their compasses had been adjusted the pair were towed towards Cowes ; *Endeavour II* astern of the Belgian trawler *John*, and *Endeavour I* towed by the old *Irishman*, her parent ship *Viva II* not having yet turned up.

FRANKIE MURDOCH ABOARD THE JOHN

WHILE WE TOWED THROUGH THE SOLENT
MRS. SOPWITH TALKS TO ENDEAVOUR II'S
CAPTAIN AND NAVIGATOR

Arrived off Cowes, we saw *Viva II*, who reported that while adjusting her compasses, she had damaged part of her steering gear, and was unable to take *Endeavour I* in tow until this had been put right. So *Endeavour I* came to anchor off Cowes Green, while the *John* and *Endeavour II* proceeded on their way out through the Needles and across the Atlantic under perfect weather conditions, for the day was still one of warm sunshine and a light easterly following wind, the sea being perfectly calm.

It was some days before *Viva II*'s steering gear was repaired and she was able to make a start. Moreover, while *Endeavour II* arrived without any hitch, *Viva* lost her "J" boat some two-thirds of the way over, and *Endeavour I* sailed the last third alone and unaided. Then came the work of getting the two into racing trim.

Meantime, eleven days after the two British boats had started for America, *Ranger* was launched by Mrs. Harold Vanderbilt from the Bath Ironworks and within two hours of her launching her Duralumin mast had been stepped, which a few hours later she lost over the side while being towed to Newport.

It will be recalled that in the last contest, our boat *Endeavour* had undoubtedly proved the faster of the two, and Harold Vanderbilt, on whose shoulders the defence has largely fallen during these last contests, knew that they had a difficult task before them, for they had not only to catch up with *Endeavour I*, but the chances were that they had to improve upon her. And so a young designer, new to "J" class yachts, was called in to collaborate with Starling Burgess, and there was little doubt that this would give good results, for the young chap was no other than Olin Stephens, who has been so successful in designing 6 and 8-metres and ocean racing yachts ; and one wonders that such combinations have not been fostered before, as youth is full of vigour and new ideas, but is always wanting to dash along new paths, while with age come wisdom and steadiness. Events soon proved the wisdom of the innovation, for *Ranger* turned out the best "J" class yacht yet built in America ; but how much of this can be attributed to the hull of the boat and how much to the wonderful seamanship and seamanlike powers of her owner, Harold Vanderbilt, we shall never know, for it always remains true that any vessel to be successful must first of all be well designed and built, and then well sailed. Designer and builder together striving and struggling for months may improve a vessel five seconds a mile, or $2\frac{1}{2}$ minutes in a 30 mile race, but the owner can in five minutes throw away 5 minutes of time round a course, and we must always look at and study these things when we are studying racers.

For some ten years (I am now holding on firmly to the wooden arm of an old wheel back chair) I have successfully designed and built 14-foot dinghies, and a great deal of this success is due entirely to my studying the ability of the different helmsmen in the different weather conditions, as only by having a perfect knowledge of the helmsman's ability under varying weather conditions can one judge the ability of the craft he is sailing. In hard weather

I have seen one man beat another in practically sister ships by as much as 25 minutes, and the same two helmsmen in the same boats would have a very close race in light weather. This important point, the ability of the helmsman and crew (and not only their sailing ability but their knowledge of the weather, setting sails, tides, etc.) is too often lost sight of. However, one thing is certain, and that is that *Ranger* was a first class vessel.

When in America some years ago, I met Professor Kenneth S. M. Davidson with Olin Stephens towing 6-metre yachts and registering their resistance ; he had previously tested out the models of these vessels in the tank and wanted to check his figures. Before *Ranger* was put in hand Professor Davidson was called in to test various models. The first model was that of *Endeavour I*, who was so much better than *Rainbow* in the last contest ; so we see nothing was left to chance with the design and build of this new vessel. We must remember, however, that though tank tests are very valuable, in that they give one a great deal of knowledge of the model tested in the way of resistance and such things, a tank cannot design a vessel, all it can do is to tell you how good or bad the design is, no more. But at the same time we must bear in mind that Professor Kenneth Davidson had worked out a wonderful method for testing sailing models, in which the driving force of the wind, its heeling power and the leeway made are all blended in their right proportion with the resistance of the model, so that his test showed distance and speed made good to windward in different weights of wind. Such things as this enabled Starling Burgess and Olin to go ahead with the model finally chosen with great confidence.

THE DESIGNER AND OWNER TAKE A FAREWELL GLASS ABOARD AS ENDEAVOUR II STARTS ON THE LONG TOW TO AMERICA

For some years now it has been usual for the two different designers in the *America's* Cup contest to exchange plans, and Charlie Nicholson, by giving Burgess the lines of *Endeavour I*, enabled him to make an exact model of her ; and as no doubt Burgess and Olin have given Charlie the plans of *Ranger*, he will be able to test this and other models in a tank, so that the next challenger to be built will be known to be a faster model than *Ranger*. I think this exchange of plans is one of the finest things that can happen for the sport, and for this reason I gave the unsuccessful challenger from America for the New York International Canoe trophy, the lines of *Wake* which successfully defended it, and also gave the lines of *Alarm* to George Ford, captain of the American team, for with her sisters she defeated the American team in British waters last summer.

To try out *Ranger* the Americans improved *Yankee* and *Rainbow*, but from the very beginning it was seen that *Ranger* was the best of the three, and she was chosen to defend. And so she and *Endeavour II* came to the line off Newport on July 30 for the first race of the series. A comparison of sizes shows that the boats were practically alike in all dimensions, and though we called *Ranger* narrow it will be seen she has a mere 7 in. less beam than her rival.

ENDEAVOUR II

Length, overall -	135·80 ft.		Length, water-line -	86·58 ft.
Beam - -	21·58 ft.		Draught -	15·00 ft.
Displacement -	163 tons.		Sail Area -	7546 sq. ft.

Owner, T. O. M. SOPWITH   *Designer*, CHARLES E. NICHOLSON   *Builder*, CAMPER & NICHOLSON

RANGER

Length, overall -	135·10 ft.		Length, water-line -	87·00 ft.
Beam - -	20·90 ft.		Draught -	15·00 ft.
Displacement -	166·50 tons.		Sail Area -	7546 sq. ft.

Owner, HAROLD VANDERBILT   *Designer*, W. STARLING BURGESS & SPARKMAN & STEPHENS, INC.
Builder, BATH IRONWORKS

To guide *Endeavour II* were T. O. M. Sopwith, his wife, Sir Ralph Gore (relief helmsman), Frankie Murdoch, Flight Lieut. J. R. Scarlet, navigator and during the third and fourth day's race C. E. Nicholson the designer ; while the nobility on the defender were Harold Vanderbilt, owner and helmsman, his wife, Olin Stephens, his relief helmsman, W. Starling Burgess, Roderick Stephens, Arthur Knapp and Zenes Bliss his navigator.

July 21—First Race.

15 miles to windward and leeward. Wind 5 miles an hour at the start, increasing to 10 miles per hour at the finish of the race.

At the start *Endeavour* had the best of it, for *Ranger* was back on her weather quarter, and when she tacked to clear her wind *Endeavour II* covered her ; but *Ranger* escaped and with her huge headsails was sailing faster in the light air prevailing, so much so that when they came to the weather mark *Ranger* had a lead of 6 minutes and 13 seconds. On rounding the mark *Endeavour II* had two alternatives open to her :

(1) To follow after *Ranger*, a course on which she could not hope to win, or
(2) To sail high on the wind, hoping to pick up a better breeze.

She chose the latter and lost heavily by it, for when she crossed the finish line she was more than 17 minutes astern of *Ranger*.

Elapsed Times. Windward and Leeward.

							H.	M.	S.
Ranger	-	-	-	-	-	-	4	41	15
Endeavour II	-	-	-	-	-	-	4	58	20

Ranger wins by 17 minutes 5 seconds.

August 2—Second Race.

30 mile triangular course. Wind 7 miles an hour at the start, increasing to $10\frac{1}{2}$ miles per hour at the finish.

Endeavour II again had the best of the start, but once more in this light weather *Ranger* had her enormous rayon quadrilateral jib set, while Endeavour had only a working quadrilateral and a staysail ; and as it was estimated that *Ranger* was carrying 1000 square feet more than *Endeavour*, we must bear in mind the different sails carried by the two vessels. For the first four miles of this beat to windward *Endeavour* held *Ranger* back, but after that *Ranger* got away and started to work out a lead at the rate of something like $1\frac{3}{4}$ minutes to the mile, so that she rounded the buoy with a lead of 10 minutes and 25 seconds.

Over this part of the course some said that *Endeavour* was sailed too close and starved to windward during these first two races, and others that she was sheetbound, but if it is true that *Ranger* had something like a 1000 extra square feet in her headsails, the answer is more likely to be there than anywhere else, for in that light going this would give her an enormous amount of extra life and energy.

From the weather mark it was two reaches home to the finish, and *Ranger* picked up another 6 minutes on the first of these and another 2 minutes on the last :

Elapsed Times. Triangular Course.

							H.	M.	S.
Ranger	-	-	-	-	-	-	3	41	33
Endeavour	-	-	-	-	-	-	4	00	05

Ranger wins by 18 minutes 32 seconds.

After this race *Endeavour II* asked for a day off to haul out and examine her bottom, and *Ranger* took advantage of this and hauled out as well. *Endeavour's* bottom was as clean as a smelt, and so 5000 lb. of inside ballast (all she had) was taken out to liven her up in this light weather.

August 4—Third Race.

30 miles windward and leeward. Wind at the start 10 miles per hour, increasing to 13 miles per hour through the race.

As the wind was as strong at the beginning of this race as at the end of the last one, both vessels came to the line with smaller quadrilateral jibs and staysails, but even so it was estimated that *Ranger* had still 1000 square feet more sail area than *Endeavour*.

This start was Vanderbilt's, as he crossed the line three seconds after the starting signal, Sopwith following 18 seconds later on his weather quarter, and as *Endeavour* tacked to clear her wind *Ranger* tacked on top of her. After a while *Endeavour II* tacked again and *Ranger* once more covered her, then *Endeavour* tacked once more to clear her wind, and though *Ranger* started to tack on top of her a riding turn on the winch handling the upper sheet of her quadrilateral jib jambed, and she was forced back on to her old tack, so *Endeavour* escaped the blanketing *Ranger* was giving her.

RANGER'S CABINS AFT ARE FITTED OUT IN TRUE YACHT FASHION IN STRICT ACCORDANCE WITH THE RULES

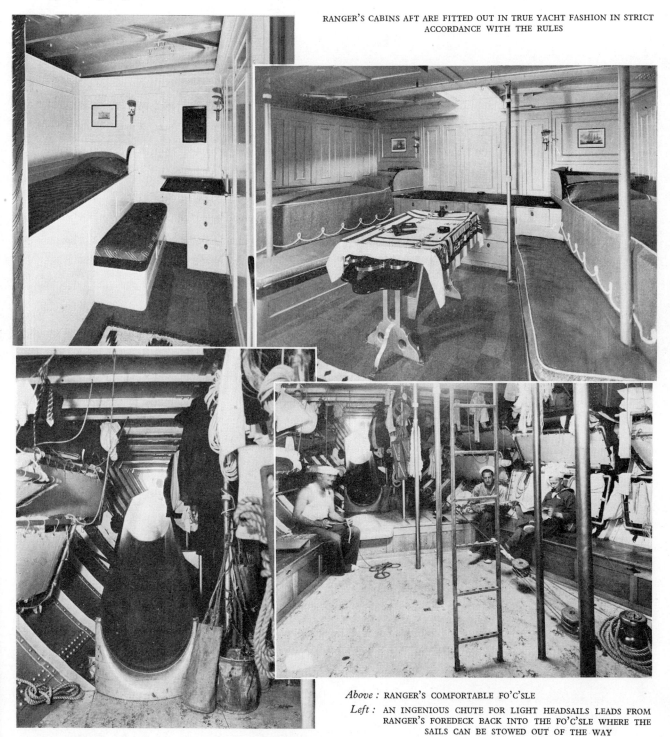

Above : RANGER'S COMFORTABLE FO'C'SLE

Left : AN INGENIOUS CHUTE FOR LIGHT HEADSAILS LEADS FROM RANGER'S FOREDECK BACK INTO THE FO'C'SLE WHERE THE SAILS CAN BE STOWED OUT OF THE WAY

One thing stood out clearly in this short tacking match, and that was that if anything the British crew handled their sheets better than the American, for not only did they harden them down more smartly, but they kept them clear, and one imagines this riding turn was the result of one of *Ranger's* crew getting over excited in the duel. As I pointed out in an earlier book, every man has a pair of hands and legs, and seamen from one country are as good as those from another, but, generally speaking, throughout the contests for the *America's* Cup the American vessels have had better designed winches and gear for handling sheets, and their smarter handling of sails was not due to better seamen but to better gear with which to work.

RANGER WITH HER DOUBLE-CLEWED GENOA JIB

On the beat to the first mark *Ranger* drew ahead, but very slowly, for she rounded only 4 minutes and 12 seconds ahead of *Endeavour*, and when we bear in mind those extra 1000 square feet in her sail area as set we realise why I say *only* 4 minutes 12 seconds in the lead. On the run to the finish line she increased this lead by 15 seconds only, so the third race was the closest.

Elapsed Time. Windward and Leeward.

								H.	M.	S.
Ranger	-	-	-	-	-	-	-	3	54	30
Endeavour II	-	-	-	-	-	-	-	3	58	57

Ranger wins by 4 minutes 27 seconds.

August 5—Fourth Race.

30 mile triangular course. Wind 11½ miles per hour at the start, increasing to 16½ miles per hour at the finish.

There was a great deal of fun before the start of this race, as *Ranger* camped out on *Endeavour II's* quarter wave and finally forced *Endeavour* over the line 9 seconds before gunfire, Vanderbilt crossing the line 5 seconds after the starting signal while *Endeavour*, having to gybe round the buoy and recross, came over 1 minute and 20 seconds later.

Once again *Ranger* had more sail area set, but with the stronger wind and our boat beginning to feel her feet this was the closest race of the series, for though *Ranger* sailed so fast to windward that she made record time for this 15 miles to windward, namely 1 hour 17 minutes and 45 seconds, *Endeavour II* was only 4 minutes 5 seconds behind her, and still bearing in mind the extra sail area of *Ranger*, and the fact that *Endeavour* started almost 1½ minutes late, we see that she was only some 2½ minutes slower in this 15 mile dead beat.

On the two remaining reaching legs of the course *Endeavour* picked up 30 seconds on the first and dropped two seconds on the last.

Elapsed Time. Triangular Course.

							H.	M.	S.
Ranger	-	-	-	-	-	-	3	07	49
Endeavour II	-	-	-	-	-	-	3	11	26

Ranger wins by 3 minutes 37 seconds.

And this fourth win in four successive races meant that once more the *America's* Cup remained on the weather side of the Atlantic.

The series had been most interesting. *Ranger* was undoubtedly the faster hull of the two craft, and added to this was the fact that she was always driven by more sail area than *Endeavour*, in spite of the fact that, of the two, *Endeavour* with her extra beam (though it was only 7 inches) was probably able to carry her sail better.

The series had been marked by the friendly way in which the races had been sailed, and looking back over the results one is tempted to say that they would have been far closer had *Endeavour* set the same amount of canvas as *Ranger* every day, and that the next challenger should have a good reliable critic watching the races from another vessel's deck, far enough away to be able to judge accurately the value of the different sails and tactics employed on both boats, as then he would be able to point out such a thing as this to the challenger after each day's race. Those on board are so close to their sails that such things do not strike them forcibly.

There is no doubt that both boats had been equally well sailed and handled, Sopwith having the best of the first two starts and Vanderbilt the best of the last two, while the crews of each had both handled their sails remarkably well throughout.

We on this side have learned some lessons, and let us hope a new challenger will soon be on her way across the Atlantic with a firm endeavour to bring back the Cup once more to these shores.

After the *America's* Cup races the two *Endeavours* took part in the American "J" class races, and finally at the end of the summer started on their way home, *Endeavour II* being towed by T. O. M. Sopwith's wonderful yacht *Philante*, which had been designed and built by Charles E. Nicholson for him, and *Endeavour I* by *Viva*. *Philante* towed *Endeavour II* across without parting a spunyarn, though in one heavy gale she had to slow down till she was practically hove to, after which she continued her way and brought her charge safely home. But on the way a very sad thing happened, for Captain Williams, *Endeavour II's* skipper, passed away. Little did I dream, when we were yarning away together aboard *Endeavour II* as she was being towed down through the Solent on her way to America, that this would be the last of the many pleasant yarns I have had with him. He was a first-rate seaman and had a charming and generous nature, and will be sadly missed by all who were fortunate enough to know him.

Endeavour I was less fortunate in her towing, for 32 hours out, when only 200 miles east of the *Nantucket Lightship*, the tow rope parted, and *Viva* returned to Newport to report that she had lost her. Though a search was made it proved fruitless, nor is this surprising, for a vessel with her colours, the white sails and blue hull, would be most difficult to see, as she would blend so well with the colour of the sea and sky, and naturally, too, she would be sailing on her way to England, not realising that the newspapers in their effort to make a story would be alarming the wives and the families of those aboard. When I first saw the reports that she was missing in the newspapers I once more thought that any political party going to the country with the object of destroying Fleet Street and the sensational press would get my vote, for as usual one saw them magnifying a small trouble till it became gigantic. Of course this not only filled their papers at the time the news was first received, but would also give them another story when *Endeavour I* was sighted as she entered the Channel, and still another when she arrived safely home ; and after all, perhaps we should not blame the newspapers so much as the people who show their eagerness for such feverish and exaggerated news.

Once again the press displayed its ignorance of the sea and ships. In one paper these words appeared : " An extra quarter of an inch fitted to the keel of *Endeavour* probably saved her by steadying her when she faced the storm of 14 days ago." As if a quarter of an inch on 15 feet draught would be noticed in the seaway running ! While another report, this time by the paper's expert, who seemingly had gone to Newport to report the races for them :

" If we had been told that a day was to come when in a hurricane *Endeavour I* would part from her escorting motor vessel and still contrive to remain afloat, we might even have made the mistake of lifting superior eyebrows or indulging in disbelieving smiles."

It is a pity such writers cannot see how stupid they make yachting and sailing seem. *Endeavour* was designed and built to the best set of racing rules yet devised for large yachts, rules that had been adopted by the most under-

ENDEAVOUR UNDER TRYSAIL

standing brains of Europe and America. Her hull was to Lloyd's rules, and her builder was none other than Charles E. Nicholson, one of the finest yacht builders the world has ever seen. Her captain too was Ned Heard, considered by most to be the best yacht skipper this side of the Atlantic, and he had a crew of first-rate seamen with him. If only the press would realise these points they would not have filled their pages with so much junk, and one would like to see a law passed that would enable wives and relations to obtain damages for the worry caused them by the feverish writing that appears in our newspapers.

I was spared most of this myself as living half a mile from the main road and two miles from the nearest town no one will deliver newspapers to me, and for twelve years the only times I have seen newspapers are on Sundays and when travelling in trains.

There was very little chance of any vessel sighting *Endeavour* on her way across, for I have been 33 days in the North Atlantic, in a sailing boat small enough to go on her deck, without sighting a vessel of any sort. When the news came that she had broken adrift I said that she would not be sighted until she was making for the entrance of the Channel and that this would be after 14 or 15 days' sailing. As it was, she was sighted within 13 days, 260 miles to the south west of the Irish Coast, and as was expected of her, she had made a fine passage. The night of the heavy gale, in which she parted her tow rope, she lay to her sea anchor with the mizen set and with no one on deck. When the storm had abated she set sail for England and home, and made a very fast passage, experiencing all sorts of weather from calm to gale, but making good time all the while, averaging 8 knots.

The rule makers are to be congratulated on their hull rules. When through the kindness of her designer, Charles E. Nicholson, I was able to publish *Endeavour's* lines, construction and sail plans in my last book, *Sail and Power*, I said : " It is probable that *Endeavour* will stand out as the sweetest vessel of all time to the 'J' class rule," and if one could only say the same of the rig produced under the rules everyone would be much happier, but these wonderful seaworthy and sturdy hulls have to change their rig from a cutter to a yawl for the Atlantic voyage. Also the weakness in their rigs is a source of great worry and concern to their owners throughout the season's racing. *Ranger*, a brand new ship with a new mast stepped, lost this over the side while being towed from her building yard to Newport, Rhode Island. We all hope that before very long the " J " class will have this, the only blemish on an otherwise perfectly clear picture, removed. Judging from past events it will, however, take years and years before those responsible for the rules will have the brains to see how much better it would be if these vessels were given rigs that were seaworthy, and so in keeping with the wonderful sea-going abilities of the hulls. The builder of *Endeavour* should be congratulated on designing and building such a lovely and seaworthy vessel, while we are all proud of the seamanlike way in which Ned Heard and his crew brought *Endeavour* home to England after her mother ship had lost her. With the two *Endeavours* safe and sound in British waters, we hope there is a good season in front of the " J " class racers next year, and that it will be graced by the appearance of one or more of the " J's " from America.

· 33 ·

12 METRES

VERONICA

Length, overall	-	69 ft. 6 in. = 21·18 m.		Length, water-line	-	45 ft. 6 in. = 13·86 m.
Beam	-	11 ft. 10 in. = 3·60 m.		Draught	-	8 ft. 11 in. = 2·71 m.
Displacement	-	25·60 tons = 26,009 kilos.		Sail Area	-	1488 sq. ft. = 138·23 sq. m.

Owner, ROBERT DUNLOP, JNR., ESQ.   *Designer*, ALFRED MYLNE   *Builder*, ALFRED MYLNE

*V*ERONICA is another example of the very fine type of vessels that has been produced to the I.Y.R.U. rules, for as will be seen from her lines she combines speed, seaworthiness and room for living aboard, and whether we look upon her as a cruiser or a racer we are bound to admire her.

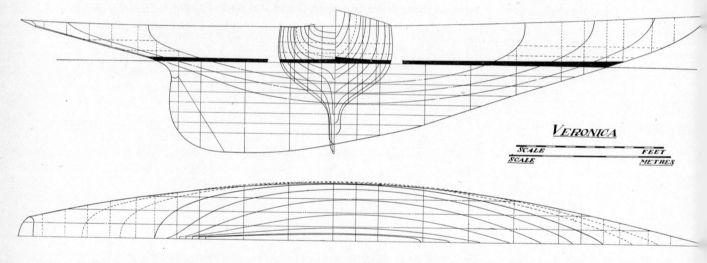

Alfred Mylne designed and built her for Sir William Burton, the President of the Y.R.A., in 1931, and in his capable hands she won a great many prizes, but for the 1936 season Sir William again went to Alfred Mylne for a new twelve, and so *Veronica* came into the market. I met Robert Dunlop when he was looking for a fast cruiser, and after looking at several boats we decided there was none to compare with *Veronica* for his purpose, for she was fast, roomy and weatherly. The only thing that needed changing to bring her to his ideal was the arrangement of her accommodation below and her rig. In travelling all over the country he had found that it was impossible to get a boat more suited to his wants than *Veronica*, and as these alterations were only minor he decided to buy her, and very wisely put his ideas for the alterations into the hands of Alfred Mylne, for who better than the designer could understand *Veronica* and her ways?

The mainmast was shortened 12 feet, and the mainboom 7 ft. 6 in., and to make up for this she was given a mizen standing 35 ft. above the deck. The result is most pleasing to look upon from a cruising viewpoint, and as the mainmast remained in its old position there was very little to alter in the way of *Veronica's* structure ; all that was needed was a mizen mast step on the counter, and the deck altered to take the mizen mast just abaft the rudder.

As a racing 12-metre *Veronica* had a fo'c'sle, pantry and galley extending back abaft the mainmast ; next came her double berthed sleeping cabin and a washroom at the after end on the starboard side and sail bin to port, abaft of which was her saloon leading up into the cockpit.

For cruising the fo'c'sle and pantry was shortened 5 ft., the pantry and galley now being divided right off from the fo'c'sle with its folding cots to port and starboard and abaft this a double berthed stateroom was arranged, and what had been the sleeping cabin was turned into a very cosy saloon. The washroom remained the same, but the

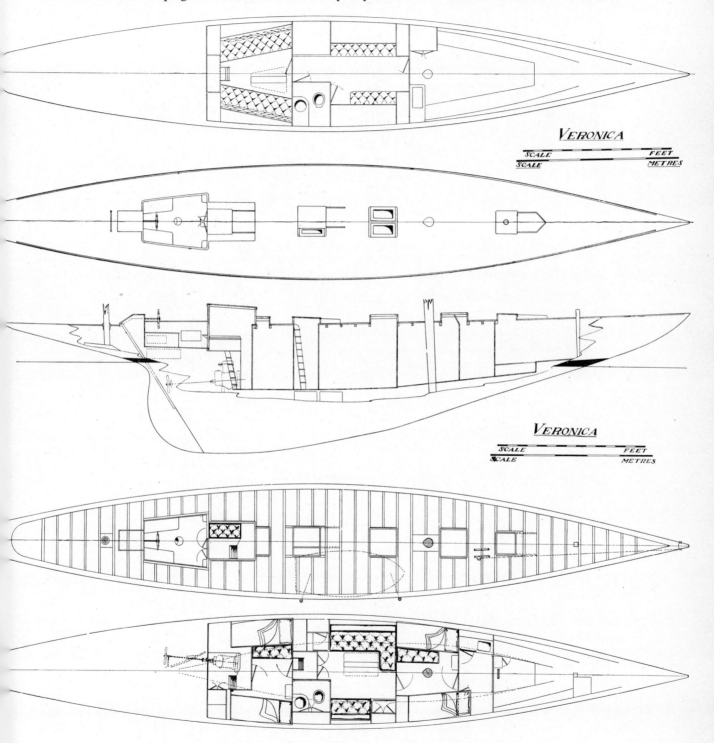

VERONICA

VERONICA

sail bin to port was turned into a sideboard, book case, glass cabinet and a wardrobe, while the saloon aft was turned into the double berthed sleeping cabin and a 15 h.p. Kelvin Ricardo engine fitted under the seat in the new deck-house, which had the fore end of the cockpit. So we see how a racing 12-metre with a few minor alterations was

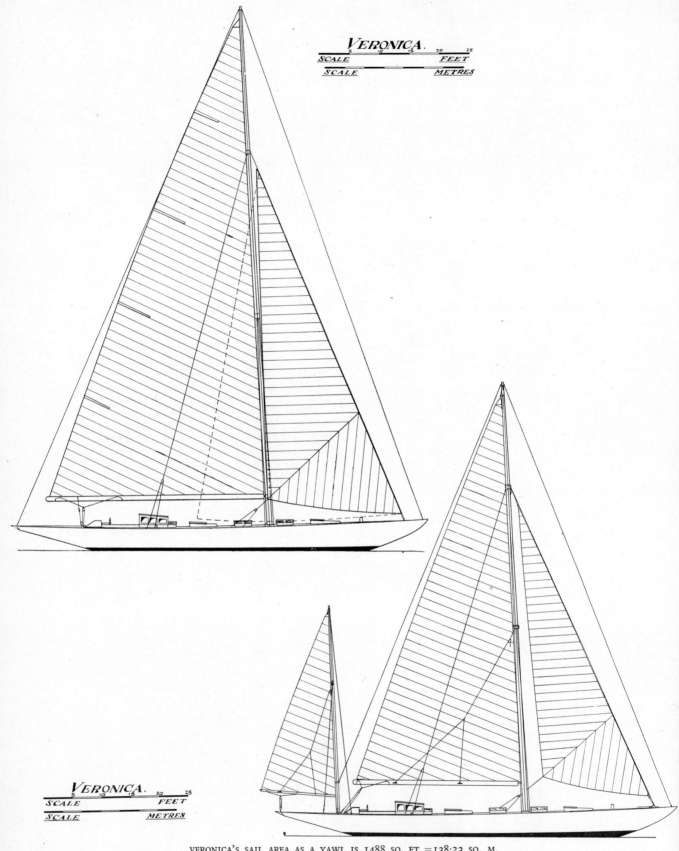

VERONICA.

SCALE   FEET

SCALE   METRES

VERONICA.

SCALE   FEET

SCALE   METRES

VERONICA'S SAIL AREA AS A YAWL IS 1488 SQ. FT. = 138·23 SQ. M.

turned into a cosy fast cruiser, who has given her new owner a great deal of pleasure. *Veronica*, in a word, is a very good argument for the present I.Y.R.U. rule for 12-metres.

THE RACING IN 1937

With the Coronation Regatta in Torbay from June 19 to July 2 the Y.R.A. fixture list was changed. Of late years the season has started on the east coast at Harwich and ended on the south coast at Falmouth, but this year the order was reversed, and Friday June 4 saw the first races, in a breeze of wind, strong enough to make the

BEFORE VERONICA WAS TURNED INTO A FAST CRUISER, SHE RACED SUCCESSFULLY IN THE TWELVE METRE CLASS

"twelves" tuck a reef in their mainsails, from the Royal Cornwall Yacht Club at Falmouth. Five "twelves" came to the line, *Trivia* (V. MacAndrew), *Little Astra* (Hugh Paul), the two new Nicholson boats, R. Fairey's *Evaine* and Hugh Goodson's *Flica*, (two older Nicholson boats) and Sir William Burton's *Marina*, designed and built by Alfred Mylne. *Marina* won this first race by 28 seconds from *Flica* with *Evaine* third :

June 4

NAME	OWNER	TIME		
		H.	M.	S.
Marina - - - -	Sir Wm. P. Burton - - -	3	3	36
Flica - - - -	H. L. Goodson - - -	3	4	4
Evaine - - - -	C. R. Fairey - - - -	3	5	33

Marina won again the next day, but this time C. R. Fairey's *Evaine* was second and Hugh Goodson's *Flica* third.

June 5

NAME	OWNER	TIME
		H. M. S.
Marina - - - -	Sir Wm. P. Burton - - -	3 23 38
Evaine - - - -	C. R. Fairey - - -	3 24 5
Flica - - - -	H. L. Goodson - - -	3 24 6
Little Astra - - -	H. F. Paul - - -	3 32 16

and by taking the third race *Marina* did the hat trick at the beginning of the season:

June 7

NAME	OWNER	TIME
		H. M. S.
Marina - - - -	Sir Wm. P. Burton - - -	3 20 58
Flica - - - -	H. L. Goodson - - -	3 22 24
Evaine - - - -	C. R. Fairey - - -	3 22 28

but then *Evaine* took the first:

June 8

NAME	OWNER	TIME
		H. M. S.
Evaine - - - -	C. R. Fairey - - -	2 56 26
Flica - - - -	H. L. Goodson - - -	2 56 48
Marina - - - -	Sir Wm. P. Burton - - -	2 57 23

Retired: *Little Astra.*

The "twelves" then left Falmouth for Plymouth Sound where Arthur Connell's *Westra* joined the class, and though she was last of the fleet on the first day she won the next three races, another hat trick.

June 11

NAME	OWNER	TIME
		H. M. S.
Flica - - - -	H. L. Goodson - - -	4 30 14
Trivia - - - -	V. W. MacAndrew - - -	4 31 22
Marina - - - -	Sir Wm. P. Burton - - -	4 34 6
Evaine - - - -	C. R. Fairey - - -	4 38 32
Little Astra - - -	H. F. Paul - - -	4 40 25
Westra - - -	A. C. Connell - - -	4 51 22

June 12

Westra - - - -	A. C. Connell - - -	3 34 55
Marina - - - -	Sir Wm. P. Burton - - -	3 38 34
Evaine - - - -	C. R. Fairey - - -	3 40 1
Trivia - - - -	V. W. MacAndrew - - -	3 41 52
Flica - - - -	H. L. Goodson - - -	3 42 38

June 14

NAME	OWNER	TIME		
		H.	M.	S.
Westra - - - -	A. C. Connell - - - -	4	40	28
Flica - - - -	H. L. Goodson - - - -	4	43	29
Marina - - - -	Sir Wm. Burton - - -	4	45	9
Trivia - - - -	V. W. MacAndrew - - -	4	46	12

Retired : *Little Astra and Evaine.*

It was now V. MacAndrew's turn with *Trivia,* for she won by 2 minutes 2 seconds from Arthur Connell's *Westra* on the last day at Plymouth :

NAME	OWNER	TIME		
		H.	M.	S.
Trivia - - - -	V. W. MacAndrew - - -	2	29	15
Westra - - - -	A. C. Connell - - - -	2	31	17
Marina - - - -	Sir Wm. Burton - - -	2	31	48
Flica - - - -	H. L. Goodson - - - -	2	34	0

Retired : *Evaine* and *Little Astra.*

And now the "twelves" had come up the coast for the Torbay Coronation Regatta, during which there were many days of light breezes and glorious weather. Here Johnny Payne's 12-metre *Vanity V* (new last year) instead of racing with the "twelves" raced in the handicap class, and caused a lot of agitation to people. So for two weeks the 12-metres experienced very pleasant weather conditions in Torbay.

June 19

NAME	OWNER	TIME		
		H.	M.	S.
Little Astra - - -	H. F. Paul - - - -	3	18	7
Marina - - - -	Sir Wm. Burton - - -	3	21	28
Westra - - - -	A. C. Connell - - - -	3	26	12
Trivia - - - -	V. MacAndrew - - -	3	32	31
Flica - - - -	H. L. Goodson - - - -	3	35	46

Retired : *Evaine.*

June 21

Marina - - - -	Sir Wm. Burton - - -	3	31	13
Westra - - - -	A. C. Connell - - - -	3	31	36
Little Astra - - -	H. F. Paul - - - -	3	35	20
Evaine - - - -	C. R. Fairey - -- - -	3	36	8
Trivia - - - -	V. W. MacAndrew - - -	3	36	16

June 22

Flica - - - -	H. L. Goodson - - - -	4	1	53
Trivia - - - -	V. W. MacAndrew - - -	4	14	38
Evaine - - - -	C. R. Fairey - - - -	4	19	14
Westra - - - -	A. C. Connell - - - -	4	25	44

Retired : *Marina* and *Little Astra.*

June 23

NAME	OWNER	TIME H. M. S.
Westra - - - -	A. C. Connell - - - -	2 57 22
Little Astra - - -	H. F. Paul - - - -	3 4 56
Marina - - - -	Sir Wm. Burton - - -	3 9 6
Flica - - - -	H. F. Goodson - - -	3 11 12
Evaine - - - -	C. R. Fairey - - -	3 27 26
Trivia - - - -	V. W. MacAndrew - - -	3 38 7

THE "TWELVES" RACING IN TORBAY

June 25

Evaine - - - -	C. R. Fairey - - - -	2 28 32
Trivia - - - -	V. W. MacAndrew - - -	2 28 56
Flica - - - -	H. L. Goodson - - -	2 29 51
Westra - - - -	A. C. Connell - - - -	2 30 6
Marina - - - -	Sir Wm. Burton - - -	2 34 0

Retired : *Little Astra*.

June 26

Little Astra - - -	Hugh F. Paul - - -	I 21 8
Evaine - - - -	C. R. Fairey - - -	I 22 48
Trivia - - - -	V. W. MacAndrew - - -	I 23 52
Westra - - - -	A. C. Connell - - -	I 26 3
Flica - - - -	H. L. Goodson - - -	I 27 40
Marina - - - -	Sir Wm. Burton - - -	I 28 13

Dartmouth. June 28

Westra - - - -	A. C. Connell - - - -	2 44 4
Evaine - - - -	C. R. Fairey - - - -	2 47 49
Trivia - - - -	V. W. MacAndrew - - -	2 50 37
Little Astra - - -	H. F. Paul - - - -	2 52 55
Flica - - - -	H. L. Goodson - - -	2 56 50

Dartmouth. June 29

NAME	OWNER	TIME		
		H.	M.	S.
Evaine - - - -	C. R. Fairey - - - -	2	43	28
Westra - - - -	A. C. Connell - - - -	2	43	52
Marina - - - -	Sir Wm. Burton - - - -	2	46	32
Trivia - - - -	V. W. MacAndrew - - - -	2	50	27
Little Astra - - -	Hugh F. Paul - - - -	2	51	20

Torquay. June 30

NAME	OWNER	H.	M.	S.
Trivia - - - -	V. W. MacAndrew - - -	12	42	25
Marina - - - -	Sir Wm. Burton - - -	12	43	10
Evaine - - - -	C. R. Fairey - - -	12	43	40
Westra - - - -	A. C. Connell - - -	12	43	59
Flica - - - -	H. L. Goodson - - -	12	44	33
Little Astra - - -	H. F. Paul - - - -	12	45	2

Torquay. July 2

NAME	OWNER	H.	M.	S.
Westra - - - -	A. C. Connell - - -	2	49	11
Evaine - - - -	C. R. Fairey - - -	2	50	33
Little Astra - - -	H. F. Paul - - - -	2	52	36
Marina - - - -	Sir Wm. Burton - - -	2	53	25
Flica - - - -	H. L. Goodson - - -	2	56	51
Trivia - - - -	V. W. MacAndrew - - -	2	57	12

July 3

NAME	OWNER	H.	M.	S.
Westra - - - -	A. C. Connell - - - -	2	44	7
Evaine - - - -	C. R. Fairey - - - -	2	44	57
Trivia - - - -	V. W. MacAndrew - - - -	2	46	21
Marina - - - -	Sir Wm. Burton - - - -	2	50	6
Flica - - - -	H. L. Goodson - - - -	2	51	28
Little Astra - - -	H. F. Paul - - - -	2	53	6

Points scored in the Coronation Regatta by First Three Yachts

NAME	OWNER	POINTS
Westra - - - -	A. C. Connell - - - -	percentage points 75·38
Evaine - - - -	C. R. Fairey - - - -	percentage points 67·27
Trivia - - - -	V. W. MacAndrew - - - -	percentage points 56·32

As the points table shows, *Westra* had come out well on top for the fortnight in Torbay. It is good for a class that a boat in her third season is still able to top it, and while it is highly probable that the newer boats were faster, to balance this was the fact that their owners and crews were new to their boats, whereas *Westra's* owner had the advantage of three seasons' experience behind him with the same vessel, so that everyone aboard knew every whim of *Westra* and was able to coax the best out of her. But as time goes on she will find it harder to hold her place amongst the newer boats, for their owners will be learning more and more about them, and will be able to sail them faster round the course.

From Torbay the racers, making their way eastward, next raced round the triangular course in Weymouth Bay. This race was won by C. R. Fairey in *Evaine*, but Sir William Burton's *Marina* was only 7 seconds behind, no more than a boat's length, so we see the racing was very keen and close throughout.

12 METRES

Weymouth. July 5

NAME	OWNER	TIME
		H. M. S.
Evaine - - - -	C. R. Fairey - - - -	2 20 42
Marina - - - -	Sir Wm. Burton - - -	2 20 49
Trivia - - - -	V. W. MacAndrew - - -	2 21 24
Flica - - - -	H. L. Goodson - - - -	2 23 35
Westra - - - -	A. C. Connell - - - -	2 23 45
Little Astra - - -	H. F. Paul - - - -	2 24 53

July 17 saw the 12-metres racing in the Solent under the Lymington Yacht Club Burgee. The winner again was C. R. Fairey in *Evaine*, with young Hugh Goodson just over a minute astern in *Flica*, the nearest boat to him, *Little Astra*, being just on 3 minutes behind him.

Lymington. July 17

NAME	OWNER	TIME
		H. M. S.
Evaine - - - -	C. R. Fairey - - - -	2 9 40
Flica - - - -	H. L. Goodson - - - -	2 10 57
Little Astra - - -	H. F. Paul - - - -	2 13 22
Trivia - - - -	V. W. MacAndrew - - -	2 10 25

Retired : *Marina.*

With a Sunday in between the "twelves" sailed on the Monday at Bournemouth in very light airs, and with *Flica* absent there were only four of them. This race was won by V. W. MacAndrew's *Trivia*, who had over a 3½ minute lead from the second boat *Evaine*.

Bournemouth. July 19

NAME	OWNER	TIME
		H. M. S.
Trivia - - - -	V. W. MacAndrew - - -	2 47 10
Evaine - - - -	C. R. Fairey - - - -	2 50 43
Marina - - - -	Sir Wm. Burton - - -	2 51 36
Little Astra - - -	H. F. Paul - - - -	2 55 0

The next time the "twelves" met there were six, and this was at the Royal Thames Yacht Club's regatta from Ryde Pier, and *Evaine* leading throughout the race won from Arthur Connell's *Westra*.

R.T.Y.C. July 24

NAME	OWNER	TIME
		H. M. S.
Evaine - - - -	C. R. Fairey - - - -	2 33 38
Westra - - - -	A. C. Connell - - - -	2 34 55
Little Astra - - -	H. F. Paul - - - -	2 35 18
Marina - - - -	Sir Wm. Burton - - -	2 36 46
Flica - - - -	H. L. Goodson - - - -	2 36 52
Trivia - - - -	V. W. MacAndrew - - -	2 39 40

The next race was won by *Trivia* with *Marina* second :

R.T.Y.C.   *July* 26

NAME	OWNER	TIME		
		H.	M.	S.
Trivia - - - -	V. W. MacAndrew - - -	3	8	40
Marina - - - -	Sir Wm. Burton - - -	3	13	55
Westra - - - -	A. C. Connell - - -	3	14	55
Flica - - - -	H. L. Goodson - - -	3	17	10
Evaine - - - -	C. R. Fairey - - -	3	17	24
Little Astra - - -	H. F. Paul - - -	3	18	26

and then it was *Evaine's* turn again with *Trivia* second :

R.T.Y.C.   *July* 27

NAME	OWNER	TIME					
		1*st* ROUND			FINISH		
		H.	M.	S.	H.	M.	S.
Evaine - - - -	C. R. Fairey - - -	1	35	6	3	36	15
Trivia - - - -	V. W. MacAndrew - - -	1	35	24	3	39	3
Little Astra - - -	H. F. Paul - - -	1	36	40	3	39	54
Westra - - - -	A. C. Connell - - -	1	42	55	3	44	50
Flica - - - -	H. L. Goodson - - -	1	43	15	3	45	38
Marina - - - -	Sir Wm. Burton - - -	1	36	40	3	47	56

The day following saw Sir William Burton bringing *Marina* in ahead of the fleet with *Trivia* second and *Evaine* third, and so well matched were these " twelves " that no one could say which would win, and seldom has better racing been enjoyed than in the 12-metre class this summer.

Royal Victoria Y.C.   *July* 28

NAME	OWNER	TIME		
		H.	M.	S.
Marina - - - -	Sir Wm. Burton - - -	4	26	21
Trivia - - - -	V. W. MacAndrew - - -	4	28	15
Evaine - - - -	C. R. Fairey - - -	4	45	18

Retired : *Westra, Little Astra, Flica.*

Marina again won on the last day of Ryde with *Westra* only sixteen seconds astern of her :

Royal Victoria Y.C.   *July* 29

NAME	OWNER	TIME		
		H.	M.	S.
Marina - - - -	Sir Wm. Burton - - -	3	12	26
Westra - - - -	A. C. Connell - - -	3	12	42
Trivia - - - -	V. W. MacAndrew - - -	3	14	13
Evaine - - - -	C. R. Fairey - - -	3	16	50
Flica - - - -	H. L. Goodson - - -	3	51	10

Retired : *Little Astra.*

The racing at Cowes starts before Cowes Week under the Burgee of the Royal Southampton Yacht Club, and in very light airs *Evaine* won this race from *Westra* by 3 minutes and 16 seconds after a long drawn out race, which, as the times will show, lasted until 5.00 in the afternoon. Johnny Payne had rejoined the class with *Vanity V* but the weather was so light that he gave up.

Royal Southampton Y.C. *July* 31

NAME	OWNER	TIME
		H. M. S.
Evaine - - - -	C. R. Fairey - - - -	4 53 10
Westra - - - -	A. C. Connell - - - -	4 56 26
Little Astra - - -	H. F. Paul - - - -	4 57 0
Trivia - - - -	V. W. MacAndrew - - -	5 1 12
Flica - - - -	H. L. Goodson - - - -	5 5 53
Marina - - - -	Sir Wm. Burton - - -	5 14 47

Retired : *Vanity V*.

Once again Cowes Week had arrived, and as we grow older the years grow shorter, so The Week always arrives before we expect it.

Years ago, when very young, I always made a point of being away from Cowes during The Week, as the town seemed full of strangers; but as the years rolled on and I came to know more and more people, The Week turned into a reunion of old friends, often friends whom I had not seen for a year. To some of these I have shown the less known parts of Cowes, for Cowes like most other towns has a great deal of interest tucked away in the background behind its streets and houses. Very few yachtsmen realise that the old mould loft of Michael Ratsey, one of our greatest yacht builders of 100 years ago, is still intact, though crumbling away, in behind the streets of Cowes. All round the sides of this mould loft there are the models of a great many of the vessels he built, most of them famous yachts in their day, some revenue cutters and traders, but for the most part sailing yachts.

The mould loft itself is built out of old ships' timbers, and the old knees are as good to-day as they were when they came out of the old ships 100 years ago, for they are of sound oak. On the beams across the mould loft floor is fastened the heavy gilt scroll work which adorned the sterns of some old vessels 100 years ago, and in this old mould loft, approached by a steep flight of rickety stairs from a bed of weeds, one is instantly wafted back a 100 years into the past, although less than 25 yards from the high street of Cowes.

In the two stories below it, also built out of old ship's timbers, are bosun's stores and a small boat building shop. The average yachtsman takes delight in associating Cowes with the firms of Ratsey & Lapthorn, the leading sail-makers of the world, of Henry Bannister, whose rope is generally recognised as the best, Benzie, the yachtsman's jeweller, Saunders-Roe, the builders of *Bluebird*, holder of the world's water record, and J. Samuel White & Co., Ltd., the famous shipbuilders, while the premier yacht club of the world, the Royal Yacht Squadron, occupies the castle built by Henry VIII for the defence of Cowes against the French. All such things are on the surface, but there are a great many other interesting features only known to locals, such as little claps and tunnels where smuggling was carried on in the years gone by—one in particular, where many of the most respected inhabitants were caught and convicted, being still much the same to-day as it was those years ago. Cowes, then, has a great deal of interest ashore as well as afloat, and though this year there were no "J" class racers or Royalty present, The Week was most enjoyable as always for all the yachting fraternity. Light weather prevailed throughout The Week, and the notable thing was that although the winds were so light all the races were completed. When we think of the three- and four-knot tides running through the Solent we realise the seamanship displayed by those sailing to get round the course with such light fickle airs, for the lighter the breeze the more important tidal work becomes, and though these races were tedious to some, they were nevertheless full of interest, as one had to think hard throughout a race, for while it is easy to sail round a course with a lot of wind, it requires skill of a high order to get round with such light airs as we had through The Week, let alone getting round faster than the rest of the class.

V. W. MacAndrew's *Trivia* won on the Monday, but *Westra* won on the Tuesday, and as Tuesday is King's Cup Race day, and the 12-metres were the largest racing class at Cowes, this meant that Arthur Connell's *Westra* won the King's Cup for 1937.

The next day C. R. Fairey's *Evaine* came in ahead, and on the Thursday *Marina* came in a half minute ahead of *Trivia*, and as Sir William had invited me on board for this race its story may prove interesting.

There were seven of us starting, and the weather-going tide being strongest close into the Royal Yacht Squadron, and as this was also the weather end of the line, there was no doubt that this was the place to start. After a lot of sailing round, most of the " twelves " were making towards the inner end of the line close hauled on the starboard tack, the weather going tide tending to push them over.

We in *Marina* had Johnny Payne just ahead to leeward, luffing out, and to weather *Westra* roaring along and calling for water as the tide soaked her on to the Fairway buoy ; for just under the Royal Yacht Squadron there was a strong south westerly breeze and the " twelves " were going along almost at their top speed, so that the latter part of the five minutes was exciting, Johnny Payne and *Westra* had the best of the start, while we were third, but tacking along the Green in the strong tide, *Evaine* caught us starboard tack, and went ahead of us. Then we all stood off for the West Lepe buoy, *Marina* rounding it fourth with *Trivia* just outside us.

FRIENDS FROM ALL PARTS MEET IN COWES WEEK. UFFA IS SEEN LISTENING TO THE WORDS OF WISDOM OF ALFRED MYLNE
VERONICA'S DESIGNER AND BUILDER

We stood across at once for the north shore and the slacker water, for it was a run against the foul tide to our next mark, Calshot Float, and once under this shore we eased the tide and were soon sailing over the ground at a good clip. But on this shore the wind was not true in strength or direction, and first it would favour one and then another of the boats. After a while it swung round more southerly, and though we were sailing by the lee we kept on this gybe as it enabled us to pass *Westra* without her being able to luff us, for she too carried her boom on her starboard and southernmost side, so though we were passing her to windward and taking her wind we were to lee-ward of her by the rules, and she was unable to luff and stop us. After we had passed we gybed over, but two of the " twelves " that had been behind now came up and passed us to weather. We were thus third round the Float buoy. On the reach from here to the north east middle we had the sad experience of watching most of the others pass us, for we had struck a soft patch in the wind. But all this was evened up soon after, for we all came into a spot with absolutely no wind at all ; it was one of those hot blistering days when the wind was caused by the sun burning up the air inshore and then sucking in the air from the sea. So the breeze, as always, was sucked in from Bembridge to Cowes and from the Needles to Cowes, and we had arrived at the calm spot between these south-east and south-west winds. We all anchored to save ourselves being swept back towards Calshot, and setting first the spinnaker and then the genoa, first on one gybe then another, we finally struggled through this calm patch. The three veterans in the class, Sir William Burton, Arthur Connell, and Johnny Payne, seemed to be best at this sort of work, and we rounded the north east Ryde Middle buoy third again, and held this across to the south east buoy. Here the wind was easterly, but we could see that off Cowes there was a strong south westerly blowing, and on *Marina* before we rounded the south-east Ryde buoy we all agreed that the fastest way back to Cowes was by the great circle course away to the northward, for the breeze was stronger and the calm patch between winds practically non-existent out this way. However, there was one boat to the northward of us, and as we converged I could not see that we had any chance at all of breaking through her lee. Sir William, however, held *Marina* head to wind, stunning the enemy without completely losing own way, and so we crept out through and could then sail away to the northward from all the rest. Fairly soon we had the pleasure of working right into the first of the westerly winds before any of the others. *Westra*, who had rounded ahead of us, was over towards Osborne Bay in a spot without any wind, while we had our rail down to a strong westerly. MacAndrew in *Trivia* had followed us out to the north, and Johnny Payne came partly out towards us, only we three going to the northward. We had a difficult time sitting on *Trivia* in the beat home to the finish line, finally crossing 29 seconds ahead of her, Johnny Payne coming only 15 seconds later, while *Westra*, the leader of those who had gambled on the shortest way home, did not cross the line until 10 minutes after *Vanity V.* Next came *Alanna*, while *Little Astra* and C. R. Fairey gave up ; and so ended a race full of interest.

It was the first time I had sailed with Sir William, and I was greatly impressed by the seamanlike manner in which he sailed his boat and looked after details. A little point, which illustrates his understanding and knowledge, came to light soon after we had left the smart breeze, which all day long had blown in Cowes Roads. *Marina* has Highfield levers, which set the backstay up with a constant tension, the great point about them being that the backstay always comes back exactly to its right spot. But, as we all know, in very light airs these should be eased, to throw a little more fulness into the luff of the jib and also liven up the mast and rig itself ; and the way this was accomplished was that a tail rope on the lever was made fast to the cleat astern, and the lever half lifted gave the exact amount of life required ; a small point, but one which shows a great understanding of the finer points in the art of sailing.

Trivia won on the Friday from Johnny Payne in *Vanity V*, and again on the Saturday, with Sir William Burton in *Marina* second, and so ended Cowes Week.

Royal London Y.C.   August 2

NAME	OWNER	TIME
		H. M. S.
Trivia - - - -	V. W. MacAndrew - - -	4 20 16
Evaine - - - -	C. R. Fairey - - -	4 21 26
Marina - - - -	Sir Wm. Burton - - -	4 21 48
Vanity V - - -	J. R. Payne - - -	4 22 46
Little Astra - - -	H. F. Paul - - -	4 43 32
Westra - - - -	A. C. Connell - - -	4 23 55
Flica - - - -	H. L. Goodson - - -	4 25 53
Alanna - - - -	C. E. A. Hartridge - - -	4 27 47

Royal Yacht Squadron.   August 3

Westra - - - -	A. C. Connell - - -	4 19 49
Marina - - - -	Sir Wm. Burton - - -	4 21 0
Vanity V - - -	J. R. Payne - - -	4 25 6
Trivia - - - -	V. W. MacAndrew - - -	5 21 8

Retired : *Alanna, Little Astra* and *Evaine.*

WHEN THE WIND CAME SOUTH-WEST WE CAME
UP ON WESTRA'S WEATHER SIDE—

BUT AS SHE CARRIED HER BOOM LIKE US TO STAR-
BOARD SHE HAD TO GIVE US A FREE PASSAGE
FOR BY THE RULES HER WEATHER SIDE WAS
HER LEE SIDE—

SO SOON WE LED THE FLEET—

BUT THIS DID NOT LAST, FOR AFTER PASSING CAL-
SHOT FLOAT . . .

SEVERAL CAME UP AND WENT THROUGH TO
LEEWARD—

BUT EVEN THOUGH THEY DREW CLEAR AHEAD
AS SHOWN IN THIS PICTURE WE REPASSED THEM
ALL ON THE BEAT AND SO WON

R.L.Y.C.   August 4

NAME	OWNER	TIME		
		H.	M.	S.
Evaine - - - -	C. R. Fairey - - - -	2	42	31
Trivia - - - -	V. W. MacAndrew - - -	2	46	5
Westra - - - -	A. C. Connell - - - -	2	52	45
Little Astra - - -	H. F. Paul - - - -	2	53	10
Alanna - - - -	C. E. A. Hartridge - - -	2	53	29
Marina - - - -	Sir Wm. Burton - - -	2	53	51

R.Y.S.   August 5

NAME	OWNER	H.	M.	S.
Marina - - - -	Sir Wm. Burton - - -	3	22	6
Trivia - - - -	V. W. MacAndrew - - -	3	22	35
Vanity V - - -	J. R. Payne - - - -	3	22	50
Westra - - - -	A. C. Connell - - - -	3	32	49
Alanna - - - -	C. E. A. Hartridge - - -	3	35	49

Retired : *Little Astra* and *Evaine*.

R.Y.S.   August 6

NAME	OWNER	H.	M.	S.
Trivia - - - -	V. W. MacAndrew - - -	3	30	40
Vanity V - - -	J. R. Payne - - - -	3	32	41
Little Astra - - -	H. F. Paul - - - -	3	35	22
Evaine - - - -	C. R. Fairey - - - -	3	35	26
Marina - - - -	Sir Wm. Burton - - -	3	35	40
Westra - - - -	A. C. Connell - - - -	3	35	50
Alanna - - - -	C. E. A. Hartridge - - -	3	38	44

R. Southern Y.C.   August 7

NAME	OWNER	H.	M.	S.
Trivia - - - -	V. W. MacAndrew - - -	3	56	34
Marina - - - -	Sir Wm. Burton - - -	4	2	32
Little Astra - - -	H. F. Paul - - - -	4	7	8
Westra - - - -	A. C. Connell - - - -	4	8	3

Retired : *Evaine*.

The racers then proceeded to Southsea and continued their way round our coast till finally *Trivia* won the last race of the season at Harwich on August 28.

Royal Albert Y.C. Regatta, Southsea.   August 9

NAME	OWNER	TIME		
		H.	M.	S.
Little Astra - - -	H. F. Paul - - - -	3	39	51
Trivia - - - -	V. W. MacAndrew - - -	3	49	47
Alanna - - - -	C. E. A. Hartridge - - -	3	50	25
Evaine - - - -	C. R. Fairey - - - -	3	51	29
Marina - - - -	Sir Wm. Burton - - -	3	52	2
Westra - - - -	A. C. Connell - - - -	3	53	22

Royal Albert Y.C.   August 10

NAME	OWNER	H.	M.	S.
Trivia - - - -	V. W. MacAndrew - - -	3	26	49
Marina - - - -	Sir Wm. Burton - - -	3	30	38
Evaine - - - -	C. R. Fairey - - - -	3	31	0
Alanna - - - -	C. E. A. Hartridge - - -	3	31	50
Westra - - - -	A. C. Connell - - - -	3	32	30
Little Astra - - -	H. F. Paul - - - -	3	34	51

Royal Cinq Ports Y.C.   August 14

NAME	OWNER	TIME		
		H.	M.	S.
Marina - - - -	Sir Wm. Burton - - -	3	39	6
Trivia - - - -	V. W. MacAndrew - - -	3	20	35

Royal Cinq Ports Y.C.   August 16

Evaine - - - -	C. R. Fairey - - - -	2	36	54
Trivia - - - -	V. W. MacAndrew - - -	2	37	50
Little Astra - - -	H. F. Paul - - - -	2	43	49

Retired : *Marina.*

Royal Temple Y.C.   August 19

Evaine - - - -	C. R. Fairey - - - -	I	28	42
Trivia - - - -	V. W. MacAndrew - - -	I	29	50
Marina - - - -	Sir Wm. Burton - - -	I	32	39
Little Astra - - -	H. F. Paul - - - -	I	37	12

Retired : *Vanity V.*

Royal Temple Y.C.   August 20

Trivia - - - -	V. W. MacAndrew - - -	2	12	3
Marina - - - -	Sir Wm. Burton - - -	2	13	53
Evaine - - - -	C. R. Fairey - - - -	2	14	56
Vanity V - - -	J. R. Payne - - - -	2	19	38
Little Astra - - -	H. F. Paul - - - -	2	21	8

Ramsgate to Southend.   August 23

Trivia - - - -	V. W. MacAndrew - - -	7	28	21
Marina - - - -	Sir Wm. Burton - - -	7	32	28
Evaine - - - -	C. R. Fairey - - - -	7	43	0
Vanity V - - -	J. R. Payne - - - -	7	54	48
Little Astra - - -	H. F. Paul - - - -	8	32	12

Royal Thames Y.C., at Southend.   August 24

Trivia - - - -	V. W. MacAndrew - - -	3	5	21
Evaine - - - -	C. R. Fairey - - - -	3	8	0
Marina - - - -	Sir Wm. Burton - - -	3	8	25
Vanity V - - -	J. R. Payne - - - -	3	8	49
Little Astra - - -	H. F. Paul - - - -	3	10	54

Southend Town Regatta.   August 25

Marina - - - -	Sir Wm. Burton - - -	4	42	5
Evaine - - - -	C. R. Fairey - - - -	4	47	15
Trivia - - - -	V. W. MacAndrew - - -	4	49	13
Little Astra - - -	H. F. Paul - - - -	5	13	26

Retired : *Vanity V.*

Royal Harwich Y.C.   August 27

Trivia - - - -	V. W. MacAndrew - - -	3	I	20
Marina - - - -	Sir Wm. Burton - - -	3	3	49
Evaine - - - -	C. R. Fairey - - - -	3	5	19
Little Astra - - -	H. F. Paul - - - -	3	14	9

12 METRES

Royal Harwich Y.C. August 28

NAME	OWNER	TIME
		H. M. S.
Trivia - - - -	V. W. MacAndrew - - -	3 56 51
Evaine - - - -	C. R. Fairey - - - -	4 6 32
Marina - - - -	Sir Wm. Burton - - -	4 6 52
Little Astra - - -	H. F. Paul - - - -	4 17 4

TABLE OF RESULTS

Counting 4 points for 1st ; 2 points for 2nd ; 1 point for 3rd ; we get the following positions for 1937 :

12-METRES

	STARTS	1st	2nd	3rd	POINTS
Trivia, V. W. MacAndrew -	41	13	11	6	80
Evaine, C. R. Fairey - - -	44	11	10	10	74
Marina, Sir Wm. Burton - -	44	9	11	11	69
Westra, A. C. Connell - -	30	7	6	3	43
Little Astra, H. F. Paul - -	41	3	1	9	23
Flica, H. L. Goodson - -	26	2	5	2	20
Vanity V, J. R. Payne - -	10	—	1	2	4
Alanna, C. E. A. Hartridge -	7	—	—	1	1

V. W. MacAndrew, a newcomer to the class, has come out top with *Trivia* after one of the finest season's racing the " twelves " have ever experienced. And so the 1937 season came to a close in British waters, and with America building up a similar class the future looks very bright for the " twelves ", as it should, for they are lovely little ships, large enough to give a great deal of comfort aboard, and yet small enough to be tacked and gybed frequently, so giving the fun of sailing a quick and responsive racer, and this with their seaworthiness is largely responsible for the ever increasing popularity of the " twelves ".

· 34 ·

8 METRES

IF

Length, overall	-	48·80 ft.	= 14·85 m.	
Beam	-	- 8·50 ft.	= 2·59 m.	
Displacement	-	8·40 tons	= 8534 kilos.	

Length, water-line	-	30·50 ft.	= 9·29 m.
Draught	-	- 6·50 ft.	= 1·98 m.
Sail Area	-	- 830 sq. ft.	= 77 sq. m.

Owner, COL. CLEAVER, D.S.O.   *Designer*, BJARNE AAS   *Builder*, BJARNE AAS

*I*F is the best hard-weather 8-metre yet seen in Norway, and looking at her lines it is easy for us to imagine her driving to windward against a strong wind and sea. Those of us who have sailed in her realise more clearly still the speed and power wrapped up in this design. The sections are those of an exceptionally seaworthy cruiser, whose

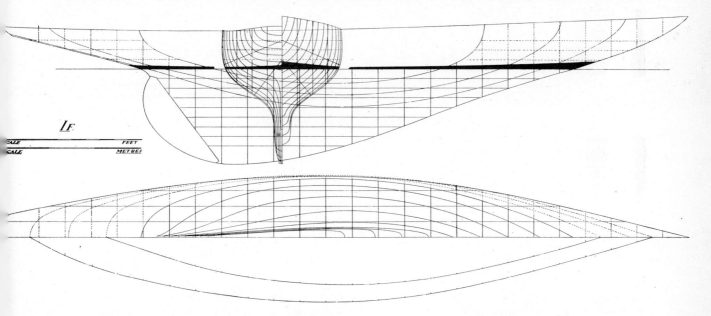

fore and aft lines are such as give her a remarkable turn of speed. Besides her evident ability to windward we can see by her clean buttock lines, which give her such a long easy run, that she is capable of high speeds off the wind, and it is a pleasure to put such a good little vessel into this book. Of late years *If* has raced in British waters, her owner, Colonel Cleaver, living aboard and sailing her round the coast to the different regattas. At night she affords him a cosy little floating home, while in the day she gives him all the pleasure of a racer, and she and her owner are well known in almost every port from the Thames to Land's End. *If* has not so far raced as an 8-metre in British waters, but as a handicap cruiser. She has proved that there is no need for the 8-metres to stay as they do in the Solent or the Clyde, and that they could very well take their owners round the coast and give them excellent sport in all the big regattas, just as the " twelves " do. And much as we in the Solent would miss the sight of so fine a class, I believe it would give the owners more fun to go racing on different courses instead of restricting themselves through-out the season to familiar waters.

The Solent and the Clyde racing was divided into two sessions as most of the " eights " went to Torquay for the Coronation Regatta from June 19 to July 3. As in past years the racing on the Solent was so keen and close that the

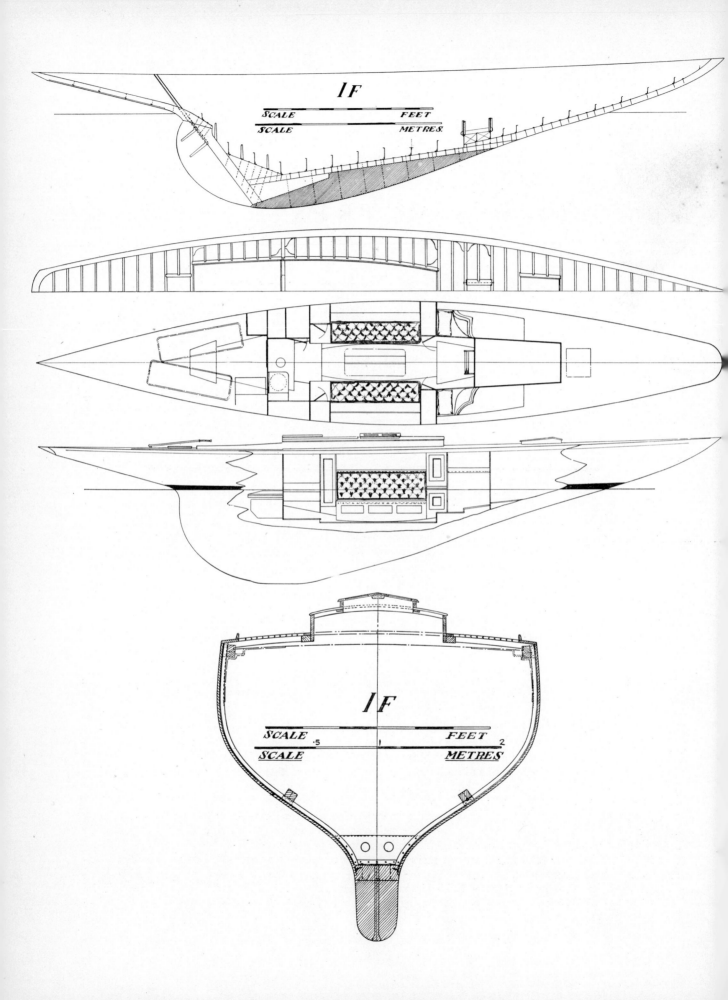

IF

SCALE — FEET
SCALE — METRES.

IF

SCALE · .5 · 1 · FEET · 2
SCALE — METRES

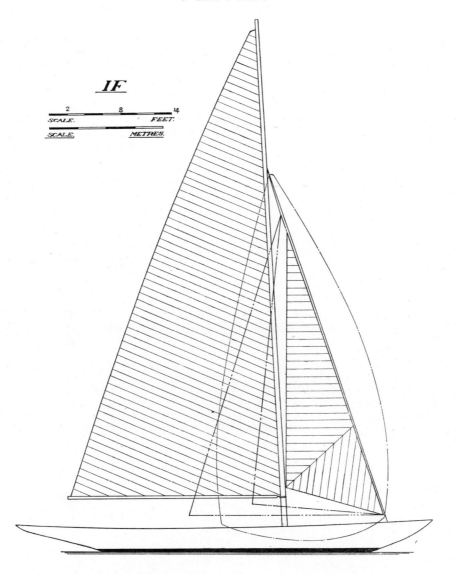

IF

SCALE. FEET.

SCALE. METRES.

THE "EIGHTS" RACING IN TORBAY

F.R.C.D.

slightest mistake cost any boat several places, and it was most difficult to say which would win. But on the Clyde things were different, for *Froya*, sailed remarkably well by J. Howden Hume, Jnr., led the fleet home more often than any other boat, so that at the end of the season she came out well on top for points.

TABLE OF CLYDE RESULTS

	STARTS	*1st*	*2nd*	*3rd*	TOTAL
Froya, J. H. Hume, Jnr. - -	36	23	5	1	29
Carol, Messrs. Hendry and Steven	39	10	10	5	25
Sappho, Sir T. C. Glen Coats -	29	3	12	5	20
Amita, J. D. McKechnie - -	37	2	9	4	15
Ailort, Geo. Jackson - - -	24	1	0	3	4

FROYA THE CLYDE CHAMPION

★   ★   ★   ★   ★

On the Solent *Wye* came out top as the following table shows :

8-METRE RECORD, 1937 (SOLENT MEDAL RACES)

	STARTS	1st	2nd	3rd	AVERAGE	POINTS
Wye -	- 55	15	6	4	1·50	76
Saskia -	- 49	8	12	5	1·24	61
Carron -	- 55	12	7	6	1·23	68
Reality -	- 56	8	12	7	1·13	63
Sagitta -	- 45	5	8	6	0·93	42
Cedora -	- 56	5	7	11	0·80	45
Folly -	- 51	4	2	9	0·60	33
Felma -	- 47	2	4	5	0·45	21

THE 8-METRE IF, WHEN RACING IN THE HANDICAP CLASS, SET A GENOA FROM HER
TOPMAST HEAD TO HER STEMHEAD

But though *Wye* topped the Solent class, *Sagitta* topped the class for the Torbay Coronation Regatta, with *Saskia* second and *Cedora* third ; and those of us who had the pleasure of watching these fine little ships racing hard throughout the summer could not help but admire them.

The French 8-metre *France* challenged for the Coup de France. F. A. Richards with *Felma* represented this country, and defended for the Royal Thames, but *France*, who had been winning in the Mediterranean through the winter, was so fast that she won this trophy in four straight races. Though we are sorry to see it leave our shores, this is tempered with real pleasure, for the French have tried and tried again over a great many years to regain the trophy, and now that they have been successful we congratulate them, and hope we shall soon be sending a challenger over capable of regaining the cup.

Early one morning shortly after the Coronation Regatta I saw Joe Oatley in an 8-metre come flying into Cowes driven along by a hard south-westerly wind. He had just arrived from Torquay. Throughout the night it had blown very hard, so hard that another "eight", *Caron II*, was dismasted when coming in for the Needles. Rigging her spinnaker boom as a mast she set enough sail on this to stop herself being driven ashore, and sailing round the back of the Wight was met and towed by the Bembridge lifeboat from Shanklin Bay into Gosport. Her dismasting drives home an interesting point, and that is that this 8-metre was such a little thoroughbred that even with only

FRANCE CAME OVER AND DEFEATED OUR BEST 8-METRE

a spinnaker boom for a mast she could be handled and kept clear of that dangerous coast in a sou'wester, a coast that in sailing-ship days claimed many victims, for with a south-west wind many a fine ship has broken up on the rocks in Brook Bay between the Needles and St. Catherine's ; and *Caron II* or any vessel that after being dismasted could still hold off such a coast on such a night is without doubt a fine type of craft. And it is because these 8-metres are such manly and capable little ships that they have such a strong appeal.

· 35 ·

6 METRES

COIMA

Length, overall - 35 ft. 6 in. = 10·80 m.	Length, water-line - 23 ft. 9 in. = 7·24 m.
Beam - - 6 ft. 0 in. = 1·83 m.	Draught - - 5 ft. 4 in. = 1·625 m.
Displacement - 4·237 tons = 4304 kilos.	Sail Area - - 465 sq. ft. = 43·19 sq. m.

Owner, BILL HORBURY   *Designer*, JOHAN ANKER   *Builder*, JOHAN ANKER

DESIGNED by Johan Anker, *Coima*, as one would expect, had a successful career. She was first owned by the Crown Prince of Norway who won a great many races with her, and this year, as the Crown Prince built a new "six", Bill Horbury was fortunate in acquiring her.

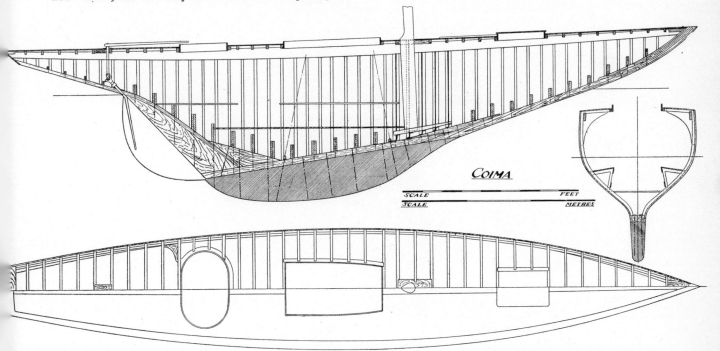

COIMA

As we look at *Coima's* lines we see that while her beam is only 6 ft., she is not so narrow as *Hakahala* with 5 ft. 9 in. beam as seen in my second book or *Maybe III* with 5 ft. 10 in. described in my third book ; but even so, *Coima* is a narrow vessel, having four beams to her water-line length, whereas we generally consider three beams make for the ideal type of craft of this size. This narrowness of beam is brought about by the displacement forced upon 6-metres by the rule, and when we think that some 80 per cent. of *Coima's* weight is in her lead keel, we realise how heavy this displacement is. However, at the I.Y.R.U. Conference this year, a minimum beam was fixed for the 6-metre class of 6 ft., or 1·83 metres, and it is hoped that this, besides barring the extremely narrow type, will also act as a check on greater length in the class, for though the narrower boats have not shown any great advantage over those with 6 ft., which for this length water-line and for this class is quite narrow, there is a strong possibility that by going narrower and longer an undesirable type of boat may be developed. However, we must look at *Coima* as the normal development of the rule, and the type of "six" the rule encourages, for she has had great success both

213

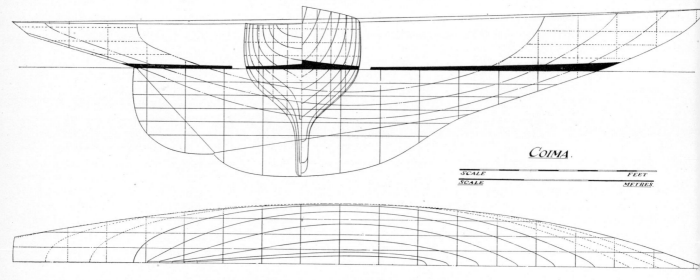

COIMA.

SCALE ——————————— FEET
SCALE ——————————— METRES

COIMA

2   4   6   8   10   12   14
SCALE ——————————— FEET
SCALE ——————————— METRES

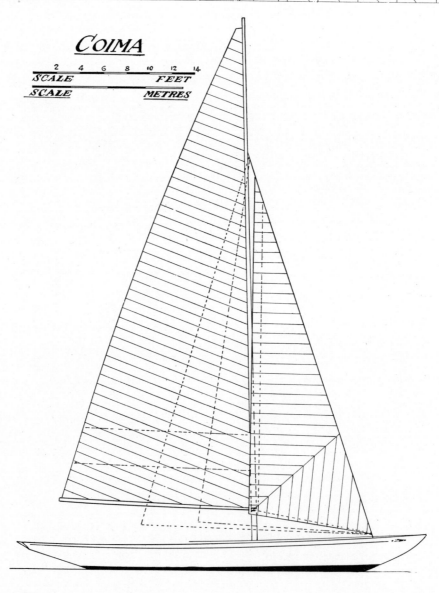

in Norway and in this country, and we must study her from a 6-metre viewpoint. When we do this we see that the designer has distributed the heavy displacement called for very well indeed, and her water-lines, buttocks and sections all tell of a sweet-lined and easily driven craft.

From her construction and arrangement plan we see that her horn timber runs away down to the main keel, and where the main keel joins the fore gripe there is a long triangular strengthening piece, and this with a long scarph between the fore gripe and the stem gives *Coima* a sturdy backbone. The heavy weight on the keels of these " sixes " necessitates their being extremely well built to endure the strains and stresses put upon them racing and sailing.

The universal joint at the rudder head worked extremely well in practice, and a study of her plans will be well repaid, for Anker is not only a designer but a builder and a first-class helmsman, and so able to design his boat with every detail of her in his mind, from the casting of her lead keel, through her building, trials, and her various races under all conditions. Little points like the width of the helmsman's cockpit, which is so wide that he can sit away down to leeward and sail on his genoa jib, tell of a perfect understanding of the problem.

The sail plan shows that the full 13 metres height allowed for the rig is taken advantage of, as is also the fore triangle height, and the 3-metre base to the fore triangle brings the mast well into the boat, so much so that it is two-fifths of the water-line from its fore end, a position that is considered by cruising people ideal for sea work. Thus a great deal of good has come from the rule, which only counts 85 per cent. of the fore triangle, and the I.Y.R.U. should be congratulated, for after many years designers have found that it encourages the mast to be in the ideal position for sea work.

SLEIPNIR II

Length, overall -	37 ft. 8 in.	= 11·48 m.		Length, water-line -	23 ft. 7½ in.	= 7·20 m.
Beam - -	6 ft. 0⅞ in.	= 1·85 m.		Draught - -	5 ft. 4 in.	= 1·65 m.
Displacement -	4·19 tons	= 4267 kilos.		Sail Area -	468 sq. ft.	= 43·53 sq. m.

Designer, ABEKING & RASMUSSEN   *Builder*, ABEKING & RASMUSSEN

Sleipnir's proportions are very similar to those of *Coima*, the great difference being that she is 2 ft. longer overall due to the fact that her buttock lines are not quite so steep ; though to appreciate how this has been done, despite

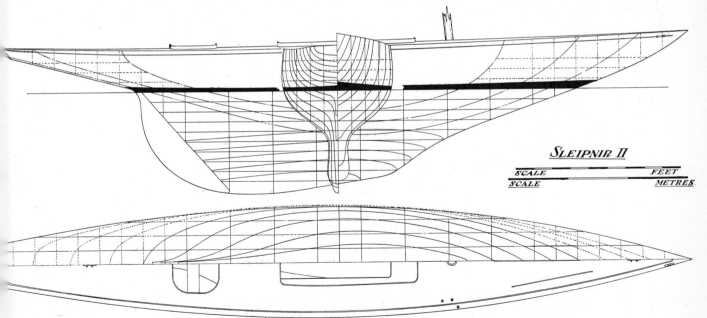

the fact that both boats have to distribute practically the same displacement, is difficult at first to realise. To find the answer to this we have to look at their lead keels, when we notice that *Sleipnir II* has a very thick fin keel, practically double the thickness of *Coima's*, and while this has the advantage of getting her lead keel very low, we have to bear in mind that she has a much thicker keel to push through the water ; and which is right it is difficult to say.

In aeroplane design the thickness of the streamline form for least resistance should be a certain proportion of the length for a certain speed, but as can easily be imagined this proportion varies with the speed, and only tank testing can tell us which is right for the fin keels of 6-metres.

Sleipnir's cockpit arrangements are practically the same as *Coima's* ; these twin cockpits have been tried and worked out on the race-course rather than on the designer's board, and it is not surprising to find the same idea in all 6-metre craft.

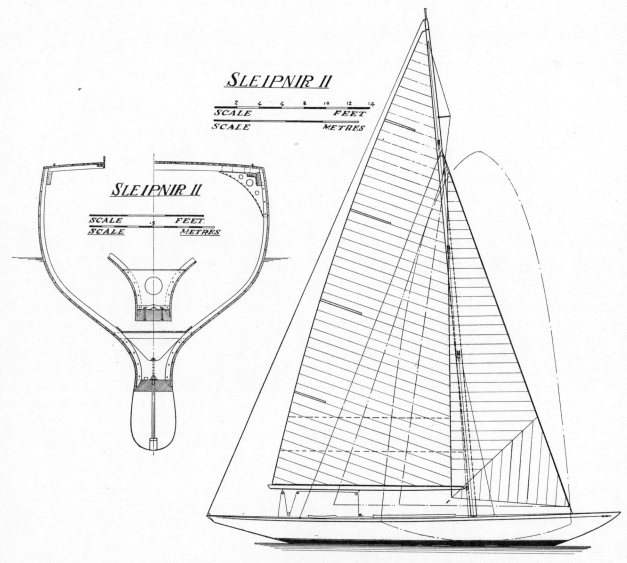

In their present sail plans, however, the proportions of *Sleipnir* and *Coima* differ, the former having a much smaller fore triangle, with the consequence that her mast is not stepped so far into her by 3 ft. 3 in. (one metre).

Sleipnir II was built in 1935 for the German Navy, and in that year won 16 prizes out of 37 starts against strong International competition.   In Hanko and Lysekil she led the fleet home, while this year she was third in Kiel Week, and winner of the German championship for the International 6-metre class.   So we see that *Sleipnir's* record is extremely good and though in her third season she is still fast enough to have won the championship of Germany for 1937.

SAGA

Length, overall	-	37 ft. 3 in.	= 11·354 m.		Length, water-line	-	23 ft. 7 in.	= 7·18 m.
Beam	-	-	6 ft. 2 in.	= 1·88 m.	Draught	-	- 5 ft. 4½ in.	= 1·64 m.
Displacement	-	4·18 tons	= 4250 kilos.		Sail Area	-	- 470 sq. ft.	= 43·66 m.

Owner, ELDON TRIMMINGHAM   *Designer*, BJARNE AAS   *Builder*, BJARNE AAS

Designed and built by Bjarne Aas for Eldon Trimmingham of Bermuda in 1935, *Saga* is one of the best hard-weather " sixes " yet built, and won the Prince of Wales' Cup Race at Bermuda early in 1936 in spite of the fact that *Indian Scout*, winner of the Gold Cup and many other important races while in European waters later that year, was racing against her.

LULU, BRIGGS CUNNINGHAM'S STEPHENS " SIX " LEADING SAGA, THE BERMUDIAN ENTRY

Again this spring when the American "sixes" went to Bermuda for the Prince of Wales' Cup *Saga* showed up well in the strong breezes, for though Briggs Cunningham's new "six" *Lulu* won the series, *Saga* defeated her in the days when it blew hard, and *Saga's* owner very sportingly suggested that the final race be called off because of the strong wind. This gesture was appreciated by the Americans, for the weather that day suited *Saga* perfectly. The final was eventually held in very light air in which *Saga* finished last, and so came out third for points over the series.

NAME			OWNER		POINTS
Lulu	-	-	Briggs S. Cunningham (U.S.)	-	34
Indian Scout	-		H. S. Morgan (U.S.) -	- -	27¼
Saga	-	-	Eldon Trimmingham (Berm.) -	-	26½
Rebel	-	-	Paul V. Shields (U.S.) -	-	21
Bob-Kat III	-		Robert B. Meyer (U.S.) -	- -	21
Viking	-	-	William Miller (Berm.) -	- -	19¼
Totem	-	-	A. E. Luders, Jnr. (U.S.)	- -	19
Light Scout	-		Herman F. Whiton (U.S.)	- -	18
Silroc	-	-	C. Raymond Hunt (U.S.)	- -	14
Marga	-	-	Eric Ahlstrom (Finland) -	- -	8

In *Saga* we have a very fine hard-weather 6-metre, and as we look at her well-rounded sections, at her clean water-lines and buttocks, we cannot but admire them ; for in spite of the heavy displacement forced upon her by the rule, they are still pleasing to the eye, for with her beam of 6·2 ft., Bjarne Aas has not gone to any extremes in narrowness of beam, and this wider beam in *Saga* makes for the type of craft we all hoped the rule would encourage. But a 6-metre is only judged by her success as a racer, and we all know that weight added to beam makes for a slower craft, and that as the I.Y.R.U. rule demands a heavy minimum displacement, designers though they would love to do so cannot design and build beamy boats to the 6-metre rule, so that though *Saga* is beamier than the other two 6-metres in this chapter she is still narrow.

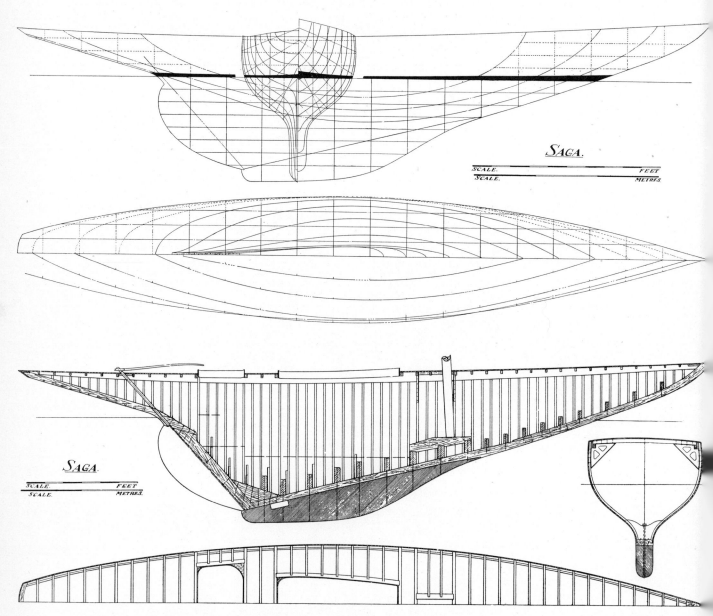

SAGA.

SCALE.   FEET
SCALE.   METRES

SAGA.

SCALE.   FEET
SCALE.   METRES.

Saga's construction plan shows that she too has a double cockpit arrangement, and that the helmsman's cockpit is wide to enable him to get to leeward and watch his headsail on a wind, and the mast is practically one-third the water-line length from its fore end. The long scarph between the stem and keel makes for a good strong joint and abaft this above the fore end of the lead keel, the mast step it will be seen spreads the thrust of the mast over three of her teak floors, for from the rudder heel forward the floors are of teak. The keel bolts run from the top of these through the bottom of the lead, so we see that *Saga's* construction is well designed and developed and a hard-weather vessel needs to be well and truly built, otherwise the weather in which she wins her races will cause her to leak or strain, so that she has to give up.

Coima's 1937 season will illustrate the 6-metre class in English waters for this year. She was shipped over from Norway early in the summer : Bill Horbury asked Stewart Morris to take her helm, and the rest of her crew

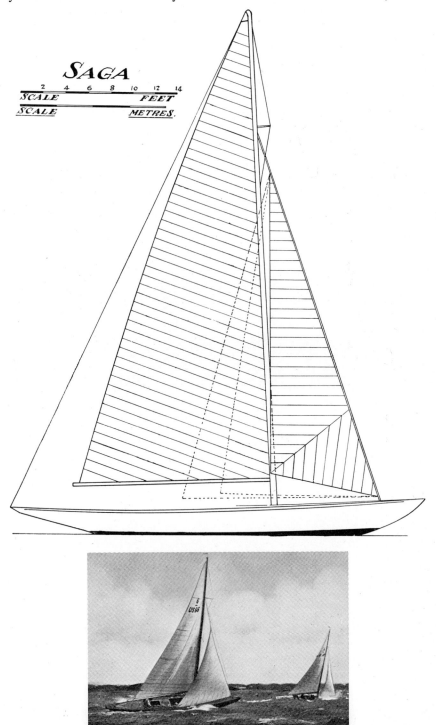

SAGA

| 2 | 4 | 6 | 8 | 10 | 12 | 14 |
SCALE   FEET
SCALE   METRES.

SAGA WORKING TO WINDWARD OF INDIAN SCOUT IN A STRONG BREEZE OF WIND

were also formed of dinghy sailors—she had no paid hands aboard at all for her races. On the Solent she did quite well before the Coronation Regatta, being always in the hunt : in seven races she had four firsts, one second, a third and a fifth, and her position as fifth is explained by the fact that she went ashore on Shrape Mud for some ten minutes, and even then only lost by forty seconds.　One day at Cowes, Bill very kindly invited me aboard for a day's sail.　It was good to be aboard her, and see the keenness with which she was handled.　Everyone on board was out

COIMA CLOSE-HAULED DURING THE CORONATION REGATTA

THE 6-METRES MADE A FINE PICTURE RACING IN TORBAY DURING THE CORONATION REGATTA

to bring *Coima* in ahead of the fleet, and after a close struggle we managed to cross the line one second in front of F. Spriggs sailing *Kyla*, with whom we had been changing places for a great part of the race.　If *Coima* could do so well in the early part of the season we all felt she would do still better at Torbay.　And so it proved : though up against stronger competition, for there were boats from Norway, Finland, Germany and Scotland against her, and though she only won one race she was generally so close to the leaders that for a long time in the week she was ahead for points. Finally H.R.H. the Crown Prince of Norway took pride of position on the last day with *Norna IV*, *Coima's* younger sister, also from the board of Johan Anker, and as the final points show, *Norna IV* only beat *Coima* by 0·64 of a point for the week, the Finnish boat being third with 68·25 points.

After the Coronation Regatta the Scottish 6-metres went back to the Clyde and the South Coast "sixes" to the Solent, for generally speaking, the class is only raced on the Solent and the Clyde. *Coima*, having now changed

CIRCE, MELITA, SENOIA, AND ESME,
OFF ASHTON, GOUROCK

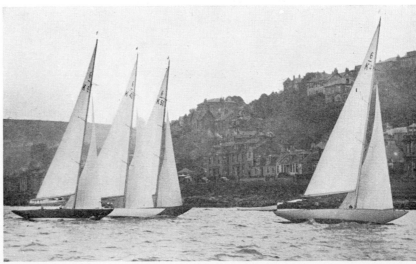

KINI, A NEW "SIX" LEADING SENOIA AND VOLGA

hands, did not do so well, for her new owner had the difficult job of getting accustomed to a new boat in the middle of a season.

At the end of the Solent season the "sixes" went to Burnham for the week, *Lalage* winning Prince George's Cup by coming out on top for points during Burnham Week.

Upon the Clyde the Scottish "sixes" gave as usual good sport to their owners, and though the Nicholson "six" *Senoia* finally came out top, and also won the Tarbet Cup, *Melita*, *Vrana* and most of the others won in their

THE CROWN PRINCE OF NORWAY'S "SIX"
CLOSE HAULED—

AND RUNNING

SOME OF THE FLEET AT TORQUAY

WITH SPINNAKERS SET

IN TORBAY

COIMA'S HELMSMAN

SIX PHOTOGRAPHS TAKEN FROM COIMA WHILE RACING IN TORBAY

turn, the races on the whole being well divided. So ended another season in British waters, a season so full of interest and good racing that we can confidently look forward to good 6-metre racing in 1938.

TABLE OF CLYDE RESULTS

	STARTS	1st	2nd	3rd	4th	TOTAL
Senoia, C. A. Allan - - -	40	10	4	3	4	21
Melita, R. M. Teacher - -	34	8	5	4	4	21
Circe, J. H. Thom - - -	39	6	6	6	6	24
Vrana, J. H. M. Clark - -	35	7	3	3	3	16
Fiona, F. A. Downes - - -	40	5	4	6	3	18
Kini, Messrs. Donaldson - -	41	2	10	5	1	18
Mara, Wm. Russell - - -	31	2	4	6	4	16
Volga, Robt. Clark - - -	36	1	2	3	4	10
Esme, I. F. Marshall - - -	23	0	1	1	1	3
Maida, K. Barge - - -	9	0	1	0	0	1

The Americans had two important cups to defend in their own waters, for they hold both the Seawanhaka and Gold Cups. Three invaders went across for the Gold Cup, Ovan Evald Elander's *Tidsforddirf II* representing the Royal Swedish Yacht Club of Gothenberg, O. Ditlev-Simonsen, Jnr.'s *Buri*, representing the Royal Norwegian Yacht Club, and G. Kyntzell's *Inga-Lill XXVI* representing the Nylundska Yakt Klubben, Helsingfors, Finland, so Briggs Cunningham's new 6-metre *Lulu* had a difficult task, for the three invaders were fast and well sailed.

The Gold Cup goes to the first 6-metre to win three races, and any boat not winning any one of the first three races has to drop out. *Buri* dropped out because of this. The American *Lulu* won the first day in a moderate breeze, and then came light weather in which the challengers were at their best, and so at the end of three races *Tidsforddrif II* had won one and so had *Inga-Lill XXVI*, *Tidsforddrif* winning the fourth race and *Inga-Lill* the fifth, so the position was that while these two needed only one race to lift the Cup, the American *Lulu* had to win the next two races to keep the Cup in American waters. All turned out well for her, as there was more heart in the breeze on the sixth day and *Lulu* came out ahead, so the contest went the full seven races, but on the last day with a breeze strong enough to cause all to reef there was no doubt that *Lulu* would win, for the invaders, though wonderful light-weather boats could not stand up to the hard breeze, and *Lulu* sailing round the course in a wonderful manner beat the Swedish boat by a minute and the Finn by half an hour, and so for another year the Gold Cup stays in America.

Buri, the Norwegian, was the challenger for the Seawanhaka trophy and ranged against her as a defender was the *Rebel*, sailed by Corney Shields, who was unbeatable, for he won three straight races and the Seawanhaka Cup remains with the Seawanhaka Club for yet another year. It would seem that the European countries have to really pull up their socks in order to win either of these trophies from the Americans, for of late years the American "sixes" have been practically invincible, the only people to beat them being the Bermudians.

One point seems to stand out clearly from all these contests, and that is, that light-weather boats do not often win a long series, for when the wind is light there are flukes and flaws in it, and the hard-weather boat is just as likely to pick up a fluke as a light-weather boat, and win in the light boat's own weather. But when it comes to a breeze of wind there is no doubt but that the hard-weather boat is bound to win, and this is a good omen, for it means that hard-weather "sixes" such as *Saga* which will be built for International events and as hard-weather boats must be sturdy and strong to endure the hard drive they get in a breeze of wind, and they must necessarily be good sea boats so though the rule makers worry and get agitated over the rules, the fact that in a long series of races the hard-weather boat stands to win will keep designers producing first-class vessels to all classes.

INTERNATIONAL 5 METRES
SVERRE II

Length, overall - 32 ft. 1⅞ in. = 9·80 m.	Length, water-line - 19 ft. 8 in. = 6·00 m.
Beam - - 6 ft. 6¾ in. = 2·00 m.	Draught - - 3 ft. 7¼ in. = 1·09 m.
Displacement - 1·82 tons = 1849 kilos.	Sail Area - - 213·10 sq. ft. = 19·80 sq. m.

Designer, KNUD H. REIMERS

THE 5-metre class is increasing in popularity in Sweden, no less than thirty-one boats having been registered and built in Sweden at the beginning of this year, while Finland, Denmark and Germany have also boats to this class. Undoubtedly the rules provide a cheap International racing class.

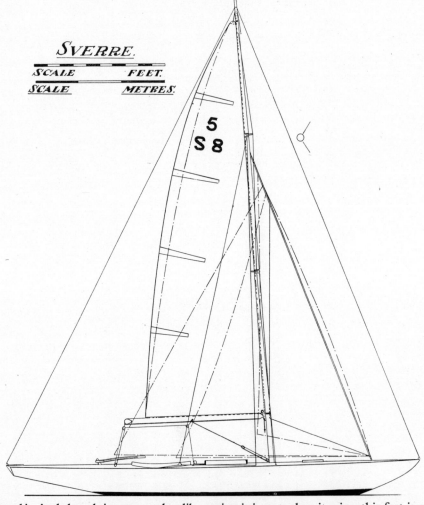

Length is speed! And though it seems rather like saying it is wet when it rains, this fact is easily lost sight of, and most classes start with fairly short boats, which with increasing years get longer and longer until the maximum

water-line length allowed by the rule, or the maximum natural length for a class is reached.   In the chapter on the
5-metre class in my last book (*Sail and Power*) I said : " It is probable that future ' fives ' will be longer on the water-
line," as " generally speaking, length can be added to designs, making the boats faster in a breeze and no slower in

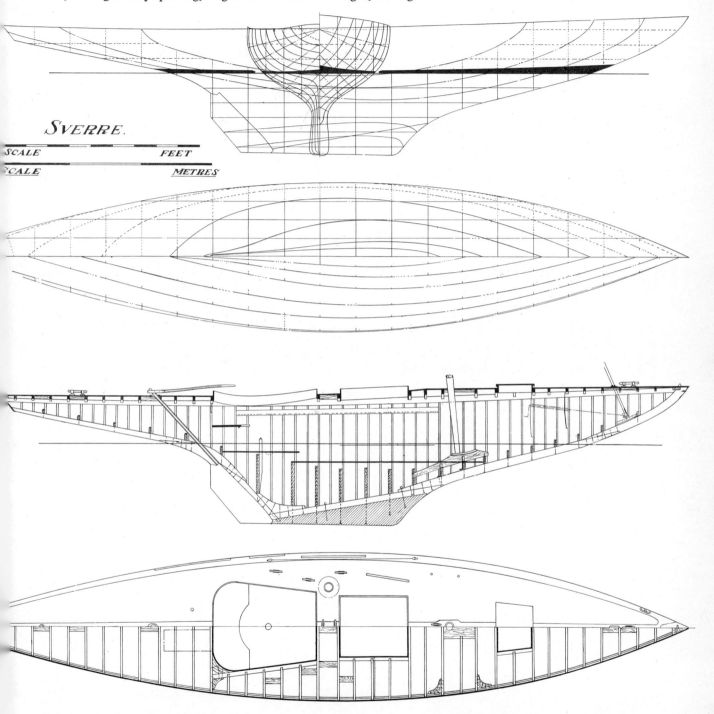

SVERRE.

SCALE   FEET

SCALE   METRES

light weather ".   This has held true for every class of racers from the " J " class down to the 6-metres, and so it is not
surprising to see that where last year's 5-metres were only 17 ft. 7 in. on the water-line, the new ones are some 2 ft.
longer.   Besides this length giving increased speed, these boats have little stability through their small draught,
and while beam will also give stability it also makes for a vessel that is harder to drive through the water ; but length
will give stability as well as beam.

P   F.R.C.D.

Sverre II is fairly normal in her dimensions, but she has 0·40 of a ton over the minimum displacement required by the rule, and as all this extra weight has gone into her lead keel, this is over a ton in weight. So we see that the designer is aiming at stability from the lead keel, and that though the International 5-metre rule calls for the minimum displacement of 1·47 tons (1500 kilos.), Knud has in this boat gone for a much heavier displacement, increasing the minimum by nearly 33 per cent., an enormous increase, while in strong contrast to this method of obtaining stability we have another design by him, *Roulette IV*, where displacement has been kept down to the minimum required by the rule, and stability is obtained by extra beam, which, however, being mostly above the water-line, will not tend to slow her.

ROULETTE IV

Length, overall -	30 ft. 4½ in. = 9·25 m.	Length, water-line -	19 ft. 0 in. = 5·79 m.
Beam - -	7 ft. 0 in. = 2·13 m.	Draught - -	3 ft. 7¼ in. = 1·09 m.
Displacement -	1·47 tons = 1500 kilos.	Sail Area - -	247·5 sq. ft. = 23·08 sq. m.

Designer, KNUD H. REIMERS

A STUDY of these two designs to the same rule by the same designer gives us much food for thought, and shows, incidentally, that so far the International 5-metre class has not settled down, for designers and owners are not sure yet exactly what pays under the rules.

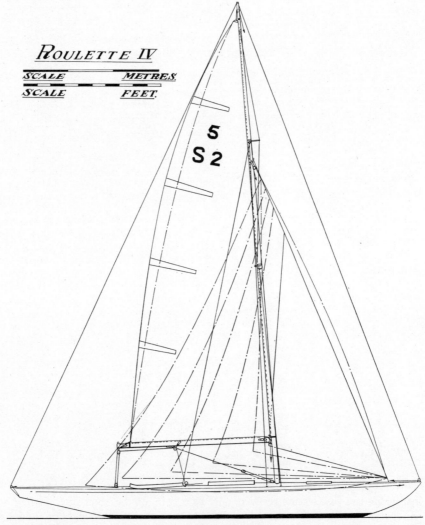

Details such as keel and rudder, cockpit, etc., are both similar, as one would expect from the same designer in the same winter to the same rule.

We see the maximum draught in each craft, and the under side of the keel is parallel with the water-line as this keeps the lead low and gives her a good grip to windward.

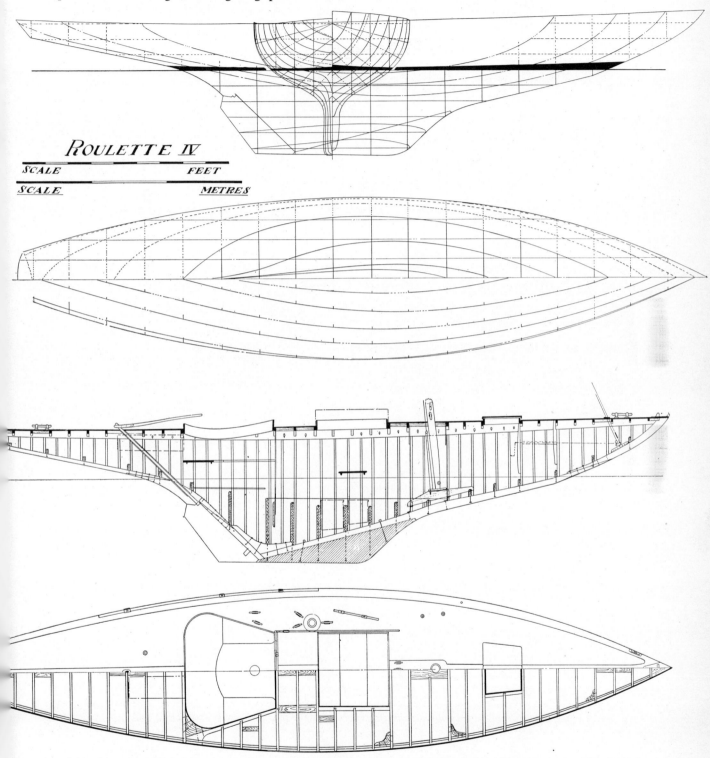

ROULETTE IV

SCALE   FEET

SCALE   METRES

The after edges of the rudders have been kept straight, so they can easily be sheathed with brass. The cockpit and deck arrangements are the same, on each boat the helmsman's cockpit growing wider at the after end to enable him to sit to leeward where he is able to watch his headsails.

When we look at the lines, if we forget the difference in the beam of these two craft, we see a great similarity between them. Both have well V'd sections forward, which makes for a healthy type of boat, and in both the beam is greatest above the water-line, while the diagonal lines in both are the sweet fair lines we look for in Knud's designs. Really these two designs differ only in that in one stability has been aimed at by extra lead in the keel made possible through exceeding the minimum displacement required, and in the other by extra beam above the water-line, and it would be interesting to race two such craft through the season to find out which is the more healthy and pleasant and which is the faster of the two.

Their sail plans, too, are somewhat similar, the only difference being that *Roulette IV* has more area, and so not such a high aspect ratio to her mainsail, for this extra sail area can only be added by lengthening the foot of the mainsail, since there is a maximum height to the mainsail and the fore triangle, and, as one would expect, both sail plans have gone to the maximum height allowed by the rule.

In *Sail and Power*, on page 284, I pointed out a mistake in the rules :

" Here again there is a flaw in the rules. Rules for spars say ' Hollow or bamboo or built mast and spars are not allowed '. This is done to keep the cost of the class down, but it is generally cheaper nowadays to build a spar of several pieces of wood, than it is to buy a solid stick free from defects, and it is not only cheaper and easier to make, but also stronger. The rule should be altered to allow of built up spars, so it would seem that a set of rules have been formed for this class, which have but two flaws in them, both of which are minor, and could be easily altered without affecting boats already built. These alterations should be beneficial to the class as the years go on, and it seems that at last this class is going ahead, though as yet no boats have been designed and built to it in British waters."

The I.Y.R.U. have straightened this point out for the same rule now reads :

Masts and Spars. Solid or built masts and spars must be made up of the same kind of material all through. The mast shall have a minimum diameter, at half the height from deck to jib halyard, of 105 millimetres.

It would now seem that the class is beginning to stand on good firm ground, and so is likely to increase in popularity and spread to more and more countries.

A striking feature with regard to the rig of these two " fives " is that where generally at the hounds we have a crosstree athwartships and two jumper struts at 30 degrees from the fore and aft line, Knud has halved the angle between the jumper struts and the crosstrees and fitted jumper struts at this angle and so done away with the cross-trees. The interesting thing to me about this was to see three different people in three different countries in the same winter all doing the same thing. In Britain Dr. Ward incorporated this feature on a cruiser he had designed and built to his ideas. She was Bermudian rigged, and in her case it worked extremely well. It often happens in this world that the same idea occurs to different people in different parts of the world much about the same time, and generally when this happens it proves that the idea is sound.

In 1933 the Royal Corinthian Club asked Malden Heckstall Smith to produce a 5-metre rule for them, and several boats were built to this rule. They raced at Burnham, but for some reason no boats were built after the first year. *Pinkus*, designed by Laurent Giles, gives us an idea of the working of that rule, and it is interesting to compare her with the two International 5-metres.

PINKUS

Length, overall -	30·02 ft.	=9·16 m.	Length, water-line -	18·84 ft.	= 5·74 m.
Beam - -	5 ft. 6 in.	=1·67 m.	Draught - -	4 ft. 9 in.	= 1·44 m.
Displacement -	1·55 tons	=1574 kilos.	Sail Area - -	255·78 sq. ft.	=23·69 sq. m.

Owner, JAMES BACON   *Designer*, LAURENT GILES   *Builder*, VOSPER & CO.

As we see, the overall lengths are much the same, but the beam is less and the draught is greater, in spite of the fact that the River Crouch, on which the Royal Corinthian " fives " raced, is very shallow. The sail area is much about the same, the height allowed in the International class being almost 33 ft., while the Corinthian rule allows 34 ft. The fore triangle heights too are very close, as the International allows 23 ft. maximum height and the Royal Corinthian 25 ft. The displacement of 1·55 tons is virtually the same as that of *Roulette IV*, practically the minimum allowed by the International rule, and so *Pinkus* tells us that the two rules bring about similar results.

Pinkus was the longest of the " fives " built to the Royal Corinthian 5-metre rule, and is also very narrow, a great deal of her displacement being tucked away in her deep-finned keel ; and in spite of the fact that she was the longest boat she did best in the light weather races.

The lines show a well balanced little vessel, and one that is very pleasant to sail, for the sections and lines are those of a fast easily driven hull and the short fin would enable her to be twisted, turned and tacked easily and quickly, for in races that only last an hour or so one needs a quick and responsive boat, as then one is able to crowd a great

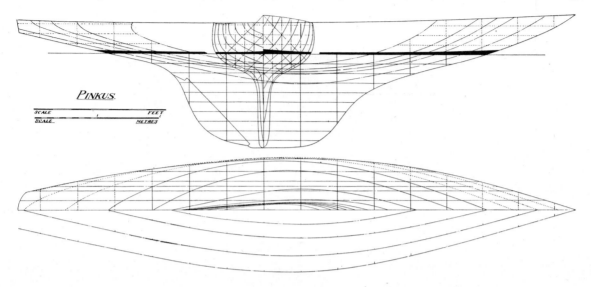

PINKUS.

SCALE ———————— FEET
SCALE ———————— METRES

deal of excitement and pleasure into a short time. For this reason it is wrong to mix up the slower and heavier cruising type with small boats used for a race lasting one to two hours.

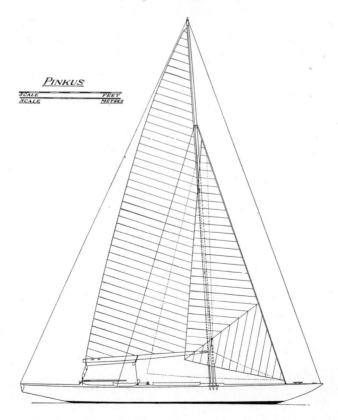

PINKUS

SCALE ———————— FEET
SCALE ———————— METRES

The construction plan shows an unusual form of construction, for the horn timber of *Pinkus* carries on forward of the sternpost and scarphs into the fore gripe, so forming the mast step and the backer for the keel bolts, which run the entire depth of the fin keel, and turn this fin keel, which might otherwise be very weak, into a very strong and sound part of the hull. When we look at the older fin keel boats, the fins and their attachment to the hull are generally a source of weakness, and the designers by adopting this unusual method have undoubtedly produced a strong hull.

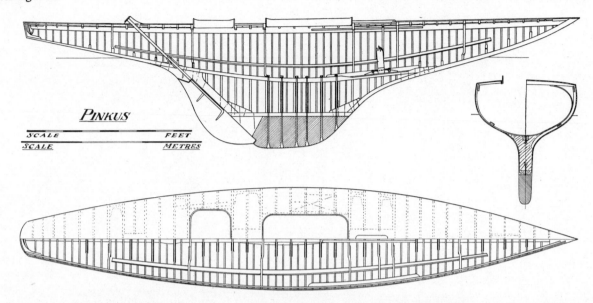

Pinkus is arranged with two cockpits, one for the helmsman and the other for her crew, and her sail plan with the mainsail and the jib going to the maximum height allowed by the rule is most efficient.

PINKUS LEADS TWO OF HER CLASS ROUND THE MARK

A copy of her rating certificate will perhaps explain the working of the rule far better than a page of words, and it seems a pity that this class, starting with five boats, did not develop and grow, for it produces interesting and sporting little boats.

ROYAL CORINTHIAN YACHT CLUB — 5 METRE CLASS

CERTIFICATE OF MEASUREMENT

Name of Yacht, "PINKUS"   *Owner,* J. S. BACON   *Designer,* J. LAURENT GILES   *Builder,* VOSPER & CO. LTD.

RATING FORMULA $\cdot 1 \times \dfrac{L \times \text{SQ. ROOT } S}{\text{CUBE ROOT } D} + \cdot 25\,(L + \text{SQ. ROOT } S) = R = 16 \cdot 4$ FT.

LENGTH OVERALL - - - - -	30·02
OVERHANG FORD. TO L.W.L. - - - 5·60	
OVERHANG AFT TO L.W.L. - - - 5·58	
SUBTRACT TOTAL OVERHANGS - - -	11·18
LENGTH ON L.W.L. - - -	18·84

MAXIMUM BEAM ON L.W.L. - - - 5·00	
¼ ,, ,, ,, ,, - - - 1·25	
1/10 ,, ,, ,, ,, - - - ·50	

D I FT. = + ·22   F = 1·75 = 1·52

QUARTER BEAM LENGTH - -   17·32

LENGTH FOR FORMULA

·5(L.W.L. 18·84 + Q.B.L. 17·32) - -	= 18·08
·005(L.W.L. 18·84 × √L.W.L. 4·34) - -	= ·40
L - - - - - - -	= 18·48

DISPLACEMENT 3490 LBS. ÷ 64   = 54·53 cu. ft.

$^3\sqrt{D}$ - - - - - - - = 3·79

SAIL AREA = 255·78 SQ. FEET - - √S = 15·99

RATING

L 18·48 × √S 15·99 = 295·49	
DIVIDE BY $^3\sqrt{D}$ 3·79 = 77·96	
MULTIPLY BY ·1 - - -	= 7·79
L 18·48 + √S 15·99 = 34·47	
MULTIPLY BY ·25 - - -	= 8·61
SUM OF PENALTIES - - -	= —
RATING - - - -	= 16·40

SAIL PLAN

MAINSAIL

LUFF—TOP OF BOOM TO BLACK BAND = A - - 30·75	
BOOM—BACK OF MAST TO BLACK BAND -11·94	
ADD DIFFERENCE BETWEEN AXES OF	
MAST SECTION - - - - ·06	
TOTAL FOR BOOM = B - - -12·00	
MAXIMUM HEIGHT OF SAIL PLAN ABOVE DECK PER	
RULE - - - - - - 34·00	
ACTUAL - - - - - - 34·00	

FORE TRIANGLE

MAXIMUM HEIGHT PER RULE - - - 25·00	
,, ,, ACTUAL = I - - - 25·00	
FORE SIDE OF MAST TO CUT OF FORESTAY ON DECK 6·71	
SPINNAKER BOOM - - - - - 6·70	
BASE = J - - - - - - 6·71	

SAIL AREAS

I × J 25·00 × 6·71 = 167·75 ÷ 2 = 83·87 × 85% 71·28	
A × B 30·75 × 12·00 = 369·00 ÷ 2 - - = 184·50	
TOTAL Y.R.A. = 255·78	

MINIMUM WEIGHT OF MAST WITH FIXED FITTINGS	
PER RULE - - - - - - 60 lb.	
ACTUAL - - - - - - - 70 lb.	
CENTRE OF GRAVITY ABOVE DECK PER RULE - 12·92	
ACTUAL - - - - - - 19·34	

LIMITS AND PENALTIES

FREEBOARD MINIMUM AT MAX. L.W.L. PER RULE	
·27 × $^3\sqrt{D}$ 1·02 + ·6 FT. - - 1·62	
DITTO ACTUAL - - - - - 1·75	
PENALTY FOR DEFICIENCY, IF ANY = — × 2 = —	
DRAUGHT MAX. PER RULE = 16% × L.W.L. 3·01 + 1·75 4·76	
,, ,, ACTUAL - - - - 4·75	
PENALTY FOR EXCESS IF ANY = — × 3 - = —	
TUMBLE HOME PER RULE = BEAM EXT. 5·50 × 2% = ·11	
,, ,, ACTUAL - - - - = ·07	
WEIGHT OF INSIDE BALLAST - - - —	
POSITION - - - - - —	

MEASURED BY   DATE   DATE OF EXPIRATION   SIGNATURE SECRETARY, R.C.Y.C.

· 37 ·

30 SQUARE METRES

Length, overall -	43 ft. 6 in. = 13·25 m.		Length, water-line -	28 ft. 6 in. = 8·68 m.	
Beam -	7 ft. 2 in. = 2·18 m.		Draught -	4 ft. 11 in. = 1·50 m.	
Displacement -	2·75 tons = 2794 kilos.		Sail Area -	323 sq. ft. = 30 sq. m.	

Owner, GEO. WANSBROUGH   *Designer*, KNUD H. REIMERS   *Builder*, UFFA FOX

AFTER a great deal of thought and hesitation the 30-square metre class has at last started in British waters, for one Sunday late in the summer of 1937, George Wansbrough, as the first passenger of a new air line, flew from London to the Isle of Wight, and as he was the first and only one it was agreed that the plane should fly over a certain field in Cowes, and if he signalled take him back to London. And that is exactly what happened. George hailing his aeroplane reminded me very much of the same chap hailing a taxi in London, and so this day saw the start of the 30-square metres in British waters.

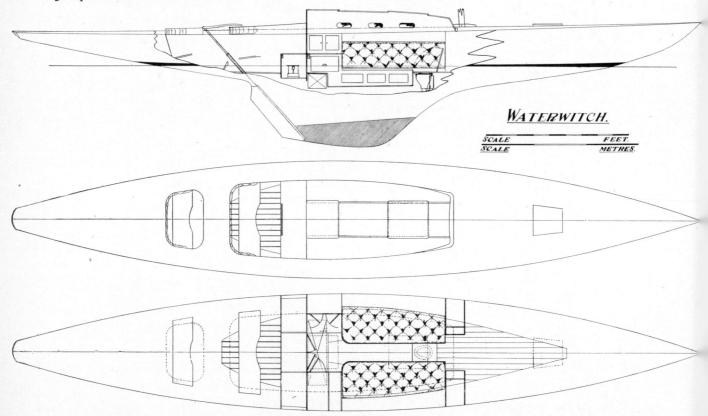

WATERWITCH.

SCALE   FEET.
SCALE   METRES.

I have always been a believer in the Skerry Cruiser classes, for their rules produce a fast type of craft that gives a great deal of pleasure to those sailing it, and also at the same time they produce a very sturdy little vessel, one that is both strong and seaworthy as the lines and construction plan of *Waterwitch* clearly show. So seaworthy are these little boats that the water-line length 28 ft. 6 in. was chosen, as it would enable them to take part in the races across channel under the Royal Ocean Racing Club's rules to such ports as St. Malo and Oistrehem, etc., and it is probable that these little vessels will do a great deal of this type of racing.

The hull rates very badly by the rule, but as the sail area to drive it is so small it levels things up, and the Royal Ocean Racing Club rule seems so well balanced that these craft, though not being designed at all to this rule, will nevertheless rate fairly under it, so that their chance of success is no greater or less than the more normal type of vessel.

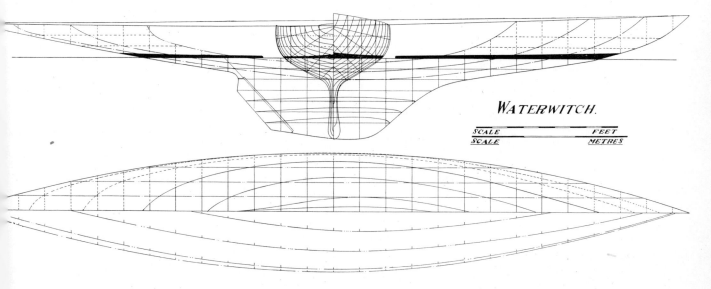

WATERWITCH.

The lines are those of a normal 30-square metre, long and easily driven, while her keel is kept down to the minimum length allowed by the rule. The sail plan is to the maximum height allowed, for while a few years ago we were

THE TWO "THIRTIES" CLOSE HAULED—

AND RUNNING GIVE US A GOOD PICTURE OF THE CLASS

allowed to increase the height of sail plan as long as punishments were taken, it was decided to put the limit at 12·70 metres and therefore we have a proportion of three and half times the main boom for the luff of the sail, which gives a very efficient shaped sail for windward work.

Once it was known that a 30-square metre had been ordered for racing on the Solent, several people who had wanted one now decided to build to the class, and while some were ordered in England others were put in hand in Sweden, so that soon there were half a dozen being built, enough to ensure the future of the class. The Skerry Cruisers with their liveliness and buoyant hulls are a type that appeal to many people, and it would seem now the class has been started in British waters it will prosper and grow. The following cables, though short, tell a great deal, namely, that two British 30-square metres will be racing in American waters at the end of next summer, and it is hoped that some Scandinavian "thirties" will be going across too, and that these will race at Cowes during The Week on their way out to America.

WATERWITCH TIMBERED OUT READY FOR DIAGONALS AND PLANKING

THIS SHOWS HER LONG RUN

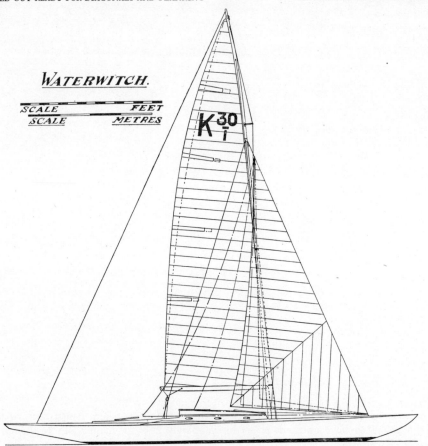

Sent October 5, 1937.

COMMODORE, Beverly Yacht Club, 53 State St., Boston, Mass.

Can you please accept challenge for Team Races next summer in 30-square metres. Suggest five races between August 15 and 27. Two boat teams to represent each country. UFFA FOX, Cowes, England.

Received October 7, 1937.

Splendid idea, delighted to accept challenge Team Races as suggested. Await with interest further details by mail. ROBERT W. CUMMING, Beverly Yacht Club.

Received October 8, 1937.

Reference your cable to Beverly Yacht Club. Do you agree that boats be designed and built in country they represent. Wire reply. PAUL DUDLEY DEAN, 30-Square metre Association, 1 Federal Street, Boston, Mass.

THE FIRST NINE DIAGONALS ON WATERWITCH SHOW HOW THEY TIE HER DEEP AND SLENDER KEEL

Sent October 10, 1937.

PAUL DUDLEY DEAN, 30-Square metre Association, 1 Federal St., Boston, Mass.

We suggest boats be built in country they represent, but may be designed anywhere in the world, as Holland, Denmark, etc., have at present no racing boat designers but many capable builders. UFFA FOX.

Sent October 10, 1937.

COMMODORE, Beverly Yacht Club, 53 State St., Boston, Mass.

Please accept challenge for Team races in 30-square metres from Island Sailing Club, Cowes, two boats to represent each country. Series of five races between August 15 and 27. This enables us to race Cowes Week. We hope Swedish, German, etc., will race at Cowes on their way to America. UFFA FOX.

· 38 ·

22 SQUARE METRES

AEOLUS YACHT CLUB'S "B" CLASS SKERRY CRUISER

Length, overall -	36 ft. 2¼ in. = 11·03 m.	Length, water-line	21 ft. 8 in. = 6·60 m.
Beam - -	6 ft. 8 in. = 2·03 m.	Draught - -	4 ft. 3½ in. = 1·30 m.
Displacement -	1·85 tons = 1879 kilos.	Sail Area - -	236 sq. ft. = 22 sq. m.

Owner, AEOLUS YACHT CLUB   *Designer*, BERTIL BOTHEN

THOSE of us who have met the Aeolus Club at Gothenburg have at once been impressed by their vigour and hospitality. This vigour is shown in their fostering the "B" class 22-square metres, and also in their efforts to develop the Ljungstrom rig. The plans of their 22-square metres for this year illustrate the good work done by this club.

All classes develop towards the longer hull until the final limit by the rule is reached. The "J" class in a very few years has grown to the maximum length of 87 ft. allowed, and no one would dream of building an International 14-footer that was shorter than the 14 ft. maximum. This same striving for length has caused the Baltic-class designers to produce very long boats, and the "B" class rule for the 22-square metres is an effort to check this length, and also to keep the cost of the racers down.

The rule is exactly as the International square metre rule but with heavier penalties for length, thus holding the latter in check. The rule in addition, forces builders to use only Swedish-grown timber, and Swedish sails, and iron must be used instead of lead for the keel, all of which keeps the cost of these "B" class 22-square metres low. These plans show the "B" class 22-square metre built as a lottery boat by the Aeolus Club for 1937.

In the lines plan we see the long, sweet, and easily driven hull produced by the rules. I have put in the points from which measurements are taken to control the design, and we see that the length used in sailing is the one that governs the design, and a designer increasing this length beyond the ideal given in the rule, namely, 7·30 metres, is penalised by having greater beam and displacement thrust upon him, all of which has to be driven by the same sail area, 22 square metres. The rule, in fact, undoubtedly tends towards a more roomy craft.

The following notes, very kindly written for me by Bertil Bothen, the designer of this vessel, give us an exact idea of just how the rule works, and he ends up by saying that even with these heavier penalties the "B" class boat has gone beyond the ideal length which the framers of the rule imagined to be the limit these boats would ever reach. But a designer needs a great deal of stopping when it comes to length ; the only thing that really stops him is a fixed limit such as I suggested in my first book, when I was talking, of course, of the I.Y.R.U. rule for 12, 8 and 6-metres (*Sailing, Seamanship and Yacht Construction*, p. 189).

Explanatory Note by the Designer Bertil Bothen

" (In the following notes the ordinary 'square metre' Skerry Cruisers are referred to as A-boats, while the Aeolus "B" class Skerry Cruisers are called B-boats.)

The B 22-square metre boats are built in accordance with all the stipulations governing the 22-square metre class of the Skerry Cruiser rule, but certain restrictive regulations have been added with a view to preventing extreme designs in order to keep the price down.

The B-boats must be built of home-grown wood and home materials. They must have iron keels, canvas-covered decks, solid spars. Nor are bent masts allowed. The 'ideal in length' has been reduced from 7·80 metres for the A-boats to 7·30 metres for the B-boats, and the minimum freeboard has been increased from 400 mm. (A-boats) to 460 mm. (B-boats). The height of the sail plan is maximum 10·50 metres as against 11·15 metres for the A-boats. Sails must be made in Sweden and must not number more than five, *i.e.* mainsail, working jib, storm jib, genoa and spinnaker.

As regards maximum height of sail measurement, it should be noted that in the A-boats this is measured from deck level, while in the B-boats it is measured from the designed load water-line.

The height of the fore triangle is two-thirds of the maximum height of the sail plan, that is, the proportion is the same as for the A-boats.

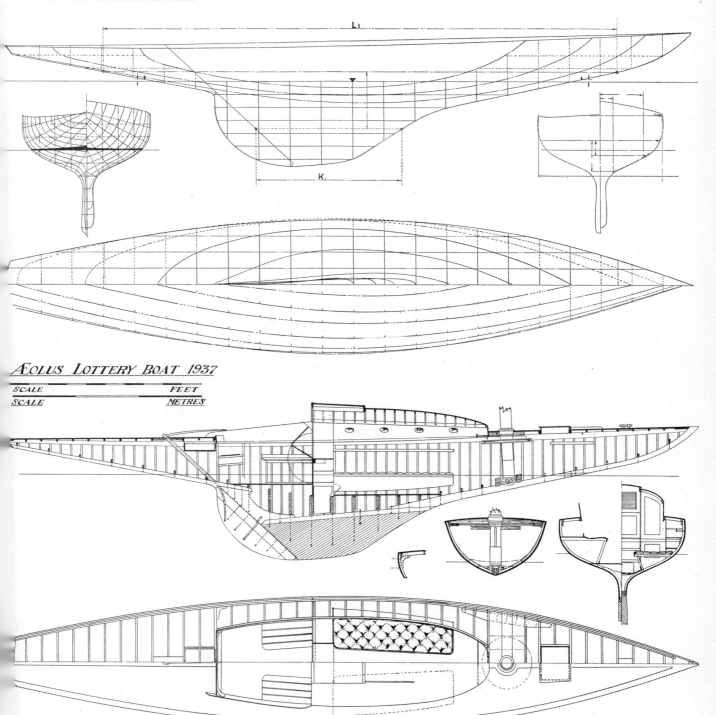

ÆOLUS LOTTERY BOAT 1937

SCALE ———————— FEET

SCALE ———————— METRES

Minimum displacement on 'ideal length' is the same as for the A-boats, but as the 'ideal length' is shorter for the B-boats, their displacement is proportionately greater. It is only when going beyond the 'ideal length' that the more severe penalties for extreme designs show their influence on the hull of the B-boats as compared to that of the A-boats.

Any increase of the length beyond that termed the 'ideal length' (7·30 metres) must be compensated by :

(1) An increase of displacement to at least 25L² (L is the actual measured length). Displacement of the A-boat need only be increased to 21·50L².

(2) An increase for the mean beam by 0·20(L × − 7·30), that is, twice the increase necessary for the A-boat, which is 0·10(L × − 7·80).

(3) An increase of freeboard after the same formula as that governing the A-boat. But as this increase is applied, in the case of the B-boat, for a length that is 0·50 metre shorter than in the case of the A-boat the freeboard of the B-boat is always kept higher.

(4) An increase of the keel length to at least 0·275L as against 0·2305 for the A-boat.

In common with the A-boat, the B-boat has long ago gone beyond the 'ideal length' but her development has of necessity occurred along more healthy lines."

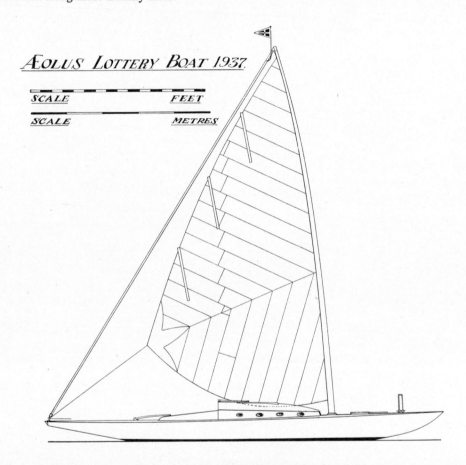

ÆOLUS LOTTERY BOAT 1937.

SCALE   FEET

SCALE   METRES

The accommodation and construction plan shows that, while cheaper materials are used, the very fact that an iron keel has to be deeper for the same weight than a lead one straightens out the fore gripe so that it is easily obtained from a straight piece of wood, whereas this same member in an " A " class Skerry Cruiser has a great curve in its after end where it meets the main keel ; so we see that these rules make for even cheaper hulls than at first thought. These plans show the Ljungstrom rig coming down through the deck forward of the cabin top, this making for a roomier and pleasanter cabin. This arrangement, however, because it is further forward and away from the iron keel, which is fighting to keep the vessel upright while all the mast's energies are directed to laying her on her beam ends, causes far greater twisting strains to be set up than in the ordinary rig, though these are somewhat cancelled out by the fact that having no shrouds, forestays, etc., there can be no heavy downward thrust on the keel such as found in the ordinary type of masting and rigging. For this reason the longer mast step, which designers are always forced to fit to counteract these strains, is missing.

In the section at the mast we see the huge roller close up under the deck beam round which a rope is rove and which revolves or spins the mast round to reef the sail, while the sail plan shows the Ljungstrom rig as fitted to this year's Aeolus Yacht Club's 22-square metre Skerry Cruiser.

The battens, it will be seen, are plumb, and they have to be as otherwise they would not roll round the mast as the sail was rolled up.

A great friend of mine, Ture Rinman, wrote to me about this rig, and I do not think I could do better than to quote his letter. (If we are amazed at the perfect English used by Ture, it must be remembered that he lived in England for some time, where he was always known as " Pure " Rinman.

" Goteborg.   3/3/37.

Dear Uffa,

Dag Lindstrand showed me your letter, and he is now having the designer (Mr. Bertil Bothen) draw plans for you. They will be sent in a day or two. The rig, of course, is not designed by him but by Mr. Frederick Ljungstrom, who has patented it. He, by the way, is the father of the Ljungstrom turbine business (big thing) and a whale on aerodynamics and scientific sailing and such like.

Dag said you had asked him to give you his ideas on the rig. He will do so, and no doubt it will be quite correct. But the fact is that most members of the Club committee are very very anxious to further this rig, which is

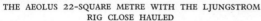

THE AEOLUS 22-SQUARE METRE WITH THE LJUNGSTROM RIG CLOSE HAULED

THE LJUNGSTROM-RIGGED 22-SQUARE METRE ("B" CLASS) RUNNING BEFORE AN 18 MILE AN HOUR BREEZE IN SMOOTH WATER

quite right of them. But it may be that their enthusiasm should also be taken into consideration. I think Dag and I will say the same about the rig and its performance—but if we both say it in our different ways, it may help you to get a better idea.

I have followed the L-rigged boats closely, and all the races, and this is what they have, so far, taught me :

On the whole the L-rig shows up best when beating to windward and running before the wind, when the two sails open up, so that she gets twice the sail area. Her weak point is reaching. When beating, the mast is spun so that the slit for the sail points forward, or almost forward. The sail then leaves the mast in a curve to leeward, which is quite unbroken and aerodynamically ideal. When tacking, the mast must be spun round to cause the same effect on the other tack.

As to different strengths of wind : a fresh or strong wind is best, light winds not so good. When racing against other 22-square metres of the ' B ' class with traditional Marconi rigs, the L-rigged boats have proved absolutely superior in fresh winds, and in light winds comparable to the better of the other boats (beaten by one or two of the class but leaving the rest behind).

In a fresh wind, too, the L-boats point rather higher in the wind than the others ; in light airs there is no appreciable difference.

The strongest point for the L-boats when racing :

They can absolutely moderate their sail area according to the changes in the wind and points of sailing. In light airs ordinarily rigged boats have an advantage, for they carry the genoa jibs, which gives them about 36 square metres of sail (while rating as 22 square metres). Then, the L-rigged yachts have, of course, only their rated area. When running dead before the wind the L-boats get larger sails than the others, but then, it is generally a short distance you can run dead before it in a race.

In strong or fresh winds, on the other hand, the favour is all for the L-rigged boats. The others start with one or two or more reefs and a small jib, and the L-boats also roll a few turns in their masts. For beating, the sail favours are, then, even. But beating is the strong point of the L-boats, so they are generally a good way ahead at the first mark. Then, when rounding for the reach, they let out all or as much as they like of their sails, and it takes no time at all. Just a pull at the rope that spins the mast and a trimming of the sheet. The other boats generally do not shake out reefs for the reach, as it delays, and also there may be another beat ahead. So, the L-rigged boats, when reaching (their weak point) have the advantage of sails exactly large enough for reaching, while the others have too small sails. The same applies to running—only in an even more marked degree. And if there should be another beat to windward afterwards the reefs are taken in quicker than you can describe it in the L-boats, whereas the others, if they have shaken out reefs, must either be delayed reefing again or carry too large sails.

Also in squally weather you can moderate all the time so that you have exactly the right amount of sail whatever it is blowing.

For passage or ordinary pleasure sailing, it is perhaps the most safe rig in existence for you can never be surprised by a rise in the wind so sudden that there is not time for spinning the mast a few times and so shortening sail. Further it is almost ridiculously handy in a congested yacht harbour. Just like a motor boat. You shorten sail as you like and moderate all the time while creeping into your berth.

Further points. You eliminate the wind resistance in stays and spreaders. Also, with a stayed mast safety lies in proper staying. If stays stretch without your noticing it, you may be in for it in hard weather. But with an L-mast there is nothing to stretch; if the mast is made right it stands whether you look after it or not.

And surprisingly, it does stand. I have gybed in one of these boats when she was carrying far too much sail (it was done in order to demonstrate) and there didn't seem to be any dashed strain on the mast at all! Never have I experienced so 'soft' gybes as in these boats.

Adverse people say : ' My gosh, what an awful thing! Are we to start sailing with ball bearings and oil cans?'

I think that is damned silly, for the rig is undoubtedly a development and may perhaps lead to something revolutionary—and yet it will be many years before I have one in my boat. Why? Well, I like the sight of an ordinary rig too much, and the work with it and the inefficiency of it and all its dear old faults, and I won't be without them.

Faults I have found (or think I have found) :

The mast must be stepped so far forward that there is an unhealthy distance between the lead keel (which must be lifted when the boat heels) and the mast (which must do the lifting or the twisting). Also when beating against a head sea my impression is that these boats get rather heavy by the head from having the mast so far forward. I therefore think it is necessary that another type of hull is developed for these rigs. It does not matter so much with these small light 22-square metres, but when you come to bigger boats that seems called for.

Well, that's that. As regards the 22-square metres ' B ' class, they were introduced in 1929, and the first one to have an L-rig was last summer. They are good, seaworthy little boats, with a fine turn of speed and they are very cheap for you can build them for about two-thirds of the cost of an A1 Skerry Cruiser and that includes fee to the designer, sails and everything. They are lively and nice to race in.

Bertil Bothen, who is the designer of the club boat being built for balloting this summer (and also last year's club boat), will give you details of the restricted regulations introduced into the ordinary square metre rule in order to produce the ' B ' class boats.

Well Uffa, I am afraid I have bothered you with this long letter. Only you see I thought that you might like to have two opinions on their performances. Dag's and mine will probably tally fairly well, but he may be slightly more enthusiastic.

It boils down to this, they are superior to the old rig in fresh and strong winds (the stronger the more so)— quite strikingly superior. But in light winds they are just about the same as the old—or perhaps very slightly inferior. That, however, changes so much according to different races. With a long reach you notice the inferiority better. With much beating to windward they keep their places among the best of the others.

With many regards (and I shall never forgive you if you don't inform me in good time before you come next time so that I can arrange to take a few days off and go sailing with you). Should there ever be anything I can assist you with you must let me know.

Your friend,

TURE.

The boy Jan and the wife Zoe send their best wishes and are longing to see you again."

A paragraph from another letter of " Pure's " will throw even more light on the rig.

" Regarding the unstayed mast, it may interest you to hear that at one of the last races this season, we met with very heavy winds. It was a 25 miles' course along the coast and it blew even at the start. The wind increased, and for the last six or seven miles, the wind was blowing forty miles an hour—this figure emanates from a lighthouse on the course, where the force of the wind was measured at the time. There was a lot of reefing and a lot of bailing out water among the smaller boats in the fleet. The Ljungstrom rigged B 22-metres, of course, had no trouble at all. They just sat in the cockpit and spun the mast another turn or two, as the wind rose. Their masts, also, never gave the slightest reason for anxiety, although when reaching broadly at the end, and finally, running, they gave the boats all the sail they could carry. Never a sign of swaying about the masts, and none of the jerks felt in the other rigs when lurching in the seas or gybing.

THE NORMAL RIG OF A 22-SQUARE METRE

" Now there is another small disadvantage, and that is that as the mast is given half a turn every tack so that the sail comes from it on the lee side and takes up air foil shape, the same thing should happen in a strong breeze, so that when head to wind in tacking the sail really should be unrolled and rolled up the other way, so that it comes away from the mast sweetly to leeward, but I do not imagine anyone would be fussy enough to want to do this when the wind and sea were so great."

We must keep before us the fact that almost all of these races are held behind the Skerries, where though the sea is rough in places it is generally speaking, sheltered water, and just how this rig would behave on a coast exposed to the open Atlantic has yet to be found out. But unless we consider and study all these things from all angles there can be no progress, and in the meantime the racing craft, by developing and perfecting this rig, are doing, as they always do, the greatest service to their cruising brethren ; and when finally this rig (if it ever is) is adopted by the cruisers, all its faults as well as all its virtues will be proved and known, and so the Aeolus Yacht Club with its " B " class Ljungstrom rigged 22-square metres gives us a great deal of food for thought.

★   ★   ★   ★   ★

ROYAL SWEDISH YACHT CLUB'S BALLOT BOAT, 1935

Length, overall -   39 ft. 2½ in. = 11·95 m.   Length, water-line -   26 ft. 3 in. = 8·00 m.
Beam   -   -   6 ft. 7 in. = 2 m.   Draught   -   -   4 ft. 4 in. = 1·32 m.
Displacement   -   2 tons   = 2030 kilos.   Sail Area   -   -   236 sq. ft. = 22 sq. m.

Designer, HARRY BECKER

HARRY BECKER designed this 22-square metre in 1935 to the International 22-square metre rule, and though she is not the longest of his designs to this rule, she forms a very good contrast to the previous boat to the Aeolus " B " class rule and illustrates the difference in these two rules.

KSSS Lottery Boat 1935

We see that this vessel, while being 4 ft. longer on the water-line, has 8 in. less beam, as, while the International Skerry Cruiser rule calls for one per cent. increase in beam with increasing length, the " B " class rule calls for two per cent., which in its turn means that excess of length is held more in check by the " B " class rule.   Looking at this problem from a great distance it would seem that the Aeolus rule is a great improvement in measurement, and if only the rules specifying the materials were left free (for surely it is wrong to build of inferior materials) it might easily be a rule very acceptable for British waters, in other words that boats to the Aeolus " B " class measurement rules and to the International 22-square metre scantling rules would form a lovely little class for British or any other waters.

This design by Harry Becker was very fast in a breeze, for one day during the Jubilee races of the Royal Gothenburg Club in 1935, when it blew very hard indeed with a breaking sea, she outsailed all the International 6-metre class boats (there were 35 of them).   A photo of her chasing away for the finish line gives an idea of the wind and sea experienced that day, and when we think that in such weather such a lovely little hull was able to outsail thirty-five of the best 6-metres from all countries, we realise what manly little ships the Skerry Cruisers are, in spite or perhaps because of their delicate and lovely lines.

Though this design is here in contrast to the "B" class 22, she is only 9 in. longer on the water-line than *Vigilant*, the 22-square metre in which I sailed to Stockholm and back to Cowes in 1930, and I have yet to sail in a more

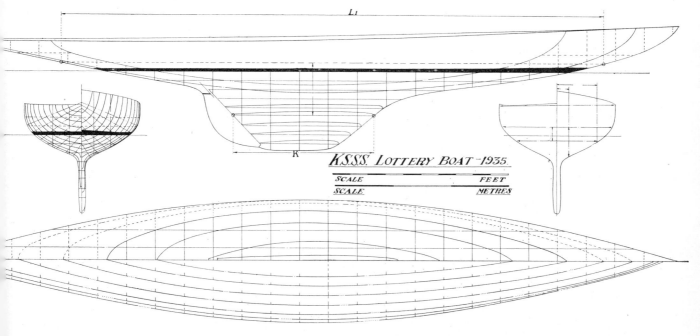

K.S.S.S. Lottery Boat -1935.

SCALE	FEET
SCALE	METRES

enjoyable racing craft than *Vigilant*, for she carried us safely through gales of wind that were recorded on shore and not by the three of us on board. In spite of this people still wonder if this type of vessel would be good in the Solent. The answer is, of course, that a vessel good in one stretch of water is sure to be good on another, and this is borne out by the fact that when the 6-metres raced this year in America, Sweden and Norway sent their best boats out,

PRETTY WORK. THE BECKER-DESIGNED 22-SQUARE METRE CHASING AWAY FOR THE FINISHING LINE AT MARSTRAND THE DAY SHE BEAT THIRTY-FIVE OF THE BEST INTERNATIONAL 6-METRES

and the racing between these and the Americans was so close that each won two races for the Gold Cup, America finally being the first country to get three firsts and so retained the Cup.

As one would expect, the lines of this 22-square metre are very easy and fair, the diagonals being particularly easy, and as I gaze at these lines and remember that I have sailed thousands of miles of open water in such a craft,

I find it difficult to realise that people cannot believe that such a vessel is so seaworthy as well as being such fun to sail.

As we study these lines we realise that they are the work of a great man, for Harry Becker is recognised as one of the best of Swedish designers to this 22-square metre rule, and these lines and the picture of this brave little ship tearing along in a breaking sea and a strong wind off Marstrand help prove this to be true and also bring home to us the fact that while the 22-square metre class produce delicate and lovely instruments with which to show our skill as helmsmen, they at the same time produce magnificent little sea boats, and so the class is suitable not only for smooth and sheltered waters but also for waters where strong winds and breaking seas are found.

· 39 ·

20 SQUARE METRES

RENJOLLE (FERRET)

Length, overall - 27 ft. 6 in. = 8·38 m.	Length, water-line - 24 ft. 6 in. = 7·46 m.	
Beam - - 5 ft. 10 in. = 1·80 m.	Draught - - 6 in. and 3 ft. 9 in. = 0·15 and 1·14 m.	
Displacement 1059 lb. = 480 kilos.	Sail Area - - 216 sq. ft. = 20 sq. m.	

Owner, R. G. W. & G. J. W. OLLERENSHAW   *Designer*, CARL MARTENS   *Builder*, JOSE VOGTENHUBER

THE 20-square metre *Renjolle* (*Ferret*), a native of the lakes of Central Europe, seems unusual to our eye used to the open sea and seaworthy hulls, for she is low and long with very little stability, due to the very narrow water-line (this 27 ft. racer has less W.L. beam than our national 12-footers) and because of this is very easily capsized.

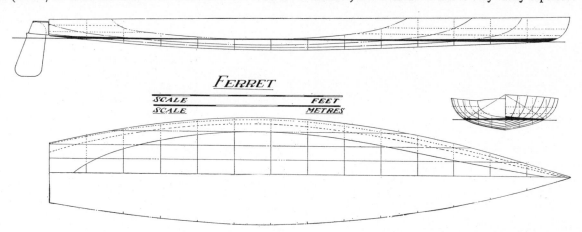

Above this hull we have 20 square metres of sail area set on very light spars, the sail being forced to take up its proper curve by battens going the full width of the sail, though very different from those used by the Chinese, for these are used to arch the sail. When once we get used to the idea of these 20 square metres we can start to admire them, because for their purpose, that of racing and sailing inland, it would be difficult to improve upon them.

In this country, on the Upper Thames, we have the one-raters, somewhat similar in their make up, but with very tall Bermudian masts, some of which are as long as 40 ft., practically double the height of this boat's sail plan. Other boats similar to these in British waters are the 200 square foot inland racers fostered by the Y.R.A. rules, which have taken the place of the old half-raters, and when we compare the 20-square metres with these we are able to judge how good the " twenties " are—better in many ways than either of their two British counterparts. Through Central Europe there are a great many sailing people, thousands of them sailing such vessels as these, and as all the clubs belong to the I.Y.R.U. it would seem that the I.Y.R.U. conference could very well bring out a rule for racing upon inland waters, one that would be acceptable not only to those on the lakes of Germany, Switzerland, Austria and such countries, but also to those racing on the Upper Thames and the Broads, the Trent, etc., in this country, and then without doubt the I.Y.R.U. would be doing a great service. I look forward to the time when such a class will be International, and races will be held on the lakes of Central Europe and on the inland waters of England, America, Canada, etc., for if only a good set of rules could be produced it would give such an impetus to the inland water sports that International Racing would soon flourish amongst the inland water clubs, whereas now countries with a seaboard take little interest in inland racing.

The lines all tell of light breezes and smooth water, for every effort has been made to produce a vessel that will glide along over the waters in the faintest of airs. All the fore and aft lines are very easy, the narrowness of the water-line being very noticeable, the rising floor and the weak sections confirming this.

FERRET SAILING THE LEEWARD LEG　　　　　　FERRET AMONG LOVELY SURROUNDINGS

From the arrangement plan we see that she is entirely decked excepting for the 9 ft. 3 in. × 3 ft. 3 in. cockpit amidships, as the low freeboard calls for a well-decked boat. It will be seen that the keel case runs well forward, and forms a stiff girder to take the thrust of the mast, and that the centre-board, as is usual with these boats, is the segment of a circle, with the rudder on the stern 9 ft. abaft the helmsman.

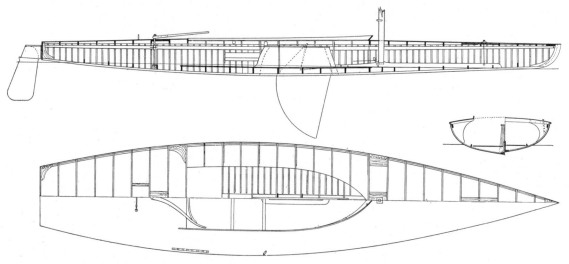

Yoke lines are needed, and these run under the deck and connect the tiller to the rudder, for a tiller would need to be 9 ft. in length and with this the helmsman would not be able to control his craft. Were the helmsman situated aft he would slow the boat up, for as we all know the more the weights are concentrated in the centre of any boat the livelier she is. But it is when we look at the sail plan that we see the most unusual features of this boat for we have a gunter lug mainsail, which is heavily arched by battens, all of which have to be inserted at exactly the right tension before she starts to sail; and generally when tacking the boom has to be given a flip in order to get them across and arch the sail the other way. One wonders if it would not be more seamanlike to give these vessels a bigger area and put restrictions on the number and length of battens, as one would then have a far more serviceable boat and one that would take far less time in preparing for a race and stowing up afterwards, for those battens right across the sail are most irritating to fit before a race and take out afterwards. When we come to the headsail we see that it is quite normal except for the fact that often a spar is used on the luff, though it is quite possible that the weight of this spar counteracts any good that it does. I was forced into using such a spar when I challenged for and won the Canoe Championship of America, and was quite delighted when I got back to British waters and could once more sail without it.

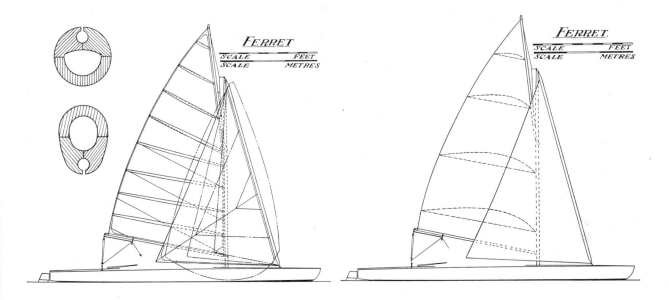

FITTING IN THE BATTENS BEFORE THE START OF THE
INTERNATIONAL RACES

THE DAY BRITAIN (IN 278) WON. NOTE BATTENS STARTING
ON ONE SIDE OF THE MAST AND FINISHING ON THE OTHER

The sail plan gives an idea of the heavy camber or the fulness thrown into the mainsail, and also the enormous round put on the leech of this sail, all of which is only made possible by the full length battens, and as one who would like to see boats of this type built to an I.Y.R.U. rule, so that they would flourish in England, and America as well as in Central Europe, I would very much like to see the battens ruled out, and extra sail area given instead. The boats would then be every bit as efficient on these lakes, but would be far more acceptable to nations unused to the battens as the mainsail would then become a seamanlike job, which could be easily reefed during a race.

Seven different countries raced in Austria in boats of this type this summer and finished in the following order :

(1) Switzerland,
(2) Italy,
(3) Hungary,
(4) Austria,
(5) Britain,
(6) Germany,
(7) France.

Our team were not only quite new to this type of boat, they had never before raced under conditions found on the lakes of Central Europe and so Britain finished fifth in the series. But these races did a great deal for us in Eng-

466 IS GYBING AND HER WHOLE CREW HAVE TO SHAKE THE MAIN-SAIL TO GET THE BATTENS TO FLIP OVER. THIS PICTURE ALSO SHOWS THE STREAKS OF WIND ON OTHERWISE GLASSY WATER

A DECENT BREEZE. THIS SHOWS THE ENORMOUS FULLNESS OF 278'S MAINSAIL

land as they brought this type of craft more forcibly to our notice, and also we had met the racers of Central Europe, and this year's racing may have far-reaching results for it may mean that boats of this type will be adopted and developed for our inland waters. If this does happen it will mean that when our team goes to Europe next time they will only be handicapped by the local conditions as they will have learnt to sail this type of craft, *Ferret's* plans therefore open up a gateway into a new field for a great many of us, and it is highly probable that many of us will roam in this new field, and get a great deal of pleasure in so doing.

INTERNATIONAL 14 FOOTERS

THUNDER

Length, overall -	14 ft. 0 in. = 4·26 m.		Length, water-line -	13 ft. 9 in. = 4·19 m.
Beam - -	4 ft. 8¼ in. = 1·42 m.		Draught -	8 in. and 5 ft. 2 in.
				0·20 m. and 1·57 m.
Displacement -	- 800 lb. = 362 kilos.		Sail Area -	125 sq. ft. = 11·61 sq. m.

Owner, PETER SCOTT   *Designer*, UFFA FOX   *Builder*, UFFA FOX

ONE of the most difficult things in this world is to convince people making rules for different classes that weight is bad. On all sides rule makers think that heavy weight is the cure for all ills in yacht design and proportion, and this in spite of the fact that one can never pick up a newspaper without seeing an advertisement on the best method to reduce our own weight. I have always argued that the only place where weight is of any use is in a steam roller, and have very seldom been listened to. I think the reason is that when there were no rules requiring a minimum displacement, boats were undoubtedly built too light, and though they gave wonderful sport they did not last long, and so made the game of yacht racing expensive. At the same time long low overhangs also came into being, and these very light and weak hulls with their overhangs left behind them the impression that overhangs were bad and lightness too was bad, and that the only thing makers of rules had to do to ensure good vessels was to continually increase the weight and discourage overhangs, the result being that this form of religion has taken a very firm hold.

Latterly it has been proved beyond doubt that moderate overhangs, because they increase the ability of a vessel in a seaway by increasing her fore and aft stability, are good ; and we are slowly learning that weight in itself is very bad, as it tends to make the craft into half-tide rocks, that are dead and lifeless to sail, and very wet in a seaway. We have instances of this in the small-metre classes, the "sixes" and "eights", for in the 6-metres 80 per cent. of the displacement is in the ballasted lead keel, which shows the result of people pinning their faith to heavy weights in rule formulae.

Ten years ago I built the 14-footer *Avenger*, and her planking was $\frac{5}{32}$ in. full in total thickness. In her we won 57 prizes in 57 starts, and I sailed her across the Channel to Havre to take part in the regatta there in 1928, and then sailed back again to Cowes. And this year, ten years after she was built, I sailed her at Lowestoft, as the winds there were too light for her owner who weighs 23 stone, and she is in even better condition to-day than she was when new. Here is conclusive proof that she was quite strong enough ; and yet in the past ten years the weight of 14-footers has been increased so much that last year we were using double the thickness of planking ($\frac{5}{16}$ in. full) all because the rule makers had increased the hull weights so much through these years. The result was that we were getting to a boat that seldom planed, and the dinghies that plane are lovely boats to sail as they are flat floored which gives initial stability, and they are very lively little chaps.

It was all very well to go on with this type of boat when we were racing amongst ourselves (the heavy flat-floored boat, that should, but seldom could, plane because of the weight in her), but last year the Canadians were sending over a team of boats, which I knew would be of the planing type such as I had developed, and which have the same spars and rig, but as they would be lighter they would plane away from our craft on the days in which we had breezes in which to plane. Because our increased weight had made planing a rare occurrence I designed a sharp-floored boat that would not plane but would, however, knife her way along to windward where she would be very fast and would also run well, but which would never plane or reach at all fast in a breeze, and then hoped that these contests would show a great deal of windward and running work and very little reaching in planing speeds. So the weight in the rule had forced me to go to an undesirable type. The midship section of *Daybreak*, Peter Scott's last year's 14-footer, shows this type of craft, and we can see from it that she is very tender and tiply, but very easily driven fast to windward and running, and slow in reaching ; and as the contest against the Canadians was held in a wind so light that they had no advantage at all from their lighter hulls, *Daybreak* had a second and two firsts in the five races against them.

Once the Dinghy Committee had seen where the excessive weight rule was taking them, they very wisely eased it, and once more the planing type of dinghy is being built, for as well as easing the weight rule, which would allow boats to plane, an additional rule was made governing the rise of floor. So while these dinghies might still, with advantage be 25 lb. lighter, the altered rules have made for far better boats in the class ; and as there are only five

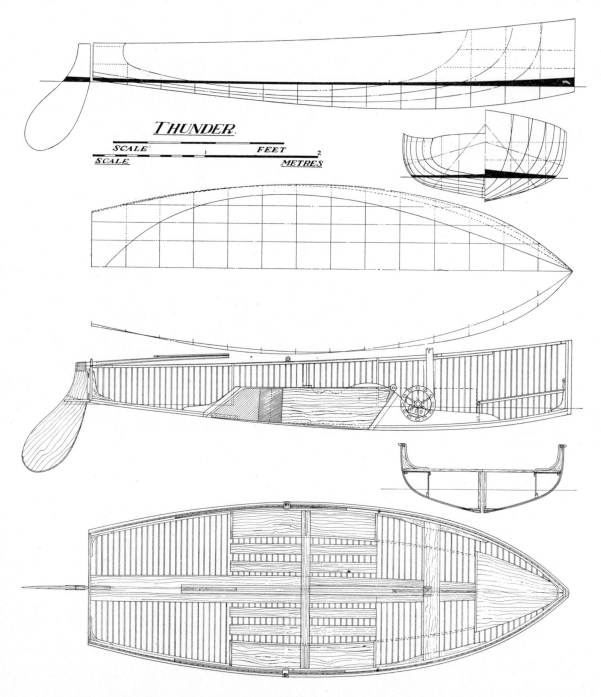

THUNDER.

SCALE   FEET   2
SCALE   METRES

of these steep-floored dinghies little harm has been done and a great deal of good by the building of them, for while they are faster to windward (two of the five were in last year's first six of the Prince of Wales' Cup and another two in the first six this year), there need only be a good reach on the course and the planing type will scuttle away from them. Therefore, we look at *Daybreak* as an undesirable type of dinghy brought about by the heavy-weight rule. Then we can look at *Thunder's* lines, the winner of this year's Prince of Wales' Cup, and rejoice that once again the planing type of dinghy has come into its own and will prosper. One only hopes that having gone through various stages from light to heavy and now back to a fairly light hull, the 14-foot rule will remain stable and produce such brave little boats from now on. It too often happens that though a rule is altered to produce a certain development, all it does is to produce the opposite, for while designers give advice at the meetings where rules are made, their advice is not always acted upon ; and as, in spite of being designers, they are human and liable to make mistakes, no doubt it is sometimes better " to bear the ills we have than fly to others that we know not of ".

The lines of *Thunder*, therefore, are those of the planing type of dinghy, which has its greatest depth forward and the long clean flat buttocks and run needed for planing.

She is built of two skins, the inner diagonal of $\frac{1}{16}$ in. and the outer fore and aft of $\frac{3}{16}$ in., making a total thickness of $\frac{1}{4}$ in., which is fastened to closely spaced Canadian rock elm timbers $\frac{1}{4}$ in. $\times \frac{3}{16}$ in. From the plans we see that her keel case is very long and forms a girder down through her centre, for as well as the strains of sailing, these little dinghies are often hoisted out of the sea full of water. Then too, they are put on trailers and travel the length and breadth of the British Isles, which greatly adds to their popularity, for fleets of them are found all round the coasts and inland also : one can race on the Upper Thames at Bourne End, the Tideway at Putney, or at Southend still further down the Thames, or off almost any part of our coasts, while the class is also raced by the Barnt Green and Midland Sailing Clubs in the Midlands. So we meet Birmingham 14-footers at Torquay and south coast dinghies in North Norfolk waters.

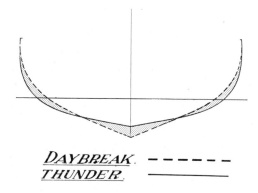

DAYBREAK. - - - - - -
THUNDER. ————————

We have usually fitted a tank, as marked solid in the plans, in the bow of the dinghies. This has the advantage of stopping water from running right into the bow, as one is coasting down a sea, but the disadvantage is that its weight is against the bow being light and buoyant. Peter accordingly did without it, but instead continued his side tanks forward as shown by the heavily dotted lines, thus concentrating his weight nearer amidships.

Usually we step the mast at the gunwale height, as this takes a little weight off the mast and helps the hull weight slightly, for the strut supporting the thwart is weighed in with the hull ; but as will be seen from the plan *Thunder's* mast went down through to the top of the keel case.

It will be noticed that the drop keel arrangement is different from before, the drop keel being hung on a bolt with rollers which run over the top of the keel case, so that the drop keel is always supported by the bolt and rollers, and even if a wire carried away no harm would be done, as the plate could not drop out through. It is an old idea of Theo. Smith, the wonderful builder of canoe yawls, and we have used it for some years on our canoes as it has so much to recommend it, such as the ease with which the plate can be lifted straight up through or shipped down through the keel slot. It will be noticed that these drop keels are ballasted, for at the same time that the hull weight was reduced the Y.R.A. rules allowed ballasted plates, which is a great advantage to the owners, for a 60 lb. ballasted plate has the same righting efficiency as one practically double its weight of uniform material, and our successful dinghies this year were sailing with 60 lb. ballasted plates, which were lighter for the owners to lift and carry about and made the dinghies more lively and more buoyant at sea. In *Thunder*, then, we have a far better dinghy than we had been developing for the last few years, and one only hopes that the rule makers will make no more changes, and that lovely dinghies of this type will continue to be built.

Practically no change at all has been made in the sail plan since *Avenger's* year, 1928 ; the only difference being that now we use three crosstrees instead of two.

As in previous years, this season's racing started at Cowes under the Island Sailing Club Burgee before Easter, and it was looked forward to with even keener interest than before as everyone wondered exactly what the boats to the new rule would be like. These first races at the Island Sailing Club are something in the nature of a mannequin parade of the new dinghies. The races proved that the new boats were undoubtedly faster and were also a better type to sail.

Stewart Morris with *Alarm* gave us a good line on the last year's boats, as she had been slightly improved by giving her a ballasted plate to the new rule.

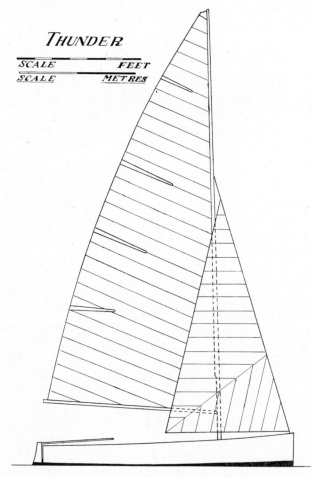

THUNDER

SCALE   FEET

SCALE   METRES

Eight dinghies came to the line for the morning's race on Saturday, March 20, and though it was early for racing in open waters, the weather conditions were ideal. Dennis Fletcher of the North Norfolk Sailing Club with his new dinghy *Mercury* led the fleet home in this race, with another new dinghy *Eriskay* second and *Alarm* third.

OWNER		NAME	CLUB				TIME		
							H.	M.	S.
1. D. Fletcher - -		*Mercury* -	N.N.S.C. -	-	-	-	11	37	30
2. Miss B. Robertson -		*Eriskay* -	U.T.S.C. -	-	-	-	11	38	8
3. S. Morris - -		*Alarm* -	Oxford & Cambridge S.S.	-			11	38	9
T. C. Ratsey - -		*Hawk* -	I.S.C. -	-	-	-	11	38	28
M. Bratby - -		*Whisper* -	Cambridge U.Cr.C.	-		-	11	39	17
W. Newbegin - -		*Pirate* -	T.U.S.C. -	-	-	-	11	39	28
J. S. Cory - -		*Mikado* -	Itchenor S.C.	-	-	-	11	40	58
G. M. Burge - -		*Lancing* -	Henley S.C.	-	-	-	11	41	32

After this race we all had lunch at the Island Sailing Club, and in the afternoon the same eight dinghies raced for the Island Sailing Club Challenge Cup, which was really a team race for the various clubs, but as it was difficult to pair off the different people for teams it was decided that the teams should consist of one boat only. After a spirited race Miss Berta Robertson's *Eriskay* won the challenge Cup for the Upper Thames Sailing Club, the Thames United Sailing Club being second and *Alarm* third. While two boats to the new rule were again first and second, it was good to see two helmsmen from the Upper Thames coming in first and second, as the great charm of the International 14-foot class is that the dinghies are equally at home on inland waters or the sea, and their helmsmen seem able to sail equally well whether in a strong wind at sea or in the light fickle breezes found on the upper reaches of the Thames.

OWNER			NAME		CLUB					TIME		
										H.	M.	S.
1. Miss B. Robertson	-		*Eriskay*	-	U.T.S.C.	-	-	-	-	3	6	22
2. W. Newbegin	-	-	*Pirate*	-	T.U.S.C.	-	-	-	-	3	7	11
3. S. Morris	-	-	*Alarm*	-	Oxford and Cambridge S.S.	-				3	7	31
T. C. Ratsey	-	-	*Hawk*	-	I.S.C.	-	-	-	-	3	7	36
M. Bratby	-	-	*Whisper*	-	Cambridge U.Cr.C.	-		-		3	8	35
J. S. Cory	-	-	*Mikado*	-	Itchenor S.C.	-		-	-	3	8	37
D. Fletcher	-	-	*Mercury*	-	N.N.S.C.	-	-	-	-	3	10	28
G. M. Burge	-	-	*Lancing*	-	Henley S.C.	-		-	-	3	14	18

That evening we had our usual dinner, with J. C. W. Damant, the Island Sailing Club's Vice-Commodore, presiding and presenting the Cup, and the evening was so enjoyable that it was late before most of us turned in. Sunday was given over to gossiping, arranging future meetings and the packing up of dinghies by their owners, who were trailing them to their various centres, for now they were to spread out like a fan all over England, some going to the south and east coasts, others to inland waters.

THIRTY-FIVE AWAY TO A GOOD START

Many attended the Torbay Coronation Regatta from June 19 to July 3, and Mrs. Richardson in *Sayanora* came out on top for points with Douglas Heard's *Huffinis* a close second after two weeks of good sport.

On July 11 many of these dinghies and owners came together once more for another big race, for it was on this day that the Itchenor Sailing Club had arranged a race for the Itchenor Gallon, a race held in Chichester Harbour where the conditions are half-way between those of the sea and those of inland waters and the popularity of this race is partly due to this, for there were no less than 35 starters in this race this year.

The London Corinthian represented that delightful village on the Thames in Middlesex, while the Barnt Green dinghy was Birmingham's representative, but Norfolk took pride of place, for Dr. Hicks won this race with *Trade Wind*, then second came the Westmorland owner, Michael Bratby, in *Whisper*, the next two places going to Norfolk again, for Dennis Fletcher came in third with *Mercury* and James Beale fourth with *Afterthought*. Then came the first of the home fleet, *Mikado*, sailed by Jack Bristow, the secretary for the race, closely followed by Major Chichester Smith in *Mirage*.

The start was against the last of the flood tide, so most of the boats crowded over to the weather shore where the tide was easier and they would have the weather berth. The wind was sou' west and had eased enough to let them carry full sail.

Four boats were over the line at gunfire and had great difficulty in getting back as the rest of the fleet were charging on past them at full speed—a boat returning has to keep out of the way. All that these four could do was to sit tight till the fleet had passed, so those that were too early were soon at the tail of the fleet.

Soon after the start Michael Bratby in *Whisper* was out in the lead. *Whisper* having started up to weather with her wind clear and in an easy tide had gone through the line with a lot of way on. At the Weir mark *Whisper* had a 50-yard lead of *Mercury*, with *Afterthought* third and *Trade Wind* fourth, these four soon drew away from the fleet and seemed to be having a race on their own. Now, whilst most followed the southern bank, Chichester Smith in *Mirage* tried the north shore, where the tide was also easier, but this manœuvre could only pay if he had a lift of wind off that shore. He failed to get it.

On this beat to windward there was just a good full sail breeze which seemed to suit the Norfolk people, for Willie Hicks had pulled out ahead, with three Norfolk boats in the first four and one from Westmorland. Evidently the dinghy sailers from farther North liked heavier winds more than those of the South, for these four were now some 300 yards ahead and close together and fighting it out.

Getting on towards the end of the beat James Beale tried the north shore, and as the tide had eased right up he picked up, passed *Whisper*, and so came into third place. It was now a reach and a run up the Emsworth channel ; inshore the ebb had started to come away while up through the middle of the channel the last drains of the flood were still making. *Whisper*, with her spinnaker pulling well, ran off up through the centre of the channel with the last of the flood.

RACING FOR THE TRENT CUP

To me it seemed that this might easily give her a place or two. However, what she had gained over this she lost, as she had held on too long, and when she took in her spinnaker to luff across for the Emsworth mark she was almost making a right angle to her old course, so, though she should have gained by her manœuvre, the extra distance she had sailed cancelled this out and she was still fourth at the top mark. On the run Dennis Fletcher had passed Willie Hicks, and these two North Norfolk boats had a duel for first place which let *Afterthought* up level with them. On the close reach down the Emsworth channel these three were abreast for the first third, but the two North Norfolk boats in the weather berth slowly drew out ahead.

It was a reach and run to the finish against the ebb tide, and *Whisper* came from fourth to second place. Dennis Fletcher remaining ahead of James Beale, these two were third and fourth, and so ended the Itchenor Gallon for 1937, the glory going to the North Norfolk boats.

The eighth boat to finish was *Fleetwing*, the first of the old boats, who had sailed remarkably well to finish within 3½ minutes of the winner and well deserved the two pint tankards she received for the first of the old boats home. *Daring*, the second of the old boats, was one minute 12 seconds behind her, all of which promises that when the helmsmen of these boats have a chance of steering a new one they will give a good account of themselves.

Stewart Morris, who presented the special prizes for the old boats, deserted the dinghies this year for the 6-metre class and only lost the championship of the class for the Coronation Regatta by 0·64 of a point to the Crown Prince of Norway, which gives an idea of the ability of the helmsmen in this class who have to be reckoned with immediately they go into any of the larger classes. Undoubtedly sailing in light centreboard boats teaches one the art of sailing as can no other craft or vessel, and the Itchenor S.C. are to be congratulated for the good they have done in this direction.

FINISHING TIMES

OWNER	NAME	CLUB	TIME		
			H.	M.	S.
1. Dr. E. W. Hicks - - -	*Trade Wind* - - -	N.N.S.C. -	4	21	10
2. M. Bratby - - -	*Whisper* - - -	C.U.Cr.C.	4	21	33
3. D. H. A. Fletcher - -	*Mercury* - - -	N.N.S.C. -	4	21	38
4. J. A. F. Beale - - -	*Afterthought* - -		4	21	45
5. J. S. Bristow - - -	*Mikado* - - -		4	23	0
6. C. H. Chichester Smith -	*Mirage* - - -		4	23	12
Mrs. C. H. Chichester Smith -	*Shadow* - - -		4	24	33
R. H. Farrant - - -	*Fleetwing* (first old boat)		4	24	42
	Alette - - -		4	24	57
P. Chandler - - -	*Rapier* - - -		4	25	58
Jack Bristow - - -	*Derring Do* - -		4	25	55
D. O. Beale - - -	*Canute* - - -		4	25	56
P. Nichols - - -	*Daring* - - -		4	26	0
N. Moore - - -	*Huffest* - - -		4	26	33
J. G. Ruston and J. R. Macdonald	*Adler* - - -		4	27	50
E. E. Jelike - - -	*Shooting Star* - -		4	28	15
H. S. Adams - - -	*Magheralin* - -		4	28	33
	Echo - - -		4	28	35
J. C. and B. J. Fearnley -	*Duet* - - -		4	29	35
E. B. Wilson - - -	*Gilette* - - -		4	32	0
	Joy - - -		4	32	12
J. C. Day - - -	*Sark* - - -		4	32	12
	Golden Eye - -		4	32	55
N. Wetherilt - - -	*Siskin* - - -		4	33	0
W. O. Bradbury - - -	*Ace* - - -		4	33	10
A. C. Brown - - -	*Flotsam* - - -		4	33	11
H. P. Dawbarn - - -	*Emily* - - -		4	33	20
	Bogey - - -		4	33	30
P. Conway Jones - -	*Timtoo* - - -		4	33	45
H. Taylor - - -	*Flare* - - -		4	35	6
O. M. Burge - - -	*Yo-Ho-Ho* - -		4	35	13
	Silver Streak - -		4	37	18
Brown and Rogers - -	*Vixen* - - -		4	37	25
	Arba - - -		4	39	40
	Imp - - -		4	40	3

On July 18 no less than nine different teams of two came to Chichester Harbour to race for the Trent Inland Waters Challenge Cup, for the Itchenor Sailing Club were the defenders. We see a distinct change in thought since 1928 and 1929, the two years when Tom Thornycroft and I, the Island Sailing Club team, won this race, for each time we suggested defending it either on the River Medina or in Chichester Harbour, and each time we were told it was the Inland Water Trophy and therefore could not be raced for on tidal and salt water. Nevertheless, it is perhaps a pity that this particular trophy has not been kept purely for inland waters, for it seems to me that unless this is done it will lose its point, as we now have three distinct challenge cups, the Prince of Wales' for the open sea, the Trent Inland Waters Cup for inland waters, and the Itchenor Gallon, which is sailed on a course giving conditions halfway between the two, and if the Trent Cup is sailed over practically the same course as the Itchenor Gallon, one or the other and possibly both will lose their attraction and popularity in the years to come.

However, there is no sign of this happening at the moment, for there were only six teams in the race last year when it was held on the Upper Thames, but this year there were no less than nine.

The first heat in the morning was won by the Itchenor team, Major C. H. Chichester Smith in *Mirage* finished second and Jack Bristow with *Mikado* third to the Thames United Sailing Club's champion, Michael Brown, in *Pirate*, and as in the afternoon the two Itchenor boats finished first and fourth they successfully defended the Cup.

CLUB	NAME	POINTS
1. Itchenor S.C. - - -	*Mirage* } - *Mikado*	74
2. North Norfolk S.C. - -	*Mercury* } - *Trade Wind*	56
3. Minima Y.C. - - -	*Daring* } - *Shooting Star*	53
4. Thames United S.C. -	*Siskin* } - *Pirate*	52
5. Royal Artillery Y.C. - -	*Fleetwing* } - *Gilette*	42
6. Ranelagh S.C. - - -	*Derring Do* } - *Shadow*	42
7. London Corinthian S.C. -	*Ace* } - *Rapier*	35
8. Tamesis Club - - -	*Duet* } - *Huff*	30
9. Henley S.C. - - -	*Lancing* } - *Yo-Ho-Ho*	18
10. Upper Thames S.C. -	*East Light* } - *Emily*	9

A VIEW OF THE MORNING RACE FOR THE TRENT CUP

START FOR THE AFTERNOON AND FINAL RACE OF THE TRENT INLAND WATER CHALLENGE CUP AT ITCHENOR

Once again all the dinghies scattered to various regattas and races on the coast and inland, and it was not until the last two weeks of August that they came together again, this time for the Oulton Broad races and Lowestoft Sea Week. These two always take the last two weeks of August, and have always been looked forward to by the dinghyites, as with the week of racing inland on the Broad, and a week at sea off Lowestoft, one gets every sort of sailing, ghosting along under trees in water like glass, or plunging into the steep tumbling breaking seas found off Lowestoft.

The great event of this meet this year was the Prince of Wales' Cup, which is the championship of the sea for dinghies, this taking the Thursday of Lowestoft Sea Week.

With 46 entries for this race, which is recognised as the contest for the Championship of OPEN boat sailing, the Royal Norfolk and Suffolk Y.C. was faced with many unusual problems, the chief being that of recalling any over the line at the start. But, as in the past ten contests, one saw printed on the Racing Instructions : " Exception to Y.R.A. Rule 28. Any dinghy over the line at the start may be disqualified without being recalled."

Though this convenient rule has never before been brought into action, it was this time in order to warn every-one that it was the committee's weapon to ensure a fair start and that it was there to be used if required, for on the day preceding the Prince of Wales' Cup, Miss Berta Robertson, after sailing a perfect race and leading throughout the finest fleet of dinghies yet seen, was disqualified without being recalled for being a boat's length over the line at the start.

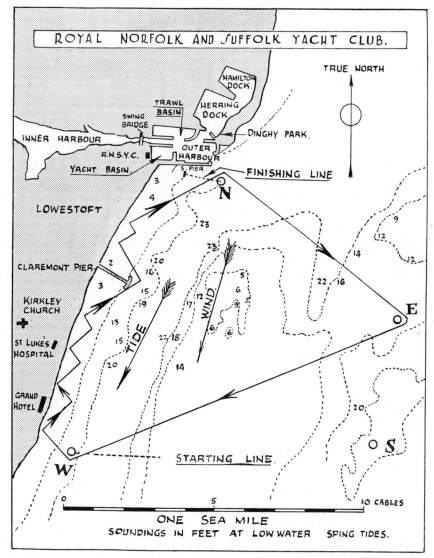

Just such incidents were in my thoughts as the committee boat steamed down to the west mark, half a mile south of the Claremont Pier, to form the starting line. With the wind north this would give a beat to windward of one mile over a foul tide to the first mark, time enough to sort every boat out, so that not only could they all start clear of each other but could round the first mark clear. Such points as these showed that the committee had carefully planned every detail of this important race, and, therefore, it was probable that, as in the ten previous championship races, there would be neither protests nor the need of them.

On first thoughts it would seem certain that any boat taking a course inshore would arrive at the weather mark first, as though there would be slightly less wind inshore there would also be much less tide. Then, one remembered that out to sea there were banks, that the tide would be weak over these, that there would be more wind out there, and that practically every boat in the race would make for the inshore course. So one felt that there was a good chance of anyone standing right off for the banks arriving at the weather mark first. Thus this race, as every race, offered problems to those in it.

All this while this great fleet fought and manœuvred for the start, and when the starting gun went the nearest to the line was some 8 ft. the right side and so all was well. Nearest was David Pollock in *Daybreak*, who, having carefully timed himself, close hauled on the starboard tack along the line, crossed immediately after gunfire at the inner end which enabled him to sail into the slack water inshore first of all.

WINNER AND RUNNER-UP—(LEFT) PETER SCOTT AND C. CURREY (THUNDER) AND (RIGHT) JOHN WINTER
AND H. L. PAXTON (LIGHTNING)

Soon he had a strong lead with most of the fleet tacking alongshore at his heels. But Mrs. Chichester Smith had started well out on the port tack, and I hoped that she would have the courage to stand right on out to sea into the stronger wind and easier tide over the banks as such a course might give her a strong lead at the weather mark, but after a while she stood inshore after the rest. So now the whole fleet were working the shore and made an inspiring picture, the cheerful white of their sails and bow waves standing out in strong contrast to the dull greyness of the North Sea.

With so many it was impossible to follow any one particular vessel's fortunes, as all over the course the different dinghies were fighting duels, for though after forty minutes of sailing the fleet extended two miles over the course no dinghy was free from attack from another. I doubt if I'll ever witness such a fine exhibition of attack, defence and counter attack as seen this day, for all around things were happening. It was rather like the days we sometimes get when we have dogs and ferrets working the steep side of a hill full of rabbits. No end of dogs, ferrets, rabbits and guns, and all the while you hear: "Look out! There he goes!" "Where?" "There." Bang, bang, bang, bang, bang. "Got 'un?" "No." And again we look out, and the same excitement over again.

Though the wind was ten miles an hour at the start it was not true in strength or direction, but only generally so, therefore, the leader, David Pollock, had a very hard battle to fight, for there were twenty boats close astern ready to jump into first place directly he sailed into a soft spot, or misjudged the strength or direction of the wind and tide in any part of the course over which he was sailing. He sailed extremely well to hold his lead for the first two rounds, for we have to remember that the first six in last year's contest were all in the race and most of them close on his heels.

Slowly yet surely these practised helmsmen came to the forefront, for one can only obtain knowledge of the sea and its ways by experience. Though there were many first-class helmsmen in this race from inland, as there have been in the past, helmsmanship itself is not enough for this event, for it demands seamanship, too, as it is raced on the sea. It is one thing to sail round a sea course, but quite another matter to race round it when all the while only ten seconds separate one racer from another. Most helmsmen in this race are of equal sailing ability, but when it comes to judgment of the sea's ways then there comes a difference, for the currents are always altering and with such sensitive and lively craft advantage can be taken of these alterations. If but one is missed the man astern takes it, and has gained the ten seconds and perhaps a little more and so comes up one place. Continually, during this race one saw this happening, so that when, after having sailed 12 miles, the leaders rounded the leeward buoy for the last mile, a beat to windward, John Winter had a short lead of Peter Scott with Stewart Morris, James Beale, Mrs. Richardson and Bruce Wolfe all close astern, and it was still any one of these helmsmen's race.

THE CRITICAL MOMENT WHEN PETER PASSED JOHN 100 YARDS
FROM THE FINISHING LINE

THUNDER CROSSES THE LINE TO WIN THE PRINCE OF WALES' CUP

JAMES BEALE CROSSES THE LINE WITH BRUCE WOLFE
TUCKED UNDER HIS LEE

AS THEY FINISHED, JAMES, BRUCE AND MRS.
RICHARDSON WERE CLOSE TOGETHER

John held his lead till some 100 yards from the finish line, when the wind, which had eased down a little, began to harden and blow stronger than at any time through the race. This increase in wind lifted *Thunder* along, so that just short of the finish line she crossed *Lightning* when on the port tack, and putting about soon after crossed the line the winner at 2 h. 10 min. 48 sec., with John Winter's *Lightning* 16 seconds astern and *Alarm* 22 seconds later. Next came James Beale in *Afterthought* with Bruce Wolfe under his lee, 5 seconds only separating these two. Mrs. Richardson was sixth, only 2 minutes 3 seconds after the winner; next came Douglas Heard and David Pollock, and one by one, sometimes two by two, the fleet finished. Last of all came *Avenger* (ten years old) with which I won this cup in these same waters many years ago.

With the end of the race came thoughts of the class and the future. These little racers have been trailed to various parts of the coasts and inland, for we have seen them giving good sport at Cowes, Itchenor, Putney, the Upper Thames, Torquay, North Norfolk and many other places as well as Lowestoft and the Broads, fine little craft brought into being by the Yacht Racing Association. When we look at the members of the Council, it seems amazing that this Council, formed of 8-metre, 12-metre and "J" class owners, could have produced such craft, but nevertheless it is so.

Then we look further into it and see that, though there are but five "J" boats, there are four "J" boat owners on the Council, and representing 400 14-footer owners racing to-day there is but one, Stewart Morris, on the Council. Now, everyone loves to make an Aunt Sally of our Y.R.A. and to say they never have a thought below a 12-metre, but here is a shot at the small-boat owners all over the country. The rules you race under and that are used all over the world are the work of the Y.R.A.; to all you dinghy owners who have had such fine sport in your dinghies, and in doing so have given a great deal of pleasure to others, I ask this question : "Are you a member of the Y.R.A.?" "No, I never thought of it." Well, apply for membership, cough up your two guineas per annum, and help the Y.R.A., for, as you see by its present list, it needs small-boat people both as members and on its Council.

OWNER	NAME	CLUB	TIME	
			M.	S.
1. Peter Scott	*Thunder*	C.U.Cr.C.	0	0
2. J. K. Winter	*Lightning*	C.U.Cr.C.	0	16
3. S. H. Morris	*Alarm*	C.U.Cr.C.	0	38
4. J. A. F. Beale	*Afterthought*	R.N. & S.Y.C.	1	39
5. E. B. Wolfe	*Spider*	N.N.S.C.	1	44
6. Mrs. H. Richardson	*Sayonara*	R.N. & S.Y.C.	2	3
R. D. Heard	*Huffins*	Ranelagh S.C.	2	24
D. Pollock	*Daybreak*	Cambridge	3	21
C. G. Benion	*Tuneful*	N.N.S.C.	3	41
Dr. E. W. Hicks	*Trade Wind*	N.N.S.C.	3	50
J. S. Bristow	*Mikado*	Itchenor S.C.	4	12
W. J. Borthwick	*Javelin*	Brancaster	5	7
David Beale	*Canute*	R.N. & S.Y.C.	5	13
Alan R. Colman	*Numbus*	R.N. & S.Y.C.	6	31
H. E. Loynes	*Viking*	N.N.S.C.	6	50
R. P. Hichens	*Venture II*	Cornwall	7	52
H. C. Williams	*Streamline*	R.N. & S.Y.C.	8	12
Mrs. Chichester Smith	*Mirage*	R.N. & S.Y.C.	8	22
Mrs. S. Evans	*Whirlwind*	N.N.S.C.	9	43
H. F. G. Harrison	*Vivid*	R.N. & S.Y.C.	9	58
R. C. Webster	*Black Magic*	Tamesis	10	12
Leslie Lewis	*Daddy Long Legs*	Trent	10	28
C. H. Chichester Smith	*Shadow*	R.N. & S.Y.C.	10	50
N. Moore	*Huffest*	Cambridge	11	16
Miss B. Robertson	*Eriskay*	N.N.S.C.	12	8
M. Bratby	*Whisper*	Cambridge	14	9
D. Fletcher	*Mercury*	N.N.S.C.	14	29
A. C. Brown	*Flotsam*	Thames	14	41
J. K. Maw	*Typhoon*	N.N.S.C.	16	4
E. B. Wilson	*Gilette*	Itchenor	17	43
H. P. Dawburn	*Emily*	U.T.S.C.	17	59
Miss Jamieson	*Vega*	N.N.S.C.	18	52
Lt. E. J. Lee	*Eclipse*	Royal Naval S.A.	19	21
G. M. Burge	*Lancing*	Henley S.C.	19	42
J. C. & B. J. Fearnley	*Duet*	Tamesis	22	59
T. N. Hinton	*Joy*	Rickmansworth	24	5
O. M. Burge	*Yo-Ho-Ho*	Henley S.C.	20	45
E. M. Killik	*Arba*	Thames	21	22
F. T. Walker	*Avenger*	Midland	21	24
D. G. Heath	*Arrow*	Cambridge		
R. H. Farrant	*Fleetwing*	Royal Artillery Y.C.		
H. S. Adams	*Magheralin*	Brancaster		

Dismasted : *Arrow* ; retired : *Fleetwing* and *Magheralin*.

On the Saturday of Lowestoft Week a new trophy, to be raced for every year in Lowestoft Sea Week, was sailed for, and there were no less than 34 starters. It is a race which is likely to prove very popular amongst dinghy sailors being for the Sir John Beale trophy. During his lifetime Sir John did so much for the class that he will always be considered its Father, and this race, being held in the waters he loved and sailed upon, will keep his memory green.

PRINCE OF WALES' CUP. THE FIRST SIX HELMSMEN WITH THEIR REPLICAS AND CREWS

The course was exactly that of the Prince of Wales' Cup, but starting from the same mark it was sailed the reverse way round, as the wind was north west, giving a dead beat to the first mark. F. T. Walker very kindly lent me *Avenger* for this day's race, as I wished to take part in it, and we managed to bring her in 12th. A crowd of us stood out to sea at once for the stronger breeze there and the easier tide over the banks, while the other school of thought made for and tacked along the shore, and these lost heavily by this manœuvre, for those who had boldly stood out to sea led easily round the first mark, and one wondered if it had been right in the race two days before for the Prince of Wales' Cup to go for the shore as everyone had done.

The breeze was light and fickle, but, however, Peter Scott managed to win after a keen struggle with John Winter in *Lightning* and Jason Borthwick in *Javelin*, Mrs. Richardson with *Sayonara* being fourth.

NAME		OWNER
Thunder	-	Peter Scott
Lightning	-	John Winter
Javelin	-	Jason Borthwick
Sayonara	-	Mrs. H. Richardson

This brought Lowestoft Sea Week to an end and points were counted up for the R.I.P. trophy, which was presented some years ago for the highest points gained in Lowestoft Sea Week. When those were all added up everyone was delighted to find that Mrs. Chichester Smith, sailing *Mirage*, had come out top, for she had always been close up to the leaders throughout the week, and had sailed more consistently than any one else, and without doubt she deserved the honour of coming out top of the whole week.

H. YULE OLDHAM, COMMODORE OF THE CAMBRIDGE UNIVERSITY CRUISING CLUB, TAKING A SNAP OF HIS BOYS, THE FIRST THREE, PETER, JOHN AND STEWART. THE DAY BEFORE HE SAID, " THE OUTLOOK IS BLACK, THUNDER, LIGHTNING AND ALARM "

R.I.P. TROPHY

NAME	OWNER	POINTS
Mirage - -	Mrs. C. H. Chichester Smith	44
Lightning - -	John Winter - - -	43
Shadow - -	Major C. H. Chichester Smith	40
Sayonara - -	Mrs. H. Richardson - -	40
Thunder - -	Peter Scott - - -	39
Afterthought -	James A. Beale - - -	31
Vivid - -	Hugh Harrison - - -	29
Streamline -	Claude Williams - - -	22
Alarm - -	Stewart H. Morris - -	21
Canute - -	David Beale - - -	16
Mercury - -	Dennis Fletcher - - -	11
Daddy Long Legs	Leslie Lewis - - -	9
Nimbus - -	Alan Colman - - -	8
Whisper - -	Michael Bratby - - -	4

The summer season ended as usual with the Ranelagh Trophy on the tideway at Putney over the lower half of the Oxford and Cambridge Boat race course and this year's race proved as popular as ever for no less than 38 boats travelled from all over the country to take part in this race, which was won by Bruce Wolfe in *Spider*.

The wind was light and northerly at the start, freshening during the race, and so it was a beat to windward with the tide to the first mark and then a run back round the starting line mark, four rounds of this course giving the seven mile race with a three hour time limit.

With such a fleet it was impossible to recall boats by number and the rule for recalls read as follows :

" There will be NO recall numbers. If a boat be on or across the line when the signal to start is made a horn will be sounded, and the responsibility of returning will rest with the helmsman. Any boat over the line not recrossing will be disqualified."

THE START OF THE RANELAGH TROPHY

Douglas Heard, Commodore of the Ranelagh Sailing Club in *Huffinis* was the first across the line, crossing it within half a second of the starting signal, closely followed by James Beale in *Afterthought*, while Stewart Morris, who was sailing Hugh Harrison's *Vivid*, which finished third, started third from the last.

APPROACHING THE LEE MARK—

AND ROUNDING IT

Huffinis kept her lead to the top mark with *Afterthought* pressing hard on her, but on the run back to the line *Afterthought* took the lead and the order at the end of the first round was *Afterthought*, *Huffinis* and *Vivid*, *Vivid* having worked right through the fleet in that one beat to windward. Next came *Black Magic*, *Spider*, *Mikado*, *Canute* and *Daring*. On the third beat *Huffinis* repassed *Afterthought* and these two were so interested in each other that they did not notice *Spider* who was being extremely well sailed by Bruce Wolfe, and coming so fast that she eventually passed them and took the lead, so that at the end of the third round the order was *Spider*, *Huffinis*, *Afterthought* and *Vivid*, these four being separated from the rest of the fleet by a good distance and so able to have a good race amongst themselves without worrying about the others.

On the fourth and final round *Vivid* caught and passed *Afterthought* and so came into third place, the final order being *Spider*, *Huffinis*, *Vivid* and *Afterthought*. After these four there was a space of three minutes before the fifth boat finished, while my old dinghy *Daring*, being the first boat home of those built before 1930 took special prize for the old boat class finishing nine minutes one second behind *Spider*.

NAME	OWNER	TIME		
		H.	M.	S.
1. *Spider* -	E. Bruce Wolfe - - -	3	1	59
2. *Huffinis* -	R. D. Heard - - -	3	3	18
3. *Vivid* -	J. F. G. Harrison - - -	3	4	13
4. *Afterthought* -	J. A. F. Beale - - -	3	4	48
5. *Black Magic* -	R. C. Webster - - -	3	8	4
6. *Mirage* -	Mrs. C. H. Chichester Smith	3	8	12
First of the old boats home :				
Daring - -	P. Nichols - - - -	3	11	0

So the summer season for the 14-foot class ended.

The number of entries in all the important races had been larger than ever before, and the class not only maintained but increased its popularity and now that the rules have brought back the more healthy and lively type of dinghies the class will go from strength to strength.

· 41 ·

NATIONAL 12-FOOT DINGHY CLASS

CAMBRIDGE UNIVERSITY 12-FOOTER

Length, overall -   12 ft. 0 in. = 3·65 m.   Length, water-line -   11 ft. 7 in. = 3·53 m.
Beam   -   -   4 ft. 6 in. = 1·37 m.   Draught   -   -   8 in. and 3 ft. 6 in.
                                                                                           = 0·20 and 1·06 m.
Displacement -   - 640 lb. = 290 kilos.   Sail Area   -   - 89·80 sq. ft. = 8·36 sq. m.

Owner, Cambridge U. Cruising Club   *Designer*, Uffa Fox

IN the autumn of last year, after the 12-ft. class had had its first season's racing, the dinghy committee met to discuss the rules and to see if there were any flaws in them. The making of rules is a very difficult job, and so

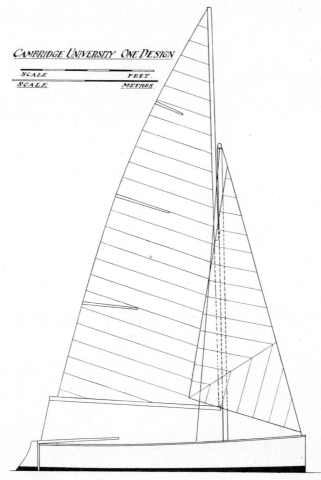

CAMBRIDGE UNIVERSITY ONE DESIGN

SCALE   FEET.
SCALE   METRES.

many people are concerned and so much talking and arguing is done that it is really difficult to decide what is vital and what is not. The 12-footer rule is no exception, for when it was being formed, Captain Boyd and myself wished to have one forcing the boats to have a certain minimum beam at the water-line, a point which makes for a steadier

265

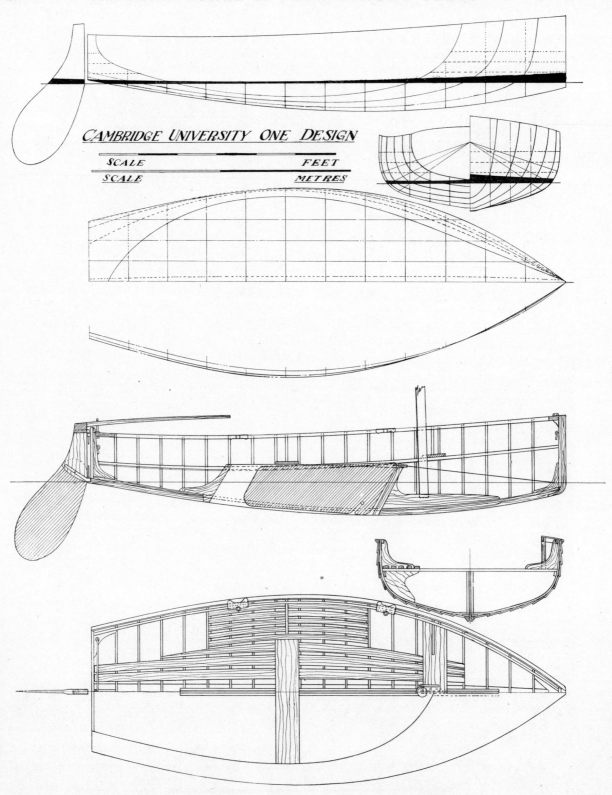

CAMBRIDGE UNIVERSITY ONE DESIGN

SCALE ——————— FEET

SCALE ——————— METRES

and easier boat to sail; but as can be imagined, with 30 people arguing and talking rules, this point was lost sight of, so when I was persuaded into the designing to this class I went for very slack bilges and a steep, rising floor, as I tried to visualise the progress made in the class over years, and hoped that this Uffa-King, as the design was named, would be so advanced that it would hold its own against all designs for some time. The set of plans of this boat will be found in my last book, and in the autumn of 1936 the committee decided to put in a rule governing the rise of floor. So the rule was made, which without barring this type of boat (for over a hundred of them had been built to this design), would prevent vessels being narrower on the water-line than this design, and the Uffa-Kings again triumphed this year, so may still be looked upon as being the fastest in the class.

The Cambridge University Cruising Club, which teaches so many men to sail at Ely, decided to build a new class, and as these would often be used by people who had never sailed before in their lives it was essential that they should be steady though fast boats, steady enough to enable the men to sail them fairly easily, yet fast enough to excite the interest of undergraduates in sailing ; and the design illustrated in this chapter is the Cambridge University 12-footer.

THE 12-FOOTERS GAVE GREAT SPORT THROUGHOUT THE SEASON AS THIS PICTURE OF PONTOON, DART, CORONATION
AND SNIPPET ROUNDING A MARK IN TORBAY SHOWS

It will be noticed that she has a firmer bilge and a flatter floor, while her water-line beam is 4 ft. 2 in., points which make for steadiness and ease of handling. With this section I have designed the fastest fore and aft lines possible, for once again we have the deep-chested type of dinghy with a long clean run and buttock lines, and these 12-footers have given a great deal of pleasure and service at Ely this year.

When we look at the arrangement plan we see that it is very similar to that of the Uffa-Kings, with the exception that here we have a lifting rudder and also a shorter drop keel, the reason for this shorter keel being the shallow and narrow waters at Ely. However, I left the drop keel case long so that a longer keel could be fitted, if any undergraduate wished to enter one of these boats for the 12-ft. National championships. But none were entered, so we have yet to know how fast these would prove when racing in the class.

The sail plan shows a gunter lug rig with bamboo spars, and while this rig is almost as effective as the Bermudian, it is not such a delicate rig to set up and handle, and will stand far more bad treatment as there are no cross-trees. In the event of a spar carrying away it is easily replaced, for we have to remember that these little boats are bound to be ill treated at times, and as it was a one-design class there is no real need to go for the more efficient but more delicate Bermudian rig, and we have always to bear in mind the job for which any vessel has been designed.

I had hoped that one of these would have been fitted with an Uffa-King plate and rig, and have been raced in the National championships in Chichester Harbour this year, as it would have been very interesting to me to have seen how she fared. For in this University 12-footer we see a dinghy designed within the class rule, which, while being ideal for any man to learn sailing in, is also fast enough to give a great deal of pleasure, and to stand a chance when racing for the championship of the class.

The 12-foot nationals raced all round the coast, and the first time they came together in any numbers was at Torquay, and as the photograph shows they gave good sport. After Torquay they all scattered to their various places around the coast and inland, coming together again for the dinghy championship races early in September, and the fact that there were 80 entries gives us an idea of the fun to be had in this vigorous class.

THE NATIONAL DINGHY CHAMPIONSHIP

GOOD STRATEGY AND FINE HANDLING BRING A WELL-EARNED VICTORY

With 80 entries the Committee had, as can easily be imagined, a very difficult task before them, and everyone was filled with admiration for the way they handled the races.

There were 11 races leading up to the final for Sir William Burton's Cup, the first 12 of each heat on September 4 qualifying for the final, which was won by A. W. B. Macdonald in *Tarandole*. He was also the winner of *The Yachting World* Points Trophy.

On the day of the final there was a very faint easterly air in the early morning, but by nine o'clock the hot sun had burnt the air up inland, so the wind came in southerly off the sea and remained true throughout the day. The Committee, however, very wisely refrained from laying the course until the last moment, and I had gone to the very top of the starting box on the roof of the clubhouse to study the different vessels sailing out to sea. As far as the

THE START OF THE FINAL

eye could reach they were all sailing to a southerly wind, and so a triangular course was laid giving a dead beat at the start from the North Buoy in the Emsworth Channel down to the buoy off the clubhouse against a flood tide of some three knots. As can easily be imagined, several dinghies got to the leeward of the line and were a long time crossing against the strong flood.

Stewart Morris in *Surprise* had the best of the start, for he and a few others very wisely kept to windward of the line until the last moment, and then dropped back on the tide just before gunfire, forging ahead immediately after. As soon as they were able they tacked to port for the slack water and eddy tide down the western shore of the Emsworth Channel. Most of the fleet were soon trailing down this shore behind Stewart Morris. A few, however, had come across to the east side of this channel, where they lost considerably on those taking the other shore, so much so that this little fleet was soon last.

Stewart had a strong lead as he arrived at Sandy Point, but here he made a mistake which cost him no fewer than 16 places. On rounding Sandy Point, where he met the full strength of the flood, he stood straight offshore for the mark, which he had no chance of weathering in the strong tide taking him to leeward. When he found he was missing the mark he did not sail back for the shore as he should have done. Instead, he made one or two short tacks against a tide that was going to leeward far faster than any dinghy could make good dead to windward, and, when he finally went back for the shore on the port tack he had dropped 16 places.

· 42 ·

INTERNATIONAL CANOE CLASS

FLYING FISH

Length, overall -	17 ft. 0 in. = 5·18 m.	Length, water-line -	16 ft. 6 in. = 5·02 m.
Beam - -	3 ft. 1⅜ in. = 0·94 m.	Draught - -	5 in. and 3 ft. 6 in. = 0·12 and 1·06 m.
Displacement -	400 lb. = 181 kilos.	Sail Area - -	106 sq. ft. = 9·84 sq. m.

Owner, PAUL CLIFT   *Designer*, UFFA FOX   *Builder*, UFFA FOX

PAUL CLIFT'S *Flying Fish* has the longest length and smallest beam permissible under the rules, and as can be seen from the lines, these dimensions produce a very easy and sweet-lined canoe.   But when we look at the

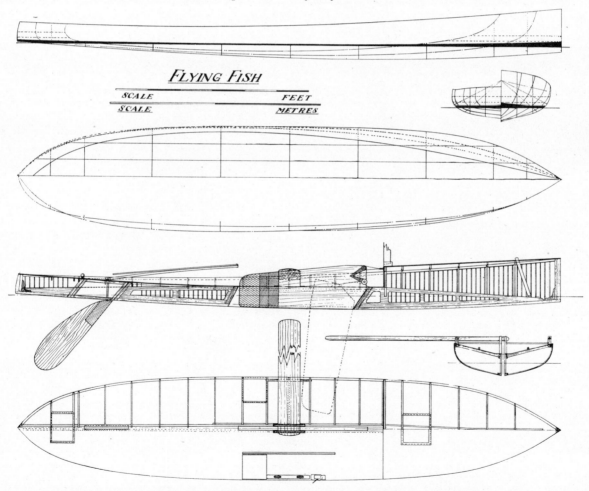

FLYING FISH

lines of these light and very fast sailing hulls we must always bear in mind that they plane two-thirds of the way round a triangular course, and even close reaching will get up and scoot along the top of the water, and for this reason their lines must be studied from a different viewpoint than that taken when studying an ordinary sailing craft.

271

The sections are V'd forward, and are gradually flattened as they go aft where they are almost flat.   The buttock lines also carry this out for they come down steeply forward, and then run aft almost parallel with the keel line, this giving the long flat run, necessary for planing.

Paul, who is unquestionably one of our finest canoe helmsmen, and I, hoped that *Flying Fish* would be the fastest ever designed and built.   Actually, the only important cup she has won has been the Quincey Cup, and this I think is due to the fact that while she is undoubtedly fast, she is most difficult to sail, so that her helmsman has to spend almost all his energies and thoughts on pure sailing, and has little left with which to study the course and the problems to be found on it.   The same thing occurred when Roger de Quincey and I challenged for, and won, the National Championship of America and the New York International Canoe Trophy.   The canoes against us there were fast and easily driven, but they took so much of their helmsman's brain and his strength of limb, that we in the heavier and more comfortable boats won enough races to bring these trophies home to England.   So while I

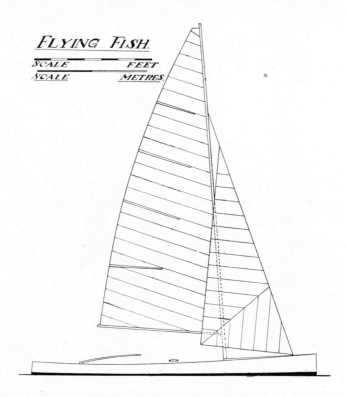

think these lines we are now looking at are very fast indeed, I do not think they are fast round a course, and the moral of all this is that designers must put into the hands of helmsmen instruments, which, while being fast, are well within their capabilities, so that plenty of spare energy, both mental and physical, is kept in reserve, for the planning of their race and the sailing of it, enabling them to conduct operations in a seamanlike manner rather than in a state of feverish excitement throughout.   It is probable that future canoes in this country will be to the maximum beam, such as *Wake*, whose plans can be seen in my last book, and who successfully defended the New York Canoe Trophy against last year's challenger.

The arrangement plan shows she is very similar to *Wake* in construction and lay-out, the difference between the two being that *Flying Fish* has a keel case which runs the entire length of the boat, whereas *Wake's* stops short forward.   The after hatch is arranged a little differently, being placed right in the stern and enabling any water to be sponged out as the canoe lies on the slipway, this one hatch taking the place of the two just forward of the rudder on *Wake*, so this year's canoe designing and building in Britain has confirmed the lesson we learnt in America, which is, that while the narrowest canoe possible is very fast, it is so difficult to handle that a good man in the widest canoe possible to the rules generally wins the race, as he has time and energy enough to study the winds, weather, tides and everything that is happening in the race, and the advantage this gives him, more than makes up for the slightly higher speed of the narrower canoe under certain conditions. This was borne out also by the races in America, for it will be remembered that after Gordon Douglas had unsuccessfully challenged for the New York Canoe Trophy last summer I presented him with the complete plans of *Wake*, and Merrill Gilbert built from these plans, but instead of building her of double skin, as we do, she was built of single thickness planking with rib and batten construction, the builder making a first-class job of her. Gordon christened his new canoe *Foxynymph*, *Nymph* being the name of his old canoe. As can be imagined she created a great deal of interest and the first race was awaited with much anxiety all round. The first race was twice round Sugar Island, and this new canoe and *Loon* had a ding-dong race the whole way round, *Loon* finally scraping home by fifteen seconds. The next race was for the Crane Trophy, and as this was in a good breeze Gordon won it easily, then came the Butler Cup and Gordon won this, Leo Friede being second. Then came the trophy race on Friday afternoon, but the wind was too hard for most, and so it was postponed until the Saturday afternoon when there was a light breeze, and Rolf Armstrong won this race fairly easily in the light going. Gordon in the new canoe was fifth and sixth for half the race, but when the breeze came a little stronger he began to travel fast, and passed all those in front of him except Rolf Armstrong, who was too far ahead to be caught.

The second and third races for the trophy were held in a good breeze, and as was to be expected Gordon won these two easily, Rolf Armstrong finishing second in one and fifth in another.

ON THE OTHER SIDE OF THE ATLANTIC, GORDON DOUGLAS WON THE AMERICAN NATIONAL SAILING CHAMPIONSHIP, THE CRANE TROPHY, AND THE PAUL BUTLER TROPHY WITH FOXYNYMPH, BUILT FROM WAKE'S PLANS

All of this brings back to my mind the pleasure that our visit to Sugar Island gave us in 1933, and recalls the many kindnesses shown to us by the American canoeists, and I only hope that some day I shall return amongst them, even if not as a racer, just to spend pleasant hours among them.

The Mab trophy was won by *Mermaid II* in a very light wind, and as this was for 16 ft. × 30 in. canoes *Foxynymph* was not eligible, and so we see that once again the beamiest canoe came out top.

The Royal Canoe Club's headquarters are at Teddington on Trowlock Island, and while no doubt back in its early years this was an ideal sailing ground, it has been so built round that it is very difficult indeed to sail a canoe there unless the wind is up and down the river, and for several seasons past the members of the Canoe Club have been wandering round to different places to find more suitable sailing waters. In these years they have tried Frencham Pond, Cowes, Aldeburgh, Langston Harbour, and have finally settled on the Sandy Point which is the eastern end of Hayling Island, for just inside Chichester Harbour there is a wonderful sailing spot at high-water, and as most important races have a time limit on them they can be sailed when all the flats are covered and there is water almost everywhere. In addition to this the Hayling Island Sailing Club has built a fine new clubhouse wherein the canoes can be stored, cars parked and the Canoe Club members housed and fed, and so most of the sailing this summer has taken place here, though as in years gone past they have trailed up to Aldeburgh for a week's sport there at the end of August.

Throughout the season the sport was good, for no canoe was outstanding. The new *Flying Fish* while being very fast reaching, has so little stability that her owner spent a great deal of his energies controlling his unstable mount, and on a wind she was almost always outpointed, but as she was travelling fast there was not much in this excepting short tacking when having to tack more often than the rest she lost to windward. *Radiant* was tuned very efficiently and seemed to be a fast all-round boat, while *Wake's* new owner has still to get really used to her, for in the winds that suited her he had *Gallant* and *Solitary Snipe* both sailing extremely well to contend with.

The 16 ft. *Defiant* is equal to *Flying Fish* in light weather, and sails very high on the wind, but being of the minimum length and beam she is the first of the fleet to get out of control when the breeze comes a little stronger, and with these points before us it is therefore not surprising to see that the cups were shared out very evenly, for no canoe was outstanding.

THE STANDARD OF CANOES AND CANOE SAILING IS NOW HIGHER THAN EVER BEFORE IN THE HISTORY OF
THE ROYAL CANOE CLUB

Billy de Quincey with *Gallant*, whose lines appear in my second book, won the Challenge Cup, Paul Clift with *Flying Fish* won the Quincey Cup, while Bee Mackinnon took the Murphy Howard Cup in *Defiant*. The Seamanship Cup was won by Billy in *Gallant* and Cyril Stollery won the Novices' Cup with *Radiant*, and *Radiant* took the Mates' Average. So ended one of the best sailing seasons the Royal Canoe Club has had, for not only have they fast and seaworthy canoes, but the standard of sailing is higher than ever before in the Canoe Club's history, and had America, as we hoped, challenged for her New York Canoe Club International Trophy, which is still this side of the Atlantic, it would have been extremely difficult to choose a defender for it, so well were the canoes and canoeists matched.

Challenge Cup	-	-	*Gallant*	-	Billy de Quincey.
Quincey Cup	-	-	*Flying Fish*	-	Paul Clift.
Murphy Howard Cup	-		*Defiant*	-	P. V. Mackinnon.
Seamanship Cup	-		*Gallant*	-	Billy de Quincey.
Novices' Cup	-	-	*Radiant*	-	Cyril Stollery.
Mates' Average*	-	-	*Radiant*	-	Cyril Stollery.
Junior Average	-	-	*Flying Fish*	-	Paul Clift.

* Cyril only beat Paul by $\frac{1}{16}$ of a point for this trophy. This, and the way the cups were shared out, show how close and keen the canoe racing was during the summer of 1937.

· 43 ·

ONE-DESIGN CLASSES

THIS chapter is written in an effort to assist, for the owners of one-designs would be very grateful if the I.Y.R.U. could find it possible to foster and encourage one-design class racing. Generally speaking, the I.Y.R.U. has mainly encouraged building to formulas or restrictions, and might be said to have taken little interest in one-design classes, for though the Union has adopted the 12-square metres and the monotypes, and years ago an International 12-ft. dinghy class, these are exceptions, and with no one to guide them the various clubs round the coasts of all countries have developed their own local one-designs. While these have given a great deal of pleasure they would give even more if there were fewer classes and they were International, so that a man racing in Ireland, another in Scotland and a third in the Solent, could ship his one-design, say, over to Stockholm or Oslo and spend a holiday racing against the Scandinavians and other nations, or that a man from the Thames Estuary could spend a summer's holiday with his one-design racing in the clear blue waters of the West Country, say, at Falmouth. Now we have only to look in *Lloyd's Register* to read of over 150 different one-design classes in British waters, and generally speaking, there are only about 12 of each class, and they are only raced in the one harbour.

It will be said that this is brought about because the conditions vary so much. But there is a great deal of non-sense talked about local conditions; for instance, a Swedish and Finnish 6-metre challenged for the Scandinavian Gold Cup and went across to America after it, and the three contestants each won two races in the contest, so that the full seven races had to be sailed before the American finally won the trophy. Yet these three boats were developed under entirely different conditions, and varied accordingly. The truth of it is that boats are driven by wind and float on the water, and wherever there is water and wind the conditions throughout the year must be very similar, the only big difference there can be is in the depth of water. The Scandinavians are blest with deep water, and indeed most places where people sail have good depth, though every so often we have a shallow harbour like Bembridge with a sturdy and strong sailing club, where a shallow-draught racer is needed similar to the Redwing class, which is included in this chapter, as such a class should be borne in mind.

So far I have only considered racing on coasts, but there should be a class for inland waters, and if it is a centre-board class it becomes cheap to run as the boats can be hauled in and out of the water without any difficulty; there is the further advantage that they are a lively and exciting type of craft to sail, whereas to sail a heavy-keeled boat on inland waters is not exciting enough. My own personal view is that the I.Y.R.U. would be doing a great deal of good if they could adopt and recommend a series of International one-design classes, for they would be encouraging and helping another class of sailors whom so far they have neglected.

The problem is full of difficulties, but as some of the finest brains in the yachting world are on the Council, these could be overcome.

First of all the classes to be adopted are very difficult to decide upon, as it is important that the best types of craft should be encouraged; then another point is that as this is an international body the designs must come from as many countries as possible, so that there is no feeling in any one country that she is being left out.

I believe that the one-design classes should range from somewhere round 40 ft. water-line down to the 20-square metre centreboard inland racer, and it would seem that the best way of arriving at the selection of designs would be to say that America and Britain have, generally speaking, developed fast seaworthy cruisers above 25 ft. on the line, that the Scandinavian countries, generally speaking, produced wonderfully cheap and fast one-designs around the 6-metre size, and that Central Europe has specialised in inland-water classes, and therefore that we should choose racers from 30 to 40 ft. water-line from Britain or America, and from 18 to 25 ft. water-line from Scandinavian countries, and a centreboard inland racer from Central Europe. Those are the lines on which I have developed this chapter. In *Stormy Weather*, *Evenlode* and *Golden Eye* we have three lovely little vessels fast enough to give a great deal of fun even when sailed in day races, and sturdy enough to take their owners round the world if they so wished, and in them we have the finest types of racing cruisers, while the smaller one-design classes are all excellent examples of the day cruisers, *Ferret* showing the type of craft developed for inland racing.

A careful study of all these plans and the problems will help us all towards the correct solution of the problem, for the examples given are as fine as can be found in this world. Supposing *Evenlode* or a similar vessel designed by

Fife was chosen as a 35 ft. water-line class ; then a committee of British yachtsmen and designers would be formed to control and settle all points arising from this class, just as the Scandinavian countries now control the Dragons ; and if the light and lively 15-square metre was chosen as a smaller class this too would be controlled by the Scandinavian Committee, while the inland waters class would be in the hands of a committee from Central Europe. Possibly a corresponding member from each country should be elected to all these committees, as then he would collect the thoughts from his country and pass them on to the committee, while the committee would send him an outline of any proposed change for his and his country's views on it ; for all we know that a single International Committee would be too big and cumbersome to deal with the problems arising.

If a range of one-design classes from 40 ft. water-line downwards could be adopted and fostered by the I.Y.R.U. and the North American Yacht Racing Union, it would save a great deal of trouble to clubs, for they would naturally adopt an International one-design class, and the state of affairs that at present exists at Lowestoft be done away with, For at Lowestoft there was a move to start a one-design class, and now they have two Dragons, two Tumlarens and two Star boats, all six racing together on a handicap basis, whereas had there been an International class they would have adopted it and they would have had six boats to one class which would have given good sport. So one hopes that the I.Y.R.U. will see its way through the difficult problem of adopting a range of one-design classes as International one-designs, for though this would mean a great deal of work for them the good which would arise from it would be well worth it.

STORMY WEATHER

Length, overall	-	53 ft. 11 in. = 16·42 m.	Length, water-line	-	39 ft. 8 in. = 12·08 m.
Beam	-	12 ft. 6 in. = 3·81 m.	Draught	- -	7 ft. 11 in. = 2·41 m.
Displacement -	20 tons	= 20,321 kilos.	Sail Area	- -	1300 sq. ft. = 121 sq. m.

Owner, PHILIP LE BOUTILLIER   *Designer*, OLIN STEPHENS   *Builder*, HENRY B. NEVINS

Three craft, designed as cruisers and for ocean racing, head the designs put forward to enable us to study the question of International one-design classes, and these three are 40, 35 and 30 ft. on the water-line. The difference

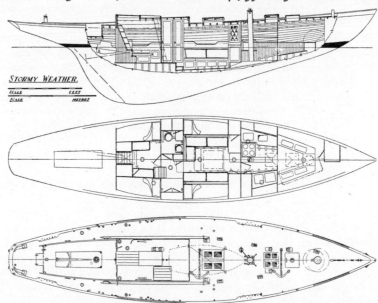

in these lengths is sufficient to give different size craft that need different crews, and in which different accommodation plans are arranged.

The first of these is *Stormy Weather*, whose plans I have taken from my *Second Book* to illustrate this chapter. When we remember that in 1935 she won the trans-Atlantic race from Brenton Reef, America, to Bergen in Norway, a distance of 3000 miles, after which she sailed down to Cowes and then won our Fastnet Race on her way home to America, finally sailing to windward across the Atlantic in the remarkable time of 23 days, we realise what an excellent little vessel *Stormy Weather* is, and what a wonderful class would be formed if there were a dozen or so such craft. They are so fast that they would give a great deal of pleasure for day sailing, and their accommodation is such that they would make wonderful cruisers and wonderful little vessels for passage races from port to port as they followed

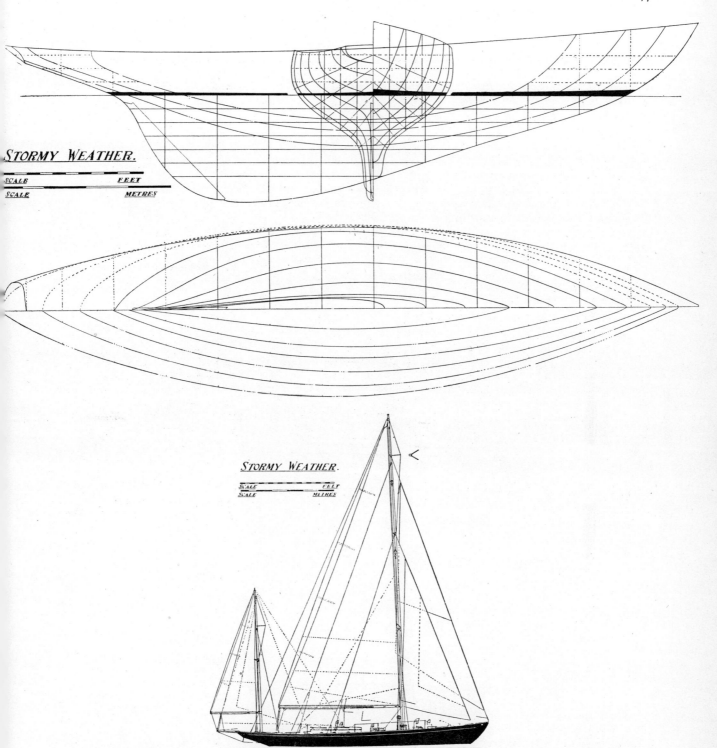

STORMY WEATHER.

SCALE   FEET
SCALE   METRES

STORMY WEATHER.

SCALE   FEET
SCALE   METRES

the regattas round the coast. By day they would form fine racers for their owners, who all the time would be taking with them a comfortable home, and no matter what the weather these little vessels are brave and good enough to go out and face it, so an owner would never need to miss any race on that account, and the picture of the pleasure such a class could and would give their owners surely makes the effort to establish such a class well worth while.

Every line of *Stormy Weather* tells of speed and comfort at sea, while the accommodation plan shows that a great deal of room is to be found below her decks, and her sail plan is one which would be fast in every kind of weather from a summer gale to light airs.

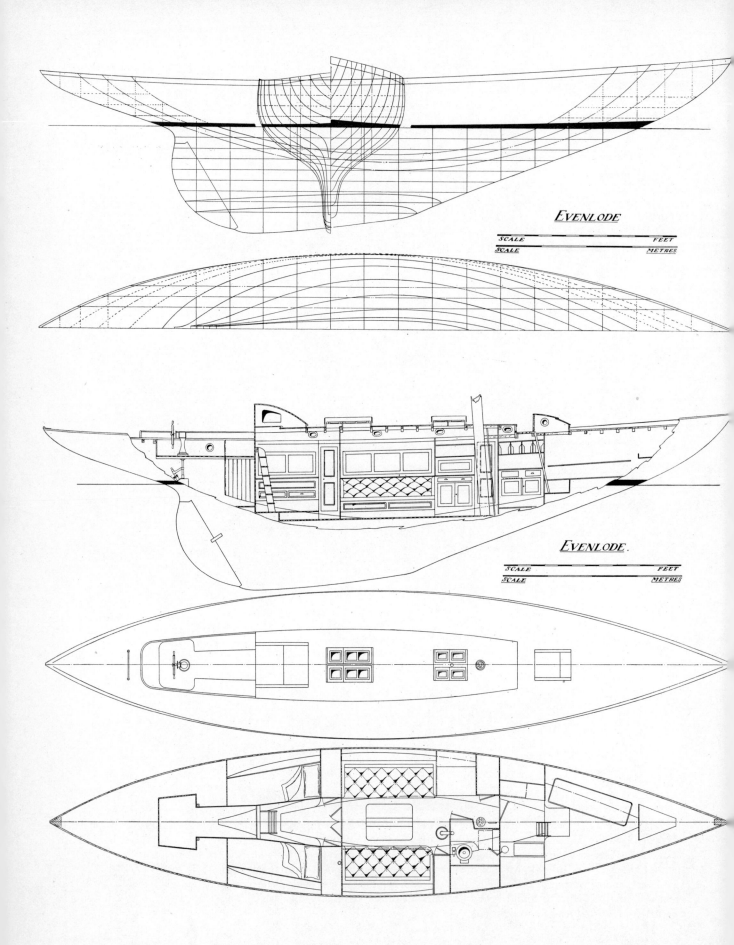

EVENLODE

SCALE   FEET
SCALE   METRES

EVENLODE.

SCALE   FEET
SCALE   METRES

EVENLODE

Length, overall -	50 ft. 6 in. = 15·39 m.	Length, water-line -	35 ft. 0 in. = 10·66 m.
Beam - -	11 ft. 0 in. = 3·35 m.	Draught - -	7 ft. 6 in. = 2·28 m.
Displacement -	13·60 tons = 13,817 kilos.	Sail Area -	1053 sq. ft. = 97·82 sq. m.

Owner, CHRIS. RATSEY   *Designer*, WILLIAM FIFE   *Builder*, WILLIAM FIFE & SON

During his long life William Fife has designed a great many sailing yachts, yachts that have given a great deal of pleasure to all lovers of the sea and ships, a great many of them being beautiful racing craft, from challengers for the *America's* Cup to the tiniest of racers, each one being well nigh perfect.

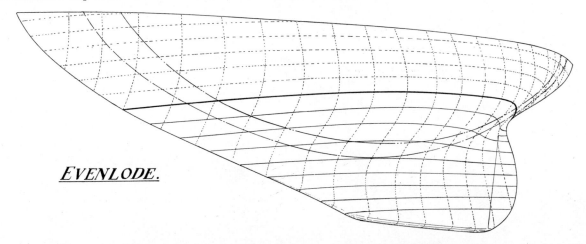

EVENLODE.

Amongst his most notable craft are the schooner *Susanne*, *Shamrock III*, and *White Heather*, while his twelve, eight and six-metre racers have long been famous all over the world. And all William Fife's knowledge and under-

SUSANNE

standing of the way of a ship at sea is behind this set of plans, so that as we look at *Evenlode* we cannot help but break one of the ten commandments which tells us we must not covet anything that belongs to our neighbours, for we would dearly love to own such a lovely little ship.

　　　The lines tell of beautiful proportions, speed and comfort at sea, and as one would expect coming from William Fife's board they are very pleasing to the eye ; the buttocks are long and fair, and the water-lines a delight to look upon.　The two lower water-lines, being shown on the lead keel, tell us that here they are true streamlines.

　　　The V'd sections forward make for ease and comfort, and these blend into the midship sections, and from there aft to the canoe stern in a manner so pleasing to the eye that they tell of a master hand.　We can gaze at the lines of *Evenlode* for a long time and then still come back to them and find delight in so doing, for to those who understand lines they bring a sense of peace and harmony, and just to gaze at them is to feel contented, for they are the work of a great artist.

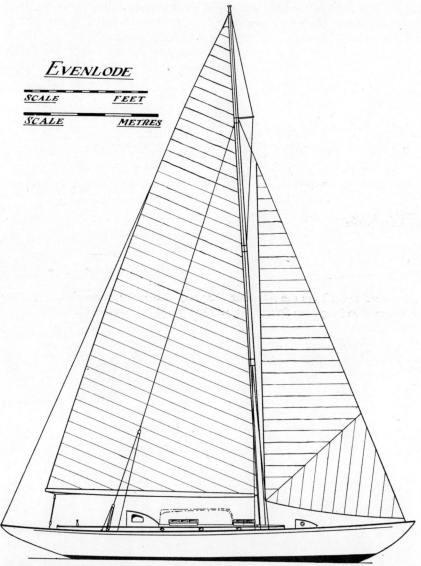

EVENLODE

SCALE　　　　　FEET

SCALE　　　　　METRES

　　　The rudder post has thirty degrees rake, for *Evenlode* is designed for sea work, and a raking rudder post, while it has the advantage of cutting down wetted surface aft, makes for a boat that is difficult to steer.　*Evenlode's* rudder may be taken as very close to the ideal rake for sea work.

　　　The accommodation shows a single berthed fo'c'sle with the galley immediately abaft it, and between this and the saloon is a wardrobe to port and washroom to starboard.　The saloon is very cosy with its settees either side.

　　　Abaft of this comes a double-berthed sleeping cabin with a companion way leading out into the watertight cockpit, while her deck plan shows a good clear deck, where one can handle and work her sails comfortably, for as will be seen from her sail plan *Evenlode* has a simple cutter rig with a single headsail.　The mast, being just about one-third of her water-line abaft its fore end, is well into the vessel, and this simple yet efficient rig drives *Evenlode* along at a good clip.

GOLDEN EYE

Length, overall -	41 ft. 3 in. = 12·56 m.	Length, water-line -	30 ft. 0 in. = 9·14 m.
Beam - -	11 ft. 0 in. = 3·35 m.	Draught - -	6 ft. 0 in. = 1·82 m.
Displacement -	10·11 tons = 10,261 kilos.	Sail Area -	917 sq. ft. = 85·18 sq. ft.

Owner, H. PRESCOTT WELLS   *Designer*, PHIL RHODES OF COX & STEVENS INC.
Builder, MINNEFORD YACHT YARD INC.

Though designed as a comfortable and sensible cruiser, or perhaps because of this, and because of the fact that her designer was Phil Rhodes, *Golden Eye* has turned out to be a wonderful little sailor, one that is able to ghost along in very light weather, and when the breeze has blown up and the weather is bad she is not only fast but comfortable.

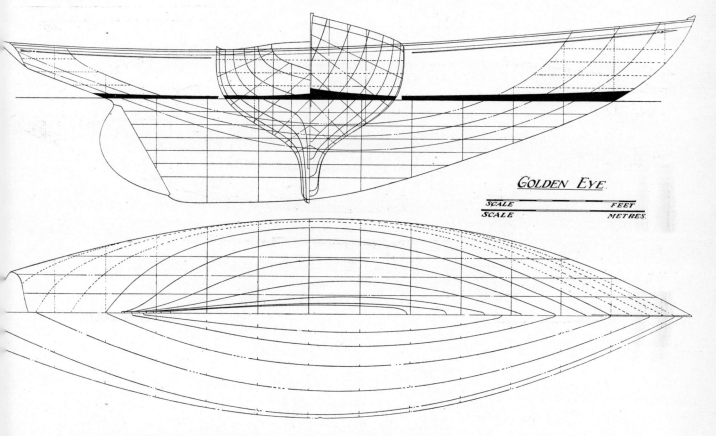

GOLDEN EYE

SCALE ——————— FEET
SCALE ——————— METRES.

As can be seen from her dimensions she is beamy, and at the same time of heavier displacement than usual these days, these two things making for comfort below decks and also comfort and safety at sea. It would be difficult to improve upon the lines of this little craft, a fact proved by her coming out top of her class in the Gibson Island race. A study of her lines will prove interesting and instructive to all, for she is another little cruiser of which Phil Rhodes may justly feel very proud.

The construction plan shows that the deckhouse, which gives her the unusual head room of 6 ft. 5 in., runs forward past the mast in order to give full head room in the double-berthed fo'c'sle cabin, but we see there is no weakness arising from this, for like the rest of her construction the strains and stresses have been thought of and prepared for.

Her accommodation plan shows that where one usually sees two pipe cots in the fo'c'sle, she has two built-in berths, and the fo'c'sle really becomes a double-berthed forward cabin, abaft of which she has a roomy galley and pantry to port, while to starboard is her washroom and farther aft her main cabin with built-in berths behind the two settees, so that below decks *Golden Eye* is a cosy little ship.

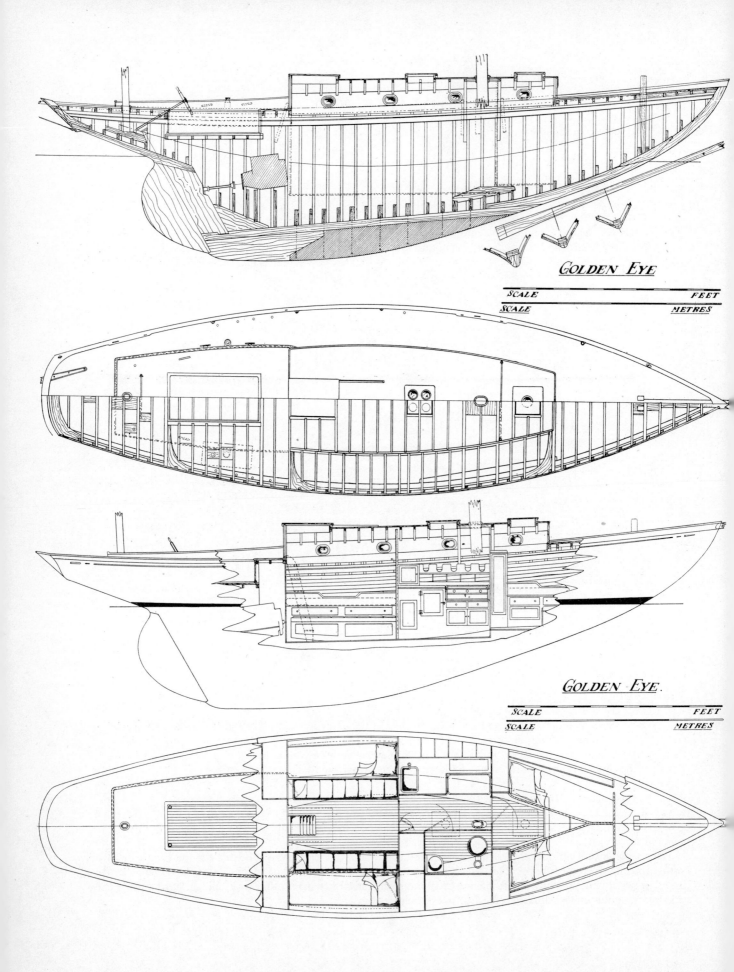

GOLDEN EYE

SCALE   FEET

SCALE   METRES

GOLDEN EYE.

SCALE   FEET

SCALE   METRES

A companion way leads out of the after hatch over the bridge deck to the cockpit, and under this her auxiliary engine is fitted, and while this is partitioned off from the accommodation it is quite accessible.

Her sail plan shows she has a double headsail yawl rig, which enables her to set combinations of sail to suit every kind of weather from the lightest air to a gale of wind, and the rig seems perfect for such a little cruiser. There is

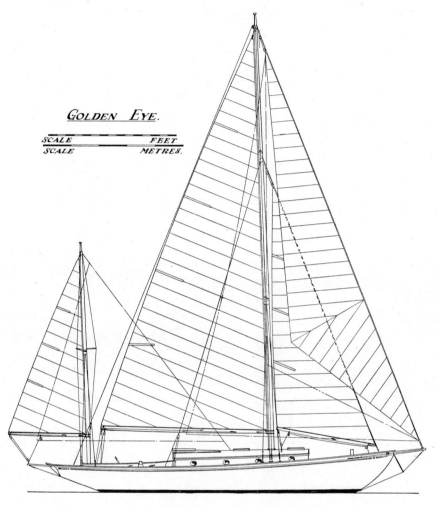

GOLDEN EYE.

only one small point I should like to see changed, and that is that the mizen staysail be tacked to the after end of the deckhouse, for my experience has been that to be really efficient the mizen staysail must not go forward of a point half-way between the main and mizen masts, as if it does it is fighting with the mainsail and the two spoil each other. In *Golden Eye* we see a perfect little cruiser with speed enough in her to win long distance races under any conditions.

LAKE ONE-DESIGN

Length, overall -	34 ft. 0 in. = 10·36 m.		Length, water-line -	23 ft. 4 in. = 7·11 m.
Beam - -	7 ft. 9 in. = 2·36 m.		Draught - -	5 ft. 3 in. = 1·60 m.
	Sail Area - - - -		444 sq. ft. = 41·24 sq. m.	

Designer, PHILIP RHODES OF COX & STEVENS INC.

This class came into being as the great lakes badly needed a one-design class that could be handled by two, and was economical in cost and upkeep, and which, at the same time, would be fast and seaworthy. It was intended that the class should be manly enough to take part in the long distance racing on the lakes, and the formation of it was tackled in an admirable manner.

Major W. F. N. Windier, of the Royal Canadian Yacht Club, appointed the committee, representing the ten Canadian and American Yacht Clubs in the Lake Racing Association, of which he is president, to promote the class.

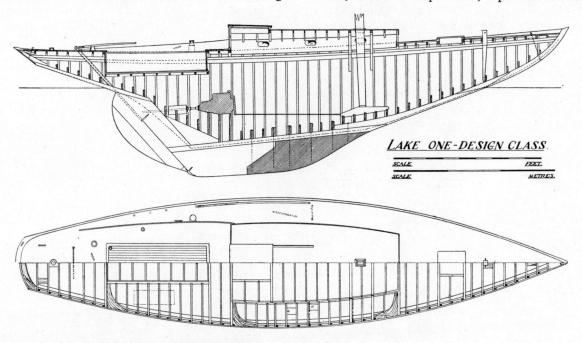

LAKE ONE-DESIGN CLASS.

SCALE   FEET.
SCALE   METRES.

The committee is formed from the following clubs :

Buffalo Yacht Club.   Crescent Yacht Club.
Kingston Yacht Club.   Olcott Yacht Club.
Oswego Yacht Club.   Queen City Yacht Club.
Rochester Yacht Club.   Royal Canadian Yacht Club.
Royal Hamilton Yacht Club.   Youngstown Yacht Club.

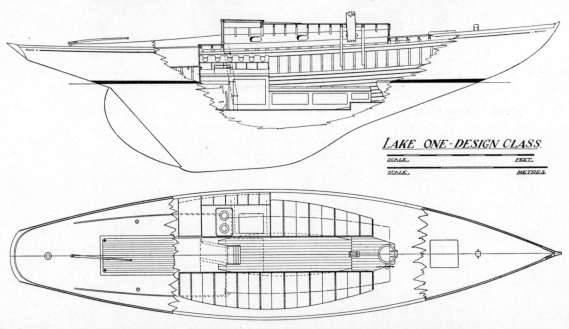

LAKE ONE-DESIGN CLASS.

SCALE.   FEET.
SCALE.   METRES.

After carefully studying a number of designs by the best Canadian and American architects, they finally selected this design by Philip Rhodes of Cox & Stevens, and looking at the plans, we heartily agree with their choice.   The lines tell of a fast, yet weatherly and seaworthy hull. The construction plan shows that it is one that will give no anxiety when the wind is strong and the sea is running high, for the mahogany planking is just on $\frac{7}{8}$ in. in thickness, and the frames only 8 in. apart.

A study of the construction plan will show that the designer has carefully considered all the stresses and strains put upon such a vessel. With no less than five feet headroom, she has a cosy cabin, the transoms of which enable three to sleep in comfort, one to port and two to starboard, while the galley and pantry is situated at the farther end of the cabin on the port side, which is, without doubt, the best place for it in such a craft, for here the motion is least, and cooking can be carried on at sea, and also the fumes from cooking quickly escape out of the hatchway, which can nearly always be left open, while the forehatch generally has to remain closed.

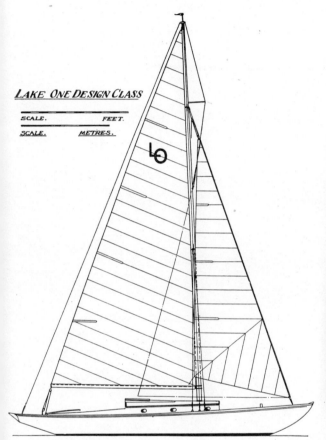

LAKE ONE DESIGN CLASS

SCALE.   FEET.

SCALE.   METRES.

A LAKE ONE-DESIGN IN A BREEZE

Under the ladder, the Sea Scout engine is installed out of the way, where it can easily be reached when needed.

The deck of this boat is fairly clear, and there is practically no need for anyone to go out of the watertight cockpit when once she is under way, as all sheets and runner falls lead back here.

The 444 square feet of sail area is well arranged, as one-quarter of it is in the headsail, and the other three parts in the mainsail, which brings the mast well aft, a point which makes for a well-behaved boat in a seaway, and one which will tend to ride quietly at her anchor. So we see that these little vessels have a great deal to recommend them. Looking at their plans, I am reminded of two French yachtsmen from St. Malo, who came to Cowes to talk over a one-design class with me. They wanted a fast little sailing craft that was manly enough to take them through the strong tidal waters from St. Malo to Guernsey and back. This class would seem to suit them, as they are speedy and seaworthy, and have cabin accommodation and cooking arrangements that would enable the racers to live aboard, and spend nights at sea if necessary, in comfort and safety.

THE BJARNE AAS CLASS

Length, overall	-	33 ft. 4 in. = 10·15 m.	Length, water-line	-	21 ft. 5 in. = 6·55 m.
Beam	-	6 ft. 9 in. = 2·05 m.	Draught	-	5 ft. 4 in. = 1·60 m.
Displacement	-	6950 lb. = 3152 kilos.	Sail Area	-	418 sq. ft. = 38·85 sq. m.

Designer, BJARNE AAS

There is no doubt that these boats are lovely little vessels. We have only to look at the lines to realise their speed, and those of us who have seen them sailing have been filled with admiration for them. The cabin enables them to be used as cruisers by any owner wishing to do so, and so it is not surprising that this class is growing in

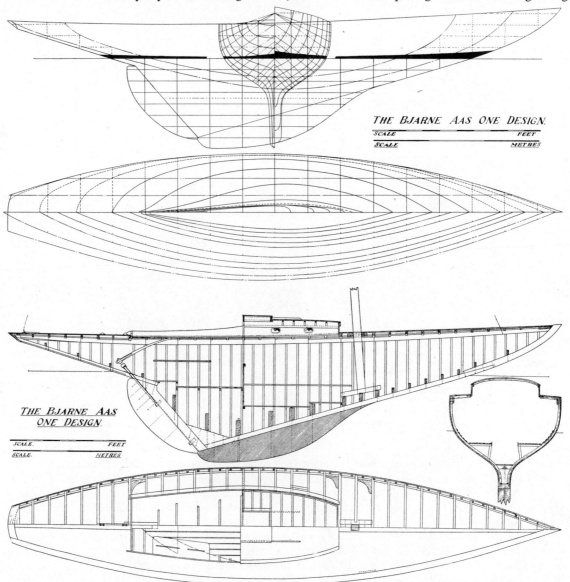

THE BJARNE AAS ONE DESIGN.

THE BJARNE AAS ONE DESIGN.

popularity. There is a large fleet of them already established on Long Island Sound, where they have given good sport, while another fleet has been formed in Bermuda, and F. G. Mitchell, the Commodore of the Royal Corinthian, is starting a fleet of them on the Crouch. As we look at them under way and their plans we realise that with their 6 ft. 9 in. beam they represent very closely the type of vessel we all hoped the 6-metre rule would produce, and so one might almost call this class a cruising type of 6-metre, and as such they have great appeal.

The sail plan is well but simply stayed under two pairs of crosstrees and a pair of jumper struts. These, with a permanent backstay aft, are sufficient to hold this rig in place, and designers, builders and rule makers may learn a great deal from a careful study of these plans.

COMMODORE F. G. MITCHELL'S BJARNE AAS ONE-DESIGN

REGULATIONS GOVERNING THE BJARNE AAS ONE-DESIGN CLASS
GENERAL

The International One-Design Class shall be controlled by regulations set forth herein, which shall be altered only by two-thirds majority vote of the Controlling Board as hereinafter set forth. It is the general purpose of the

Class to restrict fleets to active, racing yachtsmen and to a limited number of yachts for each country, to the end that an active class with reasonably stable values may be created and maintained.

It is the general intention that there shall be not more than one fleet to a country (by a country a geographical rather than a National limitation is imposed, that is, there might be a fleet in England, Canada and Bermuda or other English colony within this regulation).

In countries where yachting centres are considerably removed from each other, *i.e.* several hundred miles, the Controlling Board may, upon recommendation of the Country Class Committee involved, grant a franchise to one or more additional fleets in such country, but in that event the Class Committee of the first fleet shall remain the parent organisation for the Country in question and representation on the Control Board shall be through its Chairman.

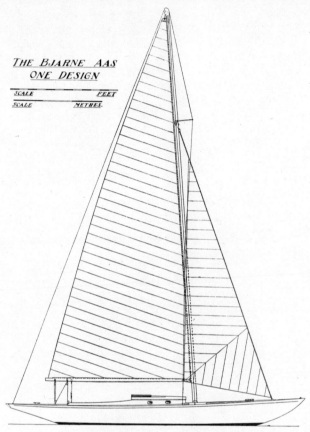

THE BJARNE AAS
ONE DESIGN

SCALE   FEET
SCALE   METRES.

CONTROL OF FLEETS

The fleet in each country shall be controlled by a Country Class Committee of not less than three Class Owners, who shall be elected once a year by the individual boat owners (one vote per boat) of the parent fleet of the Country in question ; they shall serve for one year or until their successors are elected. In the event that there should be more than one fleet in a given Country, as provided for herein, such additional fleet may, at their election, set up their own Class Committee for the handling of local problems and shall be entitled to representation on the Country Class Committee through their Chairman.

The Class Committee may during any year fill vacancies by appointment, selection being made by the majority of the Class Committee from registered owners in the Class.

The Class Committee shall within the general regulations laid down hereunder have entire control of their Country's fleet or fleets, and their decision on all matters within the Country shall be final.

CONTROLLING BOARD

The Chairman of the Class Committee in each Country shall together make up a Controlling Board of the Class, and their decisions on all matters respecting the Class shall be final. They shall elect from among their own number a Chairman who shall serve for one year or until a successor is appointed.

YACHTS

The Class shall consist of yachts as designed by B. J. Aas and covered by his plans and specifications as follows :

Working Drawing,
Sail and Rigging Plan,
Specifications as revised,
all as attached hereto.

No structural changes shall be permitted from these plans in any yacht enrolled in the Class.

Nothing herein contained, however, shall prevent any owner from making such interior changes as he wishes in the hull and/or the deck fittings, to the extent that such changes are not specifically prohibited in these regulations.

It is desirable, for the sake of uniformity, that insofar as possible all yachts enrolled in the Class shall be built by B. J. Aas at Fredrikstad, Norway. Arrangements have been made, however, which, with the approval of the Control Board, permit of yachts being constructed at other points from plans prepared by Mr. Aas, upon payment in advance of a reasonable sum, as a designer fee to Mr. Aas and an inspection fee to the Control Board for an inspector to be appointed by the Control Board. Such yachts must have a certificate from the builder that strict compliance with the plans and specifications has been maintained and such certificate must be approved and endorsed by the inspector appointed by the Control Board.

RIGGING

Rigging, as previously specified, shall comply with rigging plan attached. The use of stainless steel wire or plow steel is optional to the Country Class Committee.

SPARS

Spars shall conform to spar plan as originally designed. Masts shall not be altered in their rake or position beyond limitations allowed by the opening in the mast partner.

SPINNAKER POLE

One spinnaker pole only of a length of x ft. shall be carried.

SAILS

Only one suit of sails (whether new or old) may be added to a boat's racing equipment in any one season. A sail used in any class race becomes a part of the boat's racing inventory. Original use prior to September 1 of any year throws a sail in the current year's inventory, after September 1 in the following year's inventory, *i.e.* a new sail used after September 1 counts as an addition to the following year's inventory and precludes the possibility of the purchase of an additional sail the following year. In case of accident, however, the Country Class Committee may modify this rule, or in the case of owners who have not availed themselves of the opportunity to augment their equipment by a new suit of sails each season, the Country Class Committee may, on receipt of evidence satisfactory to it that such owner is at a disadvantage in the handling of his boat by reason of such deficiency in sails, in its discretion, waive this rule to the extent of allowing the purchase of two suits of sails (either complete or partial suits) in one season. When such exception is made by the Committee all owners in the Country involved shall be advised. Mainsail battens are limited to two measuring x ft. and two measuring x ft.

During the first season's use, after delivery of the boats from the builder, a Country Class Committee may permit one additional suit of sails.

As a means of regulating the hoist of the mainsail, all boats must be equipped with a special shackle substantially 3 in. long. This will limit the hoist of the mainsail at the top of the mast. Gooseneck tracks shall be equipped with a screw x in. from the lower end of the track for a lower stop which must at all times be kept in place. It is the purpose of this regulation to provide a mainsail with a hoist of not over x ft. Booms shall be x ft. long from the after side of the mast to the outboard end of the boom. Loose-footed mainsails are barred.

A painted band $\frac{1}{2}$ in. wide shall be marked around the boom x in. from the centre of the vertical pin in the gooseneck and jibs in practice may not be stretched beyond these marks.

Sails shall consist of a mainsail, jib and spinnaker, all of the dimensions shown on the sail plan. Spinnakers for any one class in any given Country shall be ordered in groups equal to the required number from one sailmaker and shall be assigned to owners by lot, that is, to avoid individual selection and to ensure utmost uniformity.

In practice spinnakers may be carried around the jibstay and sheets may be trimmed outside the shrouds.

PAINTING

Painting shall be optional with owners, with the exception that for the sake of uniformity in bottom finish Baltimore Bronze Bottom Paint shall be used—not less than three boats with the following exception only that owners may paint a strip around their yachts below the water-line not over 12 in. wide of any colour and or paint.

THE BJARNE AAS ONE-DESIGN
AT COWES

MINIMUM INVENTORY

Yachts participating in any Class event must carry the following minimum inventory :

  1 Anchor not less than 33 pounds,
20 Fathoms of anchor rope of at least $\frac{3}{4}$ in. diameter.
  1 30 in. Foghorn,
  4 Serviceable Life Preservers,
  1 Anchor Light,
  1 10-Quart Metal or Fibreware Bucket,
  1 Compass with a card of at least 4 in. diameter,
  1 Bilge Pump,
  1 Boat Hook.

CREW

When racing, the crew shall consist of not more than four persons, one of whom may be a paid hand, who shall, under no circumstances, handle the tiller during the races. Women, and children under 13 years of age, may be carried and not counted as crew, but a women helmsman shall count as one of the crew.

HAULING OUT

During the life of any season's official racing schedule yachts shall not be hauled out or put on the beach more than once in three weeks and then for not more than ninety-six hours, subject to tides. The first haul-out during the official racing schedule may be taken at the option of the owner or his representative. Thereafter three calendar weeks must elapse between hauls.

In the event of an accident, requiring the hauling-out of a boat other than as scheduled above, full facts must be immediately submitted to the Country Class Committee and their approval of such special haul secured. In the event of such emergency haul being approved, future hauls shall date therefrom.

CLASS INSIGNIA

The Class Insignia shall consist of a crossed " I " and " C ", in which the " I " shall be 14 in. high. Such insignia shall be carried on all mainsails situated in the upper plan of the mainsail just above the top batten. In International events participating yachts shall carry on each side of the mainsails, just above this insignia, distinguishing letters significant of their Country, at least 12 in. high. In addition to the insignia mainsails shall be marked with the proper distinguishing number of the boat.

RULES

Except as modified herein the rules of the accredited Yachting Association of the countries in question shall govern. International races shall be sailed under the direction of the Country Class Committee of the Country holding the races and the rules of the accredited Yachting Association of such country shall govern such races ; in the event that the Country holding such race shall not have such accredited Yachting Association then the rules of the North American Yacht Racing Association shall govern. Questions arising under the Class Rules shall be decided by the Country Class Committee and their decision shall be final. Owners are urged to immediately report in writing any evidence of infringement of the foregoing rules to the Country Class Committee who will investigate the boat in question and decide upon her eligibility. Boats not complying to the Class Rules may be disqualified by the Country Class Committee in all races in which violations have occurred.

November, 1936.

15 - SQUARE METRE SKERRY CRUISER

Length, overall -	33 ft. 7⅝ in. = 10·23 m.		Length, water-line -	21 ft. 8⅝ in. = 6·60 m.
Beam - -	5 ft. 9⅝ in. = 1·76 m.		Draught - -	3 ft. 9¼ in. = 1·14 m.
Displacement -	1·323 tons = 1340 kilos.		Sail Area - -	162 sq. ft. = 15 sq. m.

Designer, KNUD H. REIMERS

There are many clubs in this country racing on tidal waters, which are very confined and so not suitable for large and heavy racers, but the members would like to race little thoroughbreds, and at the same time have a small cabin or shelter. I thought of these people when I saw this 15-square metre by Knud H. Reimers ; she is a

dear little boat, and a type that would suit many districts and many people, for with her draught of 3 ft. 9 in. she would go almost anywhere, while her short keel would enable her to be twisted and tacked about as often as her owner wished without losing too much way, while the fine easy lines tell us that she would be exceedingly fast in all weathers, as well as being a brave little sea boat that would climb almost every sea that came her way, because of the reserve buoyancy above water.

The lines are those we expect to see in these small light-displacement boats so favoured on the Baltic, but of which most other countries are needlessly afraid ; for the lighter a vessel, providing she is strong, the easier she is in a seaway, the easier she is hauled out, and the less weight she needs on her lead keel. Indeed, light-displacement vessels have, it seems, advantages over their heavier sisters in most ways, for besides being capable of higher speeds in hard weather they are also less costly to transport.

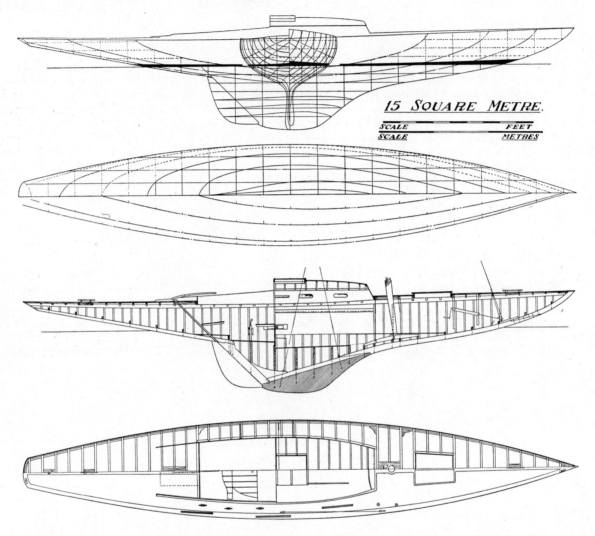

15 SQUARE METRE.

SCALE   FEET
SCALE   METRES

Even this small racer has a full-length bunk on either side of her cabin and sitting-up room in it, which means that besides being a delightful little racer she would make a week-end cruiser for her owner and would be ideal as a day cruiser, so that one could imagine this boat owner racing her hard on the Saturday, and then on the Sunday taking perhaps two of his friends for an enjoyable day's sailing, as this boat would give a great deal of enjoyment whether cruising or racing.

The sail plan is very extreme in its height, for the mainsail luff is four times that of the boom, and generally speaking it is extremely difficult to get a mainsail with a luff $3\frac{1}{2}$ times the length of the foot to stand ; but with a 3-foot rake on a mast a great deal of round can be thrown into the leech, and this with the curve in the mast above the hounds makes the sail wider aloft, and more liable to stand. However, the present day tendency is towards taller and narrower sails, and here we see this carried, I imagine, to finality. Such a sail plan uses the 15-square metre (162 square feet) to the utmost advantage and we see that this long easily driven light-displacement hull is driven by an equally long narrow and efficient sail plan, the two combined being more up to date than any other craft that it has been my lot to see.

Three different headsails are shown, the largest genoa coming well abaft the end of the main boom, so as well as the joy of sailing, the owner of such a vessel would have the joy of owning a boat that is really ahead of her time.

CONTENT ("TEAL" ONE-DESIGN CLASS)

Length, overall - 30 ft. 6 in. = 9·296 m.   Length, water-line - 20 ft. 0 in. = 6·096 m.
Beam - - 7 ft. 0 in. = 2·133 m.   Draught - - 5 ft. 0 in. = 1·52 m.
Displacement - 2·9 tons = 2946 kilos.   Sail Area - - 401 sq. ft. = 37·25 sq. m.

Designer, A. R. LUKE

A year or so ago Bernard Clay was wandering round London with a model under his arm preaching the gospel of *Teal*, but though many listened to his preachings, very few took it to heart, and it seemed to me that as his seed was falling on stony ground it bore no fruit. The reason for the ground being so stony was that most men he met were "stony broke". However, Bernard Clay asked E. Williams of Cowes to build a full-sized edition of his model and so *Teal*, the first of her class, was built.

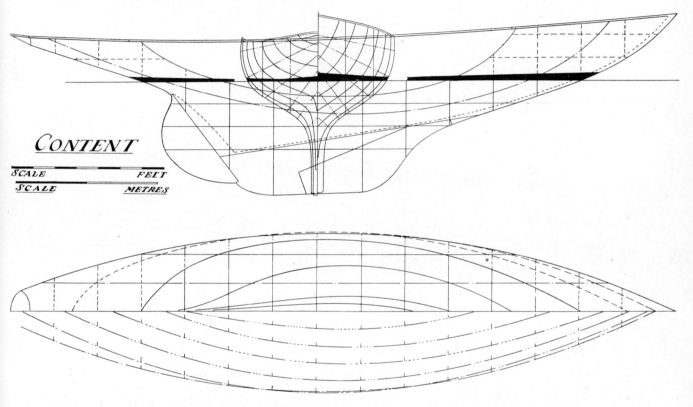

CONTENT

SCALE ——————— FEET
SCALE ——————— METRES

Like the model, *Teal* herself was a delight to the eye, as one would expect, for she was designed by Luke, of Hamble. She proved herself to be such an able boat, both as a racer and as a day cruiser that more were built to the class the following year, and to-day we have half-a-dozen boats to the "Teal" class, and there is every prospect of this class growing as the years go by.

Though a one-design class that would make good day cruisers they also conform to the Ocean Racing Club's rules very well, and for the last three years have won places in the Round the Island Race, a "Teal" winning in 1935 and 1936. This year (1937) a special handicap was put on them but even so "Teal" won third prize in a race which, lasting 14 hours, gave almost every condition of wind and sea and all points of sailing over the 54 mile course. So an account of this year's Round the Island Race, from the "Teal" class viewpoint, will illustrate the all-round ability of these little vessels.

Before starting on the race, however, it is as well to look them over :

The sections show that being unhampered by any rule she has a good flare forward and throws a great deal of water away from her deck when sailing, which is in contrast to boats to the international rule who are pinched in at the deck to save girth measurement.

The buttocks, water-lines and diagonals all give the impression of power.

The construction plan tells us that these "Teals" are built on grown frames, an important thing in a One-design class for grown frames make for a uniform shape throughout. Between these grown frames are three bent timbers.

The keel or backbone is fairly heavy, and it will be noticed in way of the mast that the stem has been left very deep with a long scarph on to the keel, a good point, as the downward thrust of the mast causes most boats to leak at this spot. In the same plan we see a very roomy cockpit and also a full-length bunk either side of the cabin. The fore hatch is a useful place from which to set and take in the spinnaker.

The sail plan is quite normal, the reason for the headsail being small and not overlapping the mainsail, is that all the owners agreed amongst themselves to keep to this sized headsail on the score of expense, for there is no doubt that while an overlapping headsail would improve the speed it would also increase the cost of racing in the class.

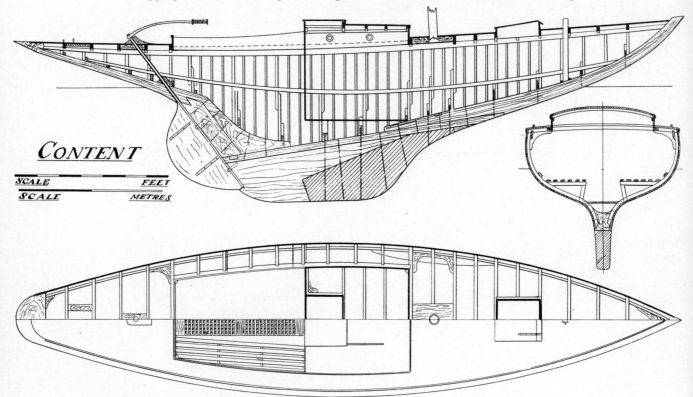

CONTENT

SCALE FEET
SCALE METRES

The mast is solid, also to save expense, and the boats are well able to carry this solid spar.

Seven years ago, Major Cyril Windelere decided that a race round the Isle of Wight would be a very sporting event. Accordingly he put up a Roman Bowl in gold as a challenge cup, and put the race in the hands of the Island Sailing Club. Once more we have an example of the good that can be done by a man with the courage of his convictions, for every year this race has increased in popularity until this year twenty-four very fine yachts came to the line. The start was at 8.30 a.m., three hours before low water and the turn of the tide at the Needles, which meant that each would carry his tide round the Bridge buoy at the Needles.

Cecil Donne had kindly asked me to go with him, when twelve hours before the race I discovered I could go, and so this race will be described from *Content's* viewpoint.

The wind was strong from the sou' sou' west and several had reefs tucked in their mainsails and were the better for this, but most of us carried full sail.

We planned to cross the middle of the line as we thought here we should have all the wind we needed, and that we should be clear of those going for the weather end and also those at the lee end of the line. With a fair tide and reaching wind it made little difference where one started on the line. So we had a fairly clear start. However, when we were off the Squadron, a hundred yards from the starting line, *Dolly Varden* had the lead of the fleet. The other large vessels having been late over the line, and taking the outer end, had sailed through the lee of everyone to windward. So with a breeze in which we would have sailed just as fast with a single reef in we all tore down to the Needles on a close reach at our maximum speeds. Our Commodore, the Hon. George Colville was the first to go through our lee with his old Solent one-design *Moby Dick*, some 5 ft. longer on the water-line, then came the new Ocean racer, *Keryl II*, 30 ft. on the water-line and presumably far faster than *Content*. When she had sailed through our lee she luffed out to windward as *Moby Dick* had done. *Maid of Malham* had already sailed past us away to leeward, and so had the Herreshoff 40-footer, *Neith*, who sailed across the Atlantic many years ago. But though *Moby Dick*,

Maid of Malham, and *Neith* drew ahead of us we held and repassed *Keryl* before reaching the Needles, rounding the Bridge buoy some five minutes ahead of her.

With the wind light and the ebb tide against us after rounding the Bridge buoy it was difficult to know what to do, and with each one making his own decision we were soon scattered over the waters outside the Needles.

Most everyone, expecting a far stronger wind with a vicious sea outside the Needles, had set smaller headsails and reefed, but we were content to watch the leaders who were far enough ahead to give us time to reef if it were needed. However, it so happened that as we drew clear of the Needles, and into the Channel the wind lightened, and the leaders had a job to stem the last of the ebb with a light failing southerly wind.

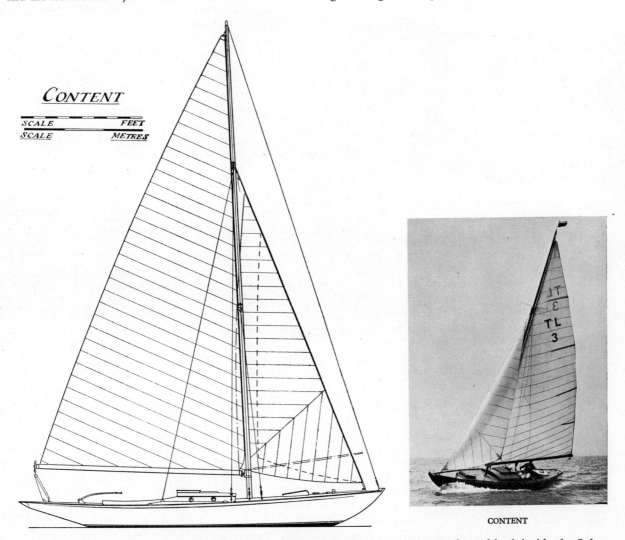

CONTENT

We rounded the Bridge buoy just ahead of *Phillipine*, the Solent one-design, and stood back inside the Solent to get the smooth water inside the Bridge buoy for a nasty tumble caused by the ebb as it runs over the Bridge would have knocked us about and shaken that light wind out of our sails. Being the only boat gliding along in smooth water, we had sailed through the fleet and were in the lead by the time we had reached Scratchels Bay. Not only had we kept in smooth water until we reached the Needles, but in this bay we had far less tide to contend with than those farther off-shore. Though the wind was light, and there was a danger of us being becalmed under the cliffs, this manœuvre had given us the lead, and we decided to carry on with it hoping to increase our lead, although no doubt the right thing to have done when we had obtained the lead was to stand off-shore against the last of the ebb and benefit by a slightly stronger breeze farther out. However, we worked close under the cliffs, and finally were becalmed in a pocket, from which we could not escape. In contrast to this, Hans Hamilton's *Solent Gipsy* had stood off on the port tack once he had rounded the Bridge buoy, and at times actually headed for St. Albans dead away from the next mark—St. Catherine's Point. Though this at first seemed the wrong thing to do, it eventually brought its reward, for he picked the first of the new breezes up, sailed right past the whole of the fleet, and was leading boat at St. Catherine's, where he made the mistake as we had, of getting in under the cliffs and being becalmed.

Unfortunately for us we were still becalmed as *Teal*, another of our one-designs, had worked her way outside of us, and picking up a breeze a hundred yards from us had sailed clear away with a lead of three or four miles before the breeze reached us. Eventually we escaped from the pocket under the cliffs, and on the way to St. Catherine's sailed past eight different boats, one of them being *Keryl*, the 30-ft. water-line ocean racer. As all this part of the course was a beat to windward in a very light air, off St. Catherine's we stood well out, for the tide was almost finished. We kept out until we judged our next tack would take us at the turn of the tide just inside the line from Dunnose to Culver Cliff. This worked out very well indeed and *Verity A*, the 26-ft. ocean racer stood out as we stood in on our last tack. When the ebb came down she had to stem the full force of it, but being just inside the bay we had far less tide to contend with. *Verity A*, without a breath of wind, started her engine and gave up. As she did this the first faint puffs of a south westerly came and setting our spinnaker we slowly drifted across Sandown Bay towards Culver Cliffs for the tide was now against us.

Well in the bay we could see *Teal*, the founder of our class, ghosting along under the cliffs. Presently she picked up a strong breeze there, and sailing past Culver Cliffs rounded the Bembridge Ledge Buoy. She was soon lost to sight sailing up through the Solent. However, the breeze was coming stronger, and as we met the strength of the tide off Dunnose it freshened enough to push us over this at a good clip, and we rushed up to the Bembridge Ledge Buoy in spite of the fact that here a strong tide was against us. Taking in our spinnaker we gybed round the buoy at 8.00 p.m., the breeze freshening fast and on the reach up to Noman's Fort, *Content* was travelling at her top speed. Inshore the tide was against us, but right out off the Nab it was slack and so *Content's* speed of just under seven knots for this part of the course may be taken as the utmost that these 20-ft. water-line boats are capable of.

As we rounded the Fort a heavy squall struck us and hove *Content* down till her cockpit coaming was in the water. Though the wind was off shore and the tide was slack, we soon had quite a popple of sea for such a small vessel. The wind threw the stinging spray over us, and though it was strenuous sailing, the eight miles from the Forts to Cowes in the twilight and darkness, were the best miles of the day.

To ease *Content* we slacked off the main sheet, for Cecil Donne, her owner, like myself, is a dinghy sailor and able to feel and ease a boat through strong squalls without reefing. However, with the wind still increasing we decided upon a reef and as *Content* is fitted with a worm reefing gear we had only to slack away on the main halyard and wind away on the handle and reef down without any slackening of pace or loss of time, for all the while *Content* was rushing along at her top speed.

Just astern was an ex 8-metre and though longer on the water-line, and a fast hull with a heavier keel, she could not be held up on her course to Castle Point, but slithered away to leeward, while we held our true course. We had to make two tacks in Cowes Roads to clear the moored yachts, and finally crossed the finishing line at 10.12.48, having been under way 14 hours, 14 hours which proved the ability of the " Teal " one-design class in every sort of weather from a calm to a strong breeze, for the breeze we finished in registered 30 miles an hour in the squalls. Times as follows :

	H.	M.	S.
Felise	8	13	32
Solent Gipsy	8	14	17
Cynthia	8	14	46
Phillipine	8	16	1
Maid of Malham	8	17	12
Neith	8	21	1
Mazurka	8	45	58
Dolly Varden	8	55	5
Helen	9	12	7
Chrisando	9	26	33
Narcissus	9	32	8
Moby Dick	9	32	24
Teal	9	40	30
Content	10	12	48
Rozelle	10	17	20
Armyne	10	28	36
Freedom	10	33	21
Keryl	10	38	0
Britt	11	0	28

Retired : *Orchis*, *Verity A*, *Allegro* and *Motihari II*.

DRAGONS

Length, overall -	29 ft. 2 in. = 8·88 m.	Length, water-line -	18 ft. 7 in. = 5·66 m.

Length, overall -   29 ft. 2 in. = 8·88 m.   Length, water-line -   18 ft. 7 in. = 5·66 m.

Beam   -   -   6 ft. 3 in. = 1·90 m.   Draught   -   -   3 ft. $9\frac{5}{8}$ in. = 1·16 m.

Sail Area   -   -   -   215 sq. ft. = 20 sq. m.

Designer, JOHAN ANKER

The Dragons, without ever being officially formed into one, have developed into what is in effect a strong and vigorous International one-design class. They have the great advantage of being controlled by the country

THE CHAMPION DRAGON

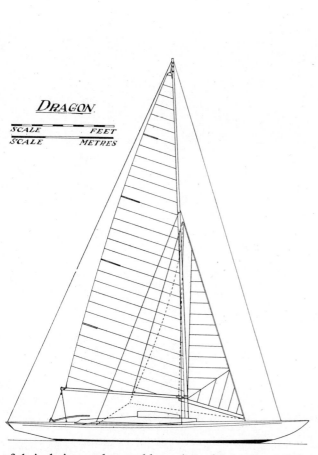

of their design, and so problems that arise can be settled quickly and easily. Every class in the world is bound to have problems arising from time to time, which often need a quick settlement, and the reason for the Dragons increasing in popularity and spreading to so many countries, is that they are undoubtedly fine little racers and day cruisers, and at the same time are very cheap, for Johan Anker, being a builder, has designed a type of craft that is very easily and cheaply constructed, yet one that at the same time is fast and seaworthy and a great pleasure to sail. These points are exactly what is required in a one-design class, for the whole point of a one-design class is to have boats that are inexpensive, and so do away with designing and building competition. These boats should be cheap to buy and run, and yet they should be boats any man would be proud to own and enjoy sailing in. The Dragons seem to fulfil all these points, and are now to be found in a great many countries in strong numbers, there being no less than seventy of them in British waters.

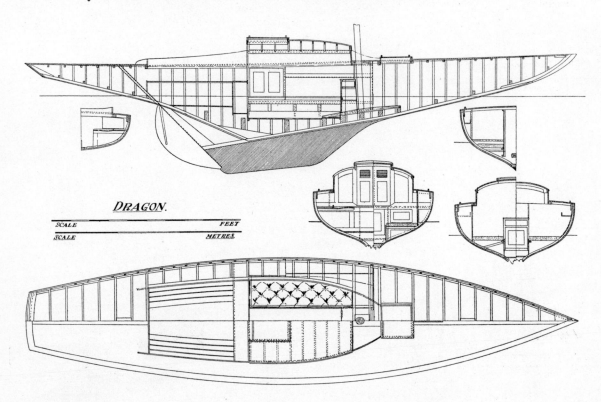

DRAGON.

| SCALE | FEET |
| SCALE | METRES. |

Looking at the plans we see that on a very fast set of lines Johan Anker has produced a fine little vessel with cabin accommodation, driven by a Bermudian cutter rig, a low fore triangle making for cheapness, as only one pair of crosstrees is needed to support the mast. The topmast stay prevents the top of the mast from going aft, while the permanent topmast backstay on the counter keeps it from bending forward ; throughout simplicity has been aimed at, and because the Dragons have the qualities sought for in one-design classes they will continue and prosper.

MYLNE 18-FOOTERS

Length, overall	-	24 ft. 9 in. = 7·543 m.	Length, water-line	-	18 ft. 0 in. = 5·486 m.
Beam	-	7 ft. 0 in. = 2·133 m.	Draught	-	3 ft. 3 in. = 0·99 m.
Displacement	-	2·05 tons = 2082 kilos.	Sail Area	-	257 sq. ft. = 23·88 m.

Designer, ALFRED MYLNE

During his lifetime Alfred Mylne has been asked to design several one-design classes, and as can be expected they have always proved to be perfect little ships for the jobs for which they were intended.

The boats to the Bombay One-Design Class which he designed many years ago have given the greatest satisfaction throughout the years they have been sailing, and the boats of this later class which he has designed for the Royal Mersey Yacht Club and the Trearddur Bay Club are sturdy little vessels, beamy and buoyant, seaworthy and robust, with short ends to save expense in building, for this was asked for by the founders of the class.

The lines show that Alfred Mylne appreciated all the problems of these two clubs, and when we look at them we see that he has produced a class which, as well as fulfilling the particular requirements, would be suitable for any waters round the British Isles and for that matter almost anywhere in the world.

These 18-footers have shallow draft, for it is only 3 ft. 3 in. or one metre, while the long keel makes for a steady boat in a seaway, and one that is easily hauled out or beached for scrubbing and repairs.

The mast, which is not quite one-third of the water-line length from its fore end, is well into the boat where she can carry it comfortably.   A long step takes the thrust from this mast.

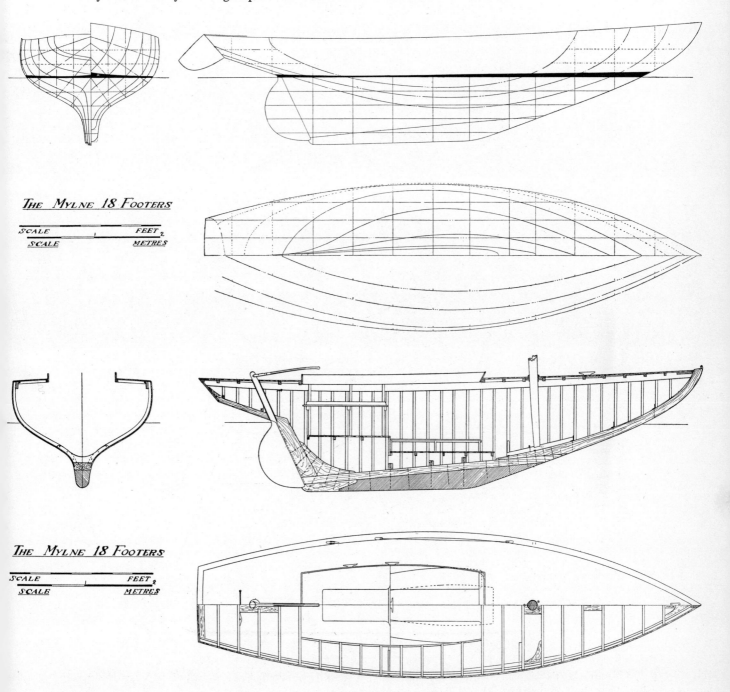

THE MYLNE 18 FOOTERS

SCALE ————————————— FEET 2
SCALE ————————————— METRES

THE MYLNE 18 FOOTERS

SCALE ————————————— FEET 2
SCALE ————————————— METRES

Her lead keel is long, and simple to cast and fit, and so makes for cheapness in building. It is bolted on with ¾ in. and ⅞ in. bolts.

At the after end of the water-line the rudder is straightforward, and everywhere one sees that while the construction is first class, economy has been studied by the designer throughout, as simplicity and strength is the impression one gets from this construction plan.

The deck plan shows the long clamp to take the strain of the mast and the pull of the shrouds on the chain plates. The beams, spaced one foot apart, make for a deck that will give no worry to owners in the years to come.

We see in the arrangement plan a large cockpit with sloping seats forward for the crew, and benches aft on a higher level for the helmsman and the man working the backstay, an arrangement very similar to that developed by the International 6-metre Class, which, as can be imagined, is as thoroughly good a one as can be devised.

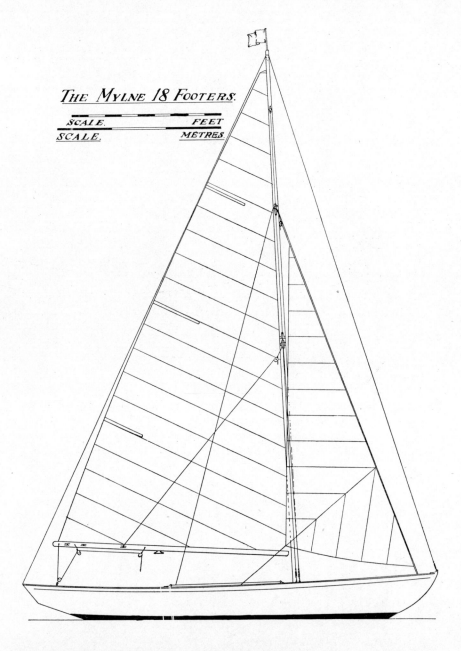

The Mylne 18 Footers.

SCALE.   FEET
SCALE.   METRES.

This little boat's sail plan continues the impression of simplicity and efficiency, as this 18-footer carries a mainsail and a staysail only, the mast needing only one crosstree to support it.

The jib halyard is 21 ft. above the deck, and at this point the mast is 4 in. in diameter, while the main halyard is 29 ft. 6 in. above the deck, where the mast is 2¼ in. in diameter. After studying these plans one is convinced that these little ships will be giving pleasure to their owners 40 years from now, just as the Redwings still do, which, as will be remembered, were designed and built over 40 years ago, and are still fast, pleasant and seaworthy boats.

REDWINGS

Length, overall -	22 ft. 1 in. = 6·73 m.		Length, water-line -	16·00 ft. = 4·87 m.
Beam - -	5 ft. 5 in. = 1·65 m.		Draught - -	2·90 ft. = 0·86 m.
Displacement -	1·23 tons = 1249 kilos.		Sail Area -	200 sq. ft. = 18·58 sq. m.

Designed and built 40 years ago by Charles E. Nicholson, the Redwings throughout those years have given a great deal of pleasure and sport, and the bright red sails, from which they take their name, have made them

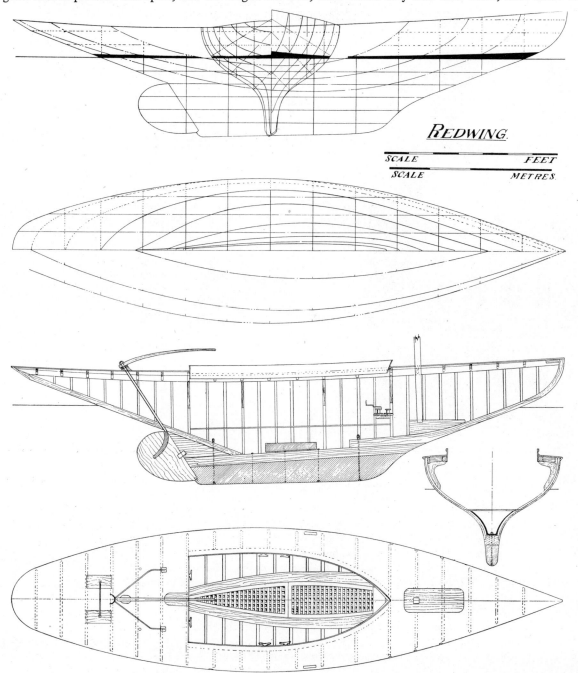

REDWING.

SCALE ——————— FEET

SCALE ——————— METRES.

easily distinguishable amongst all the other classes. In those 40 years they have raced all over the Solent, though their home port is Bembridge, and it is because most of their racing takes them in and out of Bembridge Harbour that the draught has been kept down to three feet.

This summer we hauled out Herbert Flower's *Redstart*, and as the lines of this class had been burnt, and the owner wished to have a set, we took them off, and they show what delightful little boats the Redwings are with their easy and fast lines. Even to-day 40 years after it would be difficult to think of a more suitable design to be driven by 200 sq. ft. of sail and to have such shallow draught.

In the construction plan we see the long iron keel which must have saved the hull itself a great deal of strain and damage by taking all the bumps and groundings that these boats have had in their long day.

Another interesting point in the construction is that the horn timber runs right on down to the main keel, and that she has no sternpost such as we would fit it to-day to take her rudder, the gap between the horn timber and the keel being filled by a wooden wedge, which in its turn forms the equivalent of the sternpost.

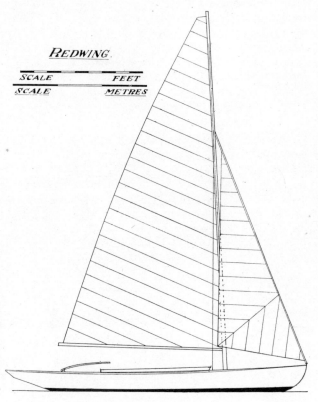

FOR FORTY SUMMERS THE REDWINGS HAVE GIVEN GOOD SPORT

There is no doubt that one of the reasons for the long life and popularity of the Redwing class is the fact that the only limit on rig was 200 square feet of actual sail area, as this left the owners free to put whatever rig they wished, and all sorts of rigs have been used, Chinese batten sails, balanced lugs, gunter lugs, gaff mainsails, the Bembridge mainsail, in which the mainsail and topsail are all one piece, and every conceivable type of sail has been used, though generally speaking, to-day the most popular rig is that shown in the sail plan, a Bermudian cutter rig. The Bembridge Redwings teach a most valuable lesson to one-designers, namely, that something must be left free for the owners to experiment and play about with, and if the hulls are one-designs and the rigs left free, this is enough to keep the class active and popular for a period of forty years, and in fact one might say for all time, as while the Redwings are now being superseded by a newer Redwing class, which will have exactly the same rules and will be by the same designer, Charles E. Nicholson, the reason for the change over is simply that some of the boats are beginning to show their age, and it was thought the time had come to lay them aside for a newer edition of the same class ; and the Bembridge Sailing Club have very wisely gone again to the same designer to design and built the new boats for them. Again the design is restricted to shallow draught and to 200 square feet of sail, in which the owner is left free to choose his mast and the type of rig providing he does not exceed the 200 square feet actual area.

FERRET

Length, overall -	27 ft. 6 in. = 8·38 m.		Length, water-line -	24 ft. 6 in. = 7·46 m.	
Beam - -	5 ft. 10 in. = 1·80 m.		Draught - -	6 in. and 3 ft. 9 in. = 0·15 and 1·14 m.	
Displacement -	1059 lb. = 480 kilos.		Sail Area - -	216 sq. ft. = 20 sq. m.	

Owner, R. G. W. & G. J. W. Ollernshaw   *Designer*, Carl Martens

(*For Lines, Construction and Sail Plans, see pages 245, 246, 247.*)

So far every boat illustrating this chapter has been of the deep-keeled type, one that derives its stability from a combination of form and keel, but in *Ferret* we have a boat that relies largely upon her crew for her ballast. This is a much livelier and faster type of craft, but one that is more difficult to sail, and so is a younger man's boat, and one, incidentally, which teaches a man far more of sailing and the strength of the wind, and far more quickly, than the heavier deep-keeled type ; she has thus much to recommend her. On top of this, such a boat is very suitable for inland waters, and has the advantage of being easily hauled out or put on a trailer and taken to different racing centres. The popularity of this type of craft can be gauged by the fact that the numbers alloted in the 22-square metre " Rennejolle " class are as high as 499 which we will call 500, and with a crew of three we see that the class affords sailing for 1500 people ; while *Ferret's* class, a 20-square metre " Rennejolle " class, has not reached such high numbers, they are getting on that way, all of which shows the need for considering centreboard classes in this series of one-designs.

Personally I should like to see this otherwise delightful little craft given a rig to the I.Y.R.U. rule in which bent spars were not allowed and only battens of a certain length and number permitted, for the long battens in these mainsails are against the class being adopted in many parts of the world, where otherwise they would be most suitable. If long battens were abolished the rig would become far more seamanlike, one would be able to reef and unreef during a race, and the problem of setting and stowing sails would be far simpler. *Ferret*, then, ends this chapter on one-designs with a plea that centreboard craft be considered.

· 44 ·

AMERICAN LONG DISTANCE RACING

GOLDEN EYE

Length, overall -	41 ft. 3 in. = 12·56 m.	Length, water-line -	30 ft. 0 in. = 9·14 m.
Beam - -	11 ft. 0 in. = 3·35 m.	Draught - -	6 ft. 0 in. = 1·82 m.
Displacement -	10·11 tons = 10,261 kilos.	Sail Area - -	917 sq. ft. = 85·18 sq. metres.

Owner, H. PRESCOTT WELLS   *Designer*, PHIL RHODES OF COX & STEVENS INC.

Builder, MINNEFORD YACHT YARD INC.

(For Lines, Construction, Accommodation and Sail Plans, see pages 281, 282, 283.)

GOLDEN EYE brings us to this year's long distance racing in America, for she came out top of her class (class B) in the 475 mile race from New London to Gibson Island at the end of June, and as we look at and admire her lines we realise that the American Cruising Clubs' rule for Ocean and Long Distance Racing must be good to encourage such a fine type of cruiser. When H. Prescott Wells ordered her design from Phil Rhodes, he asked for a beamy boat that would give comfort at sea and in harbour. *Golden Eye* is beamier and of heavier displacement than is normal in these days, but Phil Rhodes is such an artist that there is no sign of excess in any one of her lines, and it is not until we pause to consider, that we realise her width, for every line tells of a fine sea-boat that has a good turn of speed.

Her construction plan tells us that she is well and truly built, for Phil has sailed so much that he realises everything that a small vessel has to endure at sea and there is no sign of weakness in any part of her hull.

The accommodation plan shows that she is laid out so that four people can cruise in her in perfect comfort, the two double berthed cabins fore and aft being divided by the washroom to starboard and the galley and pantry to port. The fo'c'sle with its built-in berths is more of a double berthed forward cabin than a fo'c'sle as we generally think of it, and the coach roof by running forward of the mast gives full head room there, so that though only 30 ft. on the line *Golden Eye* is a remarkably roomy and compact vessel below.

Her sail plan shows the yawl rig so favoured by ocean racers ; the rig has won practically every important race in the last few years. The four last Fastnet Races have been won by yawls, *Dorade* in 1931 and 1933, *Stormy Weather* in 1935 and *Zeearend* in 1937, while the last three trans-Atlantic races have also been won by yawls, *Dorade*, *Stormy Weather* and *Roland von Bremen*. *Golden Eye's* rig is very efficient and well planned, so that it would be difficult to improve upon it, though I should like to see that mizen staysail tacked at the after end of the coach roof, for going so far forward it is fighting with the mainsail, as a mizen staysail should never be tacked forward of a spot half-way between the two masts.

One way and another *Golden Eye* fills us with contentment, for she is a perfect little cruiser, and yet one that is very fast in any weather from a calm to a gale, and as well as being fast she has a great deal of comfort above and below decks, and one could not wish for a better craft on this length water-line.

During the 475 mile Gibson Island Race this year every sort of weather was experienced, from a calm to breezes stronger than 25 miles per hour, and so the most important long distance race in America gave the competitors every variety of test. Though it was generally off the wind, there was a beat to windward for one part of the course, and the cutter *Highland Light*, who led the fleet of 35 starters across the finish line, covered the distance in 75 hours 20 minutes. Although she led the fleet she did not save her time on the next two boats to finish, as Walter Rothschild's *Avanti* crossed 13 minutes behind her, and so took first place, Rudy Schaefer's *Edlu* crossed the line 24 minutes after and took second place, *Highland Light* had thus to be contented with third place, though she had come within half an hour of the record time for the course.

Meantime *Golden Eye* had been sailing well through calms and strong winds and over a part of the course had averaged over 7½ knots, and in one squall which lasted half an hour she was smoking along at 8 knots through the water, but soon after this experienced calm weather again. However, she finally won the class B section for boats under 52 ft. overall in length, and so this year's Gibson Island race was full of interest and excitement for those taking part, and as we all know there was far more work and skill in a race under the weather conditions experienced in this year's Gibson Island Race than there is in a hard and steadier breeze, for to get the utmost out of a boat sails have to be changed every time there is a change in the strength or direction of the wind, and though the breeze was not often above 25 miles an hour in strength at any time during the race, because of the sail shifting throughout it was a hard and difficult race to sail, and one which tested the crews and vessels in it under most conditions of wind and sea.

THOUGH GOLDEN EYE HAS SAILED 3000 MILES, SHE HAS SO FAR NEVER TAKEN
SOLID WATER OVER HER BOWS

CLASS A

NAME	OWNER	ELAPSED TIME			CORRECTED TIME		
		H.	M.	S.	H.	M.	S.
Avanti - - -	W. N. Rothschild - -	75	33	27	69	49	47
Edlu - - -	R. J. Schaefer - -	75	44	45½	71	29	36½
Highland Light -	Dudley F. Wolfe - -	75	20	12	74	10	51
Mandoo II - -	D. Spencer Berger - -	77	35	24	77	35	24
Elizabeth McCaw -	R. J. Reynolds - -	80	01	06	77	43	44
Spindrift - -	W. W. Lanahan - -	83	01	42	78	09	44
Vixen III - -	John D. Archbold - -	82	39	37	80	43	10
White Cloud - -	George A. Whiting - -	83	35	02	81	17	40
Kirawan - -	Robert P. Baruch - -	93	44	23½	86	55	01½
Vryling II - -	L. B. Dunham - -	94	16	04½	87	44	26½
Sonny - - -	Albert E. Peirce - -	94	15	48	88	38	47
Valkyrie - -	Cummins Catherwood -	91	39	37	90	44	45
Nordlys - -	Chester Bowles - -	93	25	13	93	00	26
Tradition - -	F. A. Calderone - -	106	36	04	102	59	18
Nam Sang - -	Dr. P. E. Truesdale -	106	56	59	106	04	30

Teragram, D.N.F.   *Alelnaner*, T.N.T.

U

Class B

Golden Eye	-	-	H. Prescott Wells	-	-	95	48	11	82	57	58
Malabar XI	-	John G. Alden	-	-	94	36	32	83	24	58
Spookie	-	-	H. T. White, Jnr.	-	-	94	18	32	85	14	35
Cyclone	-	-	F. Jay Wells	-	-	91	53	16	85	21	38
Narada	-	-	L. Corrin Strong	-	-	106	33	58	96	12	49
Hersilia	-	-	Dexter L. Lewis	-	-	107	19	24	99	49	54
Sirocco	-	-	Paul A. Sperry	-	-	113	45	56	103	02	14
Halcyone	-	-	Wm. G. Burt	-	-	113	25	50	103	04	41
Tejeria	-	-	T. G. Hoster	-	-	120	21	27	110	18	02
Escapade	-	-	Henry G. Fownes	-	-	122	15	48	111	36	36
Pendragon	-	-	H. M. Devereux	-	-	133	29	58	120	29	18
Hawk Bells	-	-	E. H. Wardwell	-	-	139	15	57	123	22	27
Gleam	-	-	J. Leo. Flanigan	-	-	131	50	00	124	31	34
Blue Wing II	-	-	Milton J. Blair	-	-	141	30	00	129	20	14

Souvenir II, Vega, Malabar III, T.N.T.

SPECIAL CLASS

Mirage	-	-	-	A. Karl Fischer	-	-	92	18	17	92	18	17

NASSAU RACE

Earlier in the year the 184 mile race from Miami to Nassau had been won by *Stormy Weather*. It was sailed almost throughout in a fresh breeze, but as the course was for the most part close hauled and to windward the

STORMY WEATHER SMASHING HER WAY TO WINDWARD
TO WIN THE NASSAU RACE

schooners came off badly, for working to windward in a choppy sea is not a schooner's good point. D. Spencer Berger's yawl *Mandoo II* led the fleet across the finish line at the entrance to Nassau Harbour; *Stormy Weather* finishing second with 1½ hours of time allowance to spare, taking pride of place, while the 30 ft. 6 in. overall cutter *Babe*, who had been sailed by a crew of three saved her time on *Mandoo* by forty minutes, and so *Mandoo* the leader dropped back into third place.

Stormy with Rod Stephens as her crew had made the most of the good breezes they had had, Rod saying at the end that *Stormy* had never sailed better in her life, and as he has been skipper of her for the greater part of this he should know.

The converted New York " forty ", *Catherine*, had pulled out a chain plate and was dismasted during the night, but the coastguard cutter acting as a committee boat soon had her in tow, so all was well. But one wonders whether ocean racers should not be forced by the rules to carry a double set of main shrouds, so that the failure of one or a chain plate does not mean the loss of a mast, and after all the cost of this and the weight and windage would be little compared with the additional safety given to all the vessels, as this accident to *Catherine* might have had more serious consequences had there not been a good powerful tender close by. Failing this it would seem that owners should give all their gear a close inspection before starting in any race, for the rigs to-day are so designed that the failure of any one part of the elaborate system of staying a mast often means the collapse of the whole, and this should make owners inspect and survey every item and every part frequently and always very minutely before the start of any race.

MIAMI-NASSAU RACE—TABLE OF RESULTS

Start, February 9, 1937, Distance, 184 Miles

NAME	RIG	OWNER	ELAPSED TIME			CORRECTED TIME		
			H.	M.	S.	H.	M.	S.
Stormy Weather -	Yawl -	R. W. Johnson - -	30	14	30	25	12	34
Babe - -	Sloop -	H. M. Matheson	36	22	28	26	05	15
Mandoo II -	Yawl -	D. S. Berger -	28	28	35	26	45	12
Actaea - -	Sloop -	Henry Sears -	32	39	35	26	56	51
Starlight - -	Cutter -	A. B. Fay - - -	34	52	49	27	37	18
Sirocco - -	Sloop -	R. W. Robinson -	36	26	04	28	35	11
Water Witch -	Schooner -	L. W. McFarland -	34	48	54	28	36	39
Winsome Too -	Yawl -	Harkness Edwards	32	14	51	28	56	40
San Cristobal II	Schooner -	J. W. Pape -	35	10	17	29	15	07
Sonny - -	Cutter -	A. E. Peirce -	34	58	36	29	20	56
St. Clair - -	Sloop -	Henry Summerfield -	40	27	06	30	22	01
Tioga - -	Ketch -	H. E. Noyes -	31	53	24	30	43	10
Saracen - -	Cutter -	C. E. Warburton -	42	48	30	32	40	00
Shellback - -	Schooner -	R. J. Newman -	38	49	18	33	24	35
Valhalla - -	Ketch -	Willard Conrow -	50	34	28	35	23	31
Cockatoo - -	Ketch -	R. S. Evans -	50	05	23	41	47	41
Escapade - -	Schooner -	H. G. Fownes -	53	40	00	43	09	42
Katharine - -	Sloop -	R. M. Demere - -						
Voyager - -	Schooner -	A. L. DuPre - -						

Katharine, disabled, D.N.F. *Voyager*, disqualified.

TRANS-PACIFIC YACHT RACE OF 1936

Our old friend *Dorade* kept up her reputation as an ocean racer in no uncertain manner during this race, for she sailed the 2293 miles from Santa Monica to Honolulu in 13 days 7 hours 20 minutes, which averages out at 172·40 miles a day with an average speed of 7·18 knots. She was the first to finish in this race, won in her class, and also had the best corrected time of the entire fleet, and so won a very fine race for James Flood of the San Francisco Yacht Club, who now owns her, though a great deal of credit must go to Myron Spalding, who was skipper and navigator. The chart showing her course gives her best day's run as 224 miles ; the next best is 219 and the third best 216 miles, while her lowest day was 139 miles, which was the first day out, when she was not yet clear of the light weather prevailing under the land.

Dorade lead *Circe* across the finish line at Diamond Head by 13 minutes, but *Circe* a 59 ft. cutter had to give *Dorade* more than 30 hours and finally dropped into fifth place on corrected times.   To *Circe*, however, goes the

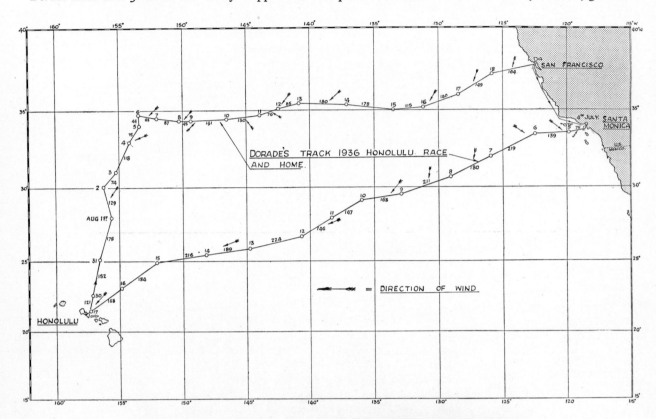

DORADE SWEEPS PAST DIAMOND HEAD TO WIN THE 1936 TRANS-PACIFIC RACE

credit for the best day's run of 254 miles, *Dorade* having the next best run of the fleet with her 224 miles, in spite of the fact that *Sartartia*, the 85 ft. schooner, and *Navigator* the 80 ft. schooner, were taking part in the race, all of which gives an idea of the wonderful seamanlike qualities of *Dorade*. The photographs illustrating this record remind us, that the passage to Honolulu makes the ideal ocean race, for it takes one from the shores of America to the Islands of the Blest, and all the way across one lives on an island, makes one's own laws and customs, and finally to arrive at such an island as Honolulu is to feel that the race has been well worth while, though after a pleasant stay *Dorade* and her crew deserted this lovely island and returned once more to San Francisco. As the chart shows, they took 20 days 16½ hours to sail the 2544 mile homeward course, their average being 123 miles a day and 5·12 knots, for *Dorade* had to come back to windward over the same ocean on which she had run with her spinnaker billowing out during the trans-Pacific race of 1936.

TRANS-PACIFIC RACE, 1936, JULY 4, SAN PEDRO

CLASS A

NAME	LENGTH OVERALL	RIG	OWNER	CLUB	ELAPSED TIME	CORRECTED TIME
	FT.				D. H. M. S.	D. H. M. S.
Navigator -	80	Schooner	G. Harton Singer -	Los Angeles Y.C. -	15 03 30 57	14 15 48 07
Sartartia -	85	Schooner	Charles Jones - -	Pacific Writers Y.C.	Scratch	14 23 31 29

CLASS B

NAME	LENGTH OVERALL	RIG	OWNER	CLUB	ELAPSED TIME	CORRECTED TIME
Dorade -	51	Yawl -	James Flood - -	St. Francis Y.C. -	13 07 20 00	11 03 29 44
Santana -	55	Schooner	W. L. Stewart, Jnr. -	Los Angeles Y.C. -	13 16 09 01	11 17 32 25
Manuiwa -	60	Schooner	Harold G. Dillingham	Pearl Harbour Y.C.	13 18 40 49	12 06 22 45
Zoe H -	65	Schooner	Ray K. Person -	California Y.C. -	13 19 50 02	12 08 08 19
Circe -	59	Cutter -	Ray Cooke - -	Seattle Y.C. -	13 07 33 49	12 10 01 11
Adore -	61	Schooner	Lee Tracy - -	Pacific Writers Y.C.	14 19 54 11	13 01 53 21
Paisano -	60	Schooner	Tom Reed - -	Pacific Writers Y.C.	14 15 06 54	13 01 58 45
Marilen -	60	Schooner	Harry B. Allen -	San Francisco Y.C.	14 19 24 05	13 05 25 52
Bali - -	67	Schooner	L. G. Monroe -	San Francisco Y.C.	18 02 17 10	15 15 20 27
Destiny -	62	Schooner	Preston Struges -	Pacific Writers Y.C.	18 14 49 38	17 02 25 19
California -	75	Schooner	J. Polkinghorne -	Vallejo Y.C. - -	19 05 54 54	17 10 06 12
Gloria -	60	Schooner	William Blackford -	Seattle Y.C. - -	20 04 00 45	18 04 07 35

CLASS C

NAME	LENGTH OVERALL	RIG	OWNER	CLUB	ELAPSED TIME	CORRECTED TIME
Flying Cloud -	45	Yawl -	James McNabb - -	Los Angeles Y.C. -	15 12 46 32	12 17 38 03
Brilliant -	49	Yawl -	Walter Franz - -	Newport Har. Y.C.	16 01 18 55	13 08 36 14
Altair -	47	Yawl -	John P. Blinn - -	Aeolian Y.C. -	16 05 46 17	13 11 02 28
Minerva -	45	Ketch -	Frank Blagen - -	Corinthian Y.C. -	16 04 21 31	13 14 46 14
White Cloud -	40	Cutter -	R. R. Pratsch - -	Tacoma Y.C. -	17 00 41 01	13 20 52 41
Naitamba -	34	Yawl -	Richard M. Smith -	Los Angeles Y.C. -	18 07 41 33	14 14 01 10
Lady Jo -	40	Schooner	Samuel Emmes - -	California Y.C. -	18 15 10 25	15 02 42 36

When loaded down for the trans-Pacific Race *Dorade* measured 52 ft. overall by 41 ft. water-line by 10 ft. 3 in. beam, 8 ft. 3 in. draught, and carried 1156 square feet of sail area, her rating being 33·70 ft. under the Honolulu Race rule.

Long distance and ocean racing has now become an active form of sport on both sides of the Atlantic and in the Pacific, and soon it will have spread to every part of the globe, for it is a manly sport, and one hopes that quite soon there will be an International Rule of measurement, and a set of International Racing rules.

So far the Cruising Club of America and the Royal Ocean Racing Club of this country and the trans-Pacific ocean racers and the long-distance racing people in Europe and the Baltic, have not come together under a common rule, and while in some ways this is to be regretted, it is, I imagine all for the best, for the longer the rule is in coming the more chance it has of being perfect and free from alterations when it finally arrives. But it would seem that the time has now come for it to arrive, as we have put behind us some years' experience of ocean racing. Possibly the

DORADE'S BOW FROM ALOFT

DORADE'S STERN FROM ALOFT

best way of the rule arriving is for the ocean racers all over the world to put their ideas before the committee of the International Yacht Racing Union and the North American Yacht Racing Union, who have had great many years' experience in framing and applying rating rules to yachts, and if a good percentage of ocean racing experts were added to the committee, a perfect International Ocean Racing Rule would soon be arrived at.

· 45 ·

GADGETS

ISLAND SAILING CLUB'S POSTPONEMENT SIGNAL

THIS chapter of Gadgets shows various small fittings or contrivances specially designed to do certain jobs, and though this chapter has been an important feature of all my books I do hope it will not take away from us the resourcefulness for which seamen the world over have been noted, and this $2\frac{1}{2}$ hour postponement signal flying from the Island Sailing Club's Yard Arm is included to emphasise the resourcefulness of seamen.

ISLAND SAILING CLUB'S POSTPONEMENT SIGNAL

The Island Sailing Club had arranged a race to Oistreham in conjunction with the French Club. The night before the race the French and English yachts taking part all thought that the start should be postponed $2\frac{1}{2}$ hours from 8.00 till 10.30 a.m. and the Y.R.A. Rule No. 9—Postponement of Race—says that one ball or shape must be hoisted for every half-hour's postponement under the answering pennant, and here we see five dark empty whisky bottles hoisted under the answering pennant, which is flying out bravely from the Yard Arm at the Island Sailing Club, a signal which everyone understood.

SELF-LOCKING DRAWERS

Dr. Ward has owned many interesting yachts in his time and aboard his latest I saw a very strong way of making a self-locking drawer. Usually these are made with a strip running along the underside of the front, but this is not a strong method, for as the drawer is slid home this strip strikes the bottom rail and soon becomes weakened until

311

it is finally knocked off and the drawer is self-locking no longer. But as will be seen from the photograph the drawers aboard Dr. Ward's boat run on a teak strip all the while, and when shut they drop down and so lock themselves,

SELF-LOCKING DRAWERS

the strain coming on the end of this strip, while to open them one has to lift the drawers $\frac{1}{4}$ in. in order to lift this strip out of its rebate and the drawer is then easily slid open. As at sea it is most important to have self-locking drawers, this photo is instructive as it shows us the strongest method of making them.

SHAMROCK III'S CLEATS

Practically every first-class vessel, from the largest to the smallest, one steps aboard, whether racing, cruising or power, has this type of cleat, which is made up by a teak bar passing through two gunmetal castings at the ideal height above the deck for the rope the cleat is intended to carry. But very often nowadays the lip is forgotten on the under and outer side of the brass castings, which forms a fairlead and takes the wear of the rope or sheet when it is being surged round the cleat. This lip is plainly seen in the upper part of the plan, for while the inner face of the

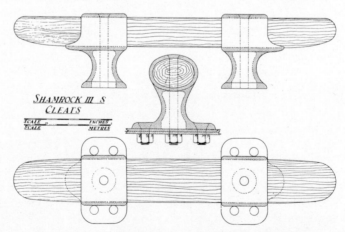

casting is square the outer and lower edge runs out something like the snout of a rhinoceros, and for the want of this I have seen many of the present-day cleats chafed badly. On one vessel where part of the sheet was wire it actually cut so much, that the outer end of the teak cleat was sawn so that it broke off and the cleat became useless. Therefore it is instructive to look back at the original of these cleats designed by William Fife as long ago as 1903 for his *America's* Cup challenger, *Shamrock III*.

Another interesting detail is that of the bolt running down through the centre of the castings and the teak bar, for this strengthens the whole job enormously, but this again is usually left out nowadays, some of the cleats having a smaller screw to keep the bar in place and others nothing at all. So this cleat finds its place here not merely to show it and to say where it originated, but more to point out faults in our present-day practice, so that yachtsmen can have them corrected.

RUNNER LEVERS

Four years ago, in my first book, Highfield's runner lever was one of the gadgets described. Since then his idea has been adapted to forestays as well as runners and backstays, and I am reproducing this gadget here, as its development makes very interesting and instructive reading. The history of this runner lever will, I hope, be an inspiration for all who think out the various details of gadgets aboard yachts, for if this lever is capable of such development it is safe to say that practically everything we use aboard our vessels is capable of similar improvement.

" The Rear-Commodore of the Royal Thames has invented many useful things for sailing vessels, and as some of these are for racers they appear in that half of the book ; but the backstay lever, which J. S. Highfield thought out and tried with great success aboard his 15-metre *Dorina*, is simple and effective, and because it always sets the backstays exactly, is very suitable for cruisers, for otherwise in the night watches it is difficult to know just how the back-

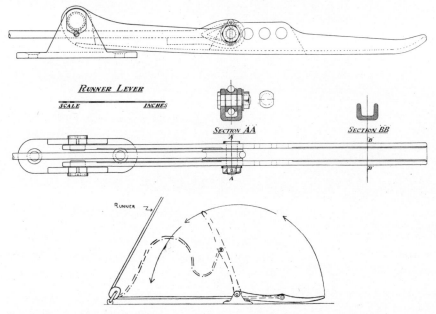

stays are set up after tacking or gybing. The lever is really a channel bar, and when it is pushed right down it is over its centre, therefore the greater the strain the less chance it has of lifting. In fact, it is impossible to lift it by the pull of the backstay, but because some rope catching under it might do this, it should have a locking catch, which would prevent a rope finding its way under.

" It would seem at first sight that there is little power in this lever, but a second thought will bring home the fact that as it begins to arrive at the spot where it is dragging home the last few valuable inches of the backstay, it is becoming increasingly powerful. *Dorina* fitted one of these on one side, and still left the ordinary backstay gear on the other side ; and the proof as to which was the better and easier, as well as the surer method, can be gauged by the fact that her crew schemed and aimed to work the lever and the unfortunate one worked the ordinary backstay on the other side. Time will see the use of this backstay lever increased in racing and cruising vessels, for it has power and adjustment combined with the advantage that the backstay is set every time to its exact tautness, there being no rope parts to stretch and give, all the power being in the lever, whose length never varies.

" On racers with twin headstays these levers can be used to slack up the stay on which no sail is set. Thus all the weight is thrown on the luff of the headsail causing it to stand much better." *

The next development of this lever that I saw was Rod Stephen's edition of it. This differed only in that where the Highfield lever had four holes, which took the bolt through the splice in the end of the runner or backstay, Rod's lever had a groove running through the inside of the channel, and in this groove the two protruding ends of a bolt through a solid thimble for the splice ran. The advantage of this was that when the runner was thrown over double

* Text and illustrations from *Sailing, Seamanship and Yacht Construction.*

the length of slack was given, for when thrown, the solid thimble could run along this groove in the channel to the end of the lever.   These levers are to be found aboard Isaac Bell's *Bloodhound*.

★   ★   ★   ★   ★

Russell Harmer, who was *Lalage's* chief gadgeteer, designed her forestay levers, which I have taken from my third book, and which were the next development I saw of the Highfield lever.

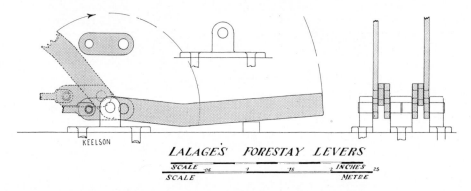

LALAGE'S   FORESTAY   LEVERS

Practically every 6-metre has twin headstays to enable her to change headsails without showing a naked fore triangle, and as it is of the utmost importance that all the load should come on the stay upon which the headsail she is using is set, these headstays must have a device for slacking off the one on which no sail is set.   Finding that the Highfield lever gave too much slack for this job, Russell Harmer designed *Lalage's* forestay levers, which gave only $1\frac{1}{2}$ in. of slack, and these were such a success that they have been used extensively by many designers and owners.

★   ★   ★   ★   ★

A still further development of this idea was used aboard *Maid of Malham*.   Her sail plan shows that while her jibstay runs to the top of the mast, the forestay has two positions, one 7 ft. abaft the forestay and the second position only 3 ft. abaft it, so that while within the rules, for it is inside the fore triangle, *Maid of Malham* could set her fore-

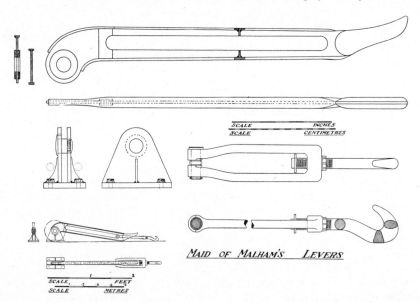

MAID   OF   MALHAM'S   LEVERS

stay either abaft or forward of the forward end of her load water-line to suit the weather conditions, and this change over of the forestay position could be made safely and in a few seconds by means of an adaptation of the Highfield lever, for having twin forestays the port lever could be thrown over and the port stay released, and as there were two legs on the short span of the deck, one leading under the after sheave and the other under the fore sheave, the forestay had only to be taken from one and hooked on to the other and then set up to be shifted, and having shifted the one it was only a matter of seconds to shift the starboard stay.

This lever was an adaptation of the slot idea that Rod Stephens put into the Highfield lever, only in this case instead of there being a groove in a channel bar it is a slot cut into a single plate, a link running up and down this slot.

*   *   *   *   *

The last, and perhaps best, because it is the most simple of all forms of this lever I saw on one of our Upper Thames raters. This was a lever shaped exactly like a croquet hoop (and for those who have not been fortunate enough to play this game, so popular with the Victorians, I must explain that a croquet hoop is like the letter U upside down in the ground through which one drives the ball). This croquet hoop on the rater was hinged on the centre line of the deck, so that it could be swung athwartships, and would lie flat either on the port or starboard side of the centre line, and the backstay led aft abreast this hoop and then ran under a sheave in the deck across to the

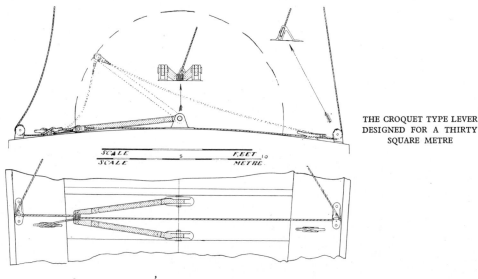

THE CROQUET TYPE LEVER DESIGNED FOR A THIRTY SQUARE METRE

WATERWITCH'S BACKSTAY LEVER

hoop, and as this hoop was 18 in. in height it gave 3 ft. of slack on one side while the other side was set taut. When tacking this rater had only to throw her croquet hoop to port, and this set up the starboard runner and gave 3 ft. of slack in the port runner. Then when she tacked she set up the port runner and released the starboard. This fitment is so simple and effective that the marvel is that we have not used it before, for it is without doubt the finest arrangement one could have for setting up and slacking off runners. Its only disadvantage is that during the throwing over of the lever, both backstays are slack for a short space of time, but as at this moment there is no weight in the headsail, for she is either tacking or gybing, it is of little consequence, for when using such a lever one should have a permanent topmast backstay leading to the deck clear abaft the main boom.

*   *   *   *   *

During Cowes Week this summer Sir William Burton very kindly invited me aboard his 12-metre *Marina* for a race. During the race I saw the answer to a point that has been in my mind for four years, over these runner levers ; that point is that while they have the great advantage that they always bring the runner back exactly to its correct position, there comes a time when with a very light wind one needs a little slack in the backstays, which in turn throws slack in the forestay, for this gives a greater fulness in the luff of the headsail, which is needed in the lightest of airs. As we had light airs on the day of this race I saw how a backstay lever could be used to give the amount of slack required, and this photograph shows *Marina's* backstay lever half cocked, for a rope tail had been spliced in the lever, and this tail belayed on the cleat immediately abaft the lever gave the slack needed.

Out on *Marina's* weather will be seen the reflection of a rival " twelve " in the still waters of the Solent, and this tells of conditions when fulness is needed in all sails, and *Marina's* half-cocked lever threw fulness in her headsail by slacking the forestay.

The rope tail, besides enabling the lever to be half cocked, has another great advantage in blowing weather. These levers want some pressing home, but the rope tail with one turn under the cleat makes the job much easier and safer, as one is able to hold every inch gained on the lever, so with both hands on the rope pulling up and a foot pressing down on the lever one is able to bang this lever home with ease and safety in the strongest of winds. Once the lever is home, while it has no tendency to lift, that tail of rope belayed on the cleat gives one a feeling of safety and comfort, for as well as holding the lever down it also prevents any stray rope from flicking under the after end of the lever and so throwing it accidentally.

THIS PICTURE SHOWS MARINA'S RUNNER HALF-COCKED

Therefore the lesson we learn from *Marina* is that every runner or forestay lever should have a rope tail to half cock it in light weather and to throw and belay, and so make safe the lever in the worst of weather.

THE SPERRY VILLIERS ODOGRAPH—NEW TYPE

When at sea, out of sight of land, we are always wondering exactly where we are, and this odograph by giving a continuous automatic recording of the vessel's track on the chart tells at a glance her position by dead reckoning, as

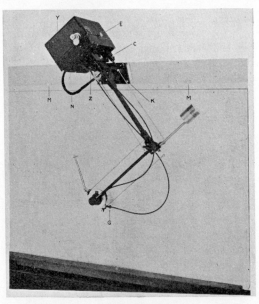

ODOGRAPH

it is operated jointly by a gyro-compass and her electric log. Such an instrument would make a fine addition to any full-powered modern cruiser, for it has the following advantages :

(1) Full view of the complete chart and full view of the plotted courses.

(2) Adaptability for any size of chart.

(3) Adaptability to any scale of chart.

(4) Enclosed mechanism minimises possible mechanical defects due to dust and sea air.

(5) Adjustments allow correction for changes of latitude scale in ocean charts.

(6) Immunity from error due to heavy motion of the ship because of rolling and gun fire, etc.

DOMIZLAFF'S PARALLEL RULER

We all know that the compass does not point to the true but to the magnetic north, and that while all compasses are in themselves true in that they point to the magnetic north when aboard a vessel in which materials such as wood, copper and bronze only are used, also that once steel in any form is introduced a further complication arises, for steel, in the form, say, of an auxiliary engine, affects the compass and we get a further error to allow for. On such a vessel the compass is not pointing to the magnetic north, due to the deviation caused by the steel aboard her, and so once we start to sail we generally have to make allowances, both for the true variation of the compass and the deviation caused by steel and such things aboard the vessel.

The first variation we read off from the chart, for on all charts there are either lines of variation or a compass rose which gives the variation, and we read variation 11° 50′ (1933) decreasing about 11′ annually, which of course is different in different places.

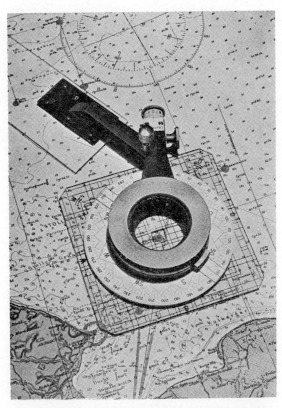

HANS DOMIZLAFF'S EQUIVALENT OF A PARALLEL RULER
CALLED A DIRKOMETER

In the longitude of the West Indies there is no variation at all, as here the compass points magnetic north, but on the European side the compass points to the west of north, while on the American side it points to the east of north, all of which is marked and shown clearly on all charts, and there has been no mystery about this since the days of Christopher Columbus.

The deviation is given to us on a card, for almost every vessel has her compass adjusted and checked frequently, and the adjuster writes down the deviation, so this is fairly straight forward too. But the irritating thing of it is that we have to apply these two corrections every time we lay a course off on a chart, and Hans Domizlaff's parallel rulers have solved this problem for us easily and kindly, so one never puts the deviation or the variation the wrong way, as it is all done automatically by his parallel rulers.

I met this ruler in his home, for during a long evening's yarn I explained to him the parallel rulers which I had used, but had not perfected and patented, consisting of an ordinary ruler working between two compasses, a square compass at the bottom representing the true north and a circular compass above representing the magnetic, a little screw enabling the magnetic compass above to be swung to coincide with the variation shown on the chart, so that with one glance one could read the true bearing from the bottom compass and the magnetic bearing on the top compass, thus eliminating any mistake from adding the variation to the course read. The reason for the true compass being made square was that it could then be laid along the line of latitude or longitude which enabled one to place it on any part of the chart.

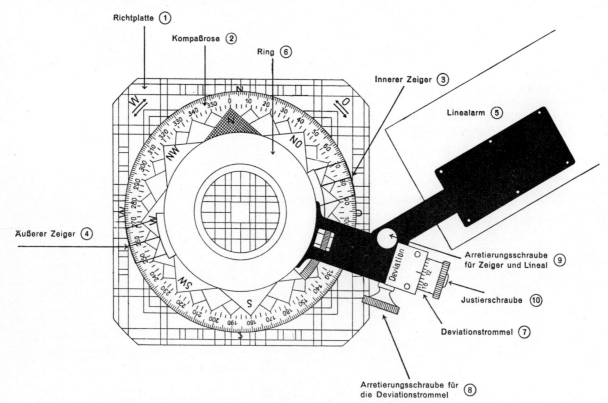

After this discussion Hans produced a dear little box in which was a far, far better arrangement of this idea, with the added refinement that one could adjust the arm for the deviation. Hans, too, had a square compass for the true and a circular one for the magnetic, which could be swung round and was adjustable to the variation, but here all likeness ceased for he had only one leg to his straight edge of glass and also he had a square hole in the centre of his two compass roses which one placed on the point of departure, and swinging the straight edge round to the required point one read off on the magnetic compass the course to be steered. And though the square and true compass had only the four cardinal points marked on it, it would be an easy matter to engrave the rest and the degrees, so that one could read both the magnetic and the true bearing of any object in the same glance. Hans Domizlaff by his patience and ingenuity has completely overcome the elements of confusion, and future years will see more and more yachtsmen using this ruler and thinking of its designer every time they do so.

TWO WAY DRAWERS

On board Oppeguard's new schooner I saw a fine arrangement for the drawers containing his crockery and silver, for when a pantry is next to the dining saloon a great deal of energy is saved ; and so most vessels are arranged in this way, Oppeguard's being no exception. At the pantry end of the dining room settee was the sideboard, the drawers of which contained the silver and crockery, glasses and such things as are used and washed up at the end of each meal.

Before the meal these are taken from the drawer and laid on the table, which is alongside the sideboard and after the meal are cleared away and taken into the pantry where they are washed.   Here is the clever point of these drawers for they can be filled with the clean silver glasses and crockery in the pantry.   These drawers slide athwartships into

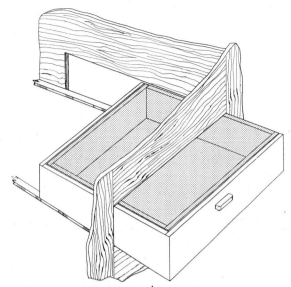

ENGINEER OPPEGUARD'S TWO-WAY DRAWERS.

the saloon or forward into the pantry all of which saves work and the pantryman from several voyages into the saloon to put away the cutlery and crockery after he has washed them up.   And so we learn from practically every boat we go aboard.

"THAT EARLY CUP OF TEA"

Even though our best friends never dare tell us, four out of five like being wakened by an early morning cup of tea, and whether this is the result of night starvation or not does not matter to us so much as having it brought to our bedside.   But when it is there we never know quite what to do with the cup and saucer.   On *Heron II* the owner

HERON'S BUNK BRACKET FOR THE EARLY CUP OF TEA

solved this problem easily, for he made a little bracket shelf with two metal clips to go down inside the bunk board, as the illustration shows.

Another method I have seen is to fit a small sliding shelf into the side of the bunk or bed, which is pulled out each morning to take the cup of sunshine that dispels any early morning gloom.

CONTENT'S MAIN HALYARD

Practically every mainsail can be hoisted on a single part, as the larger the craft the larger the crew, and almost all mainsails to-day are Bermudians, but the hoisting of the sail and the setting of it are two entirely different things, and to set it one needs extra power. *Content's* main halyard arrangement is instructive. The sail is hoisted by a single part, and then set at the finish by a tackle ; as will be seen from the sketch, the bottom part of the tackle has a strop

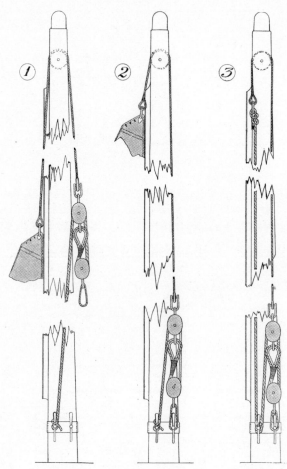

CONTENT'S MAIN HALYARDS

which is hooked over a belaying pin on the spider band, and her crew can set the sail as hard as they wish with the tackle. When lowering the mainsail the tackle is slacked off a little, the strop unhooked, and tackle and strop all go aloft as the sail comes down, being lowered on the single fall of the tackle. Once the mainsail is down and stowed, the fall of the tackle is belayed to the halyard shackles and hoisted aloft, so that the tackle is down on deck for a harbour stow.

WATERWITCH'S MAST HEAD

We all know that locking a sail aloft halves the compression strain on the mast and as to-day most of the strains to which a mast is subjected are compressive strains, designers are always endeavouring to ease these up, and this mast head designed by the owner of *Waterwitch* will be found useful, for with the passing of years many methods of locking the sail aloft will be designed and used until finally the perfect mast head arrangement is designed.

As will be seen from the plan the sheave is of fairly large diameter as this eases the friction and so makes hoisting and lowering simpler and smoother.   A long link connects the wire halyard to the shackle which takes the head board, the end of the halyard being spliced over a $\frac{3}{8}$ in. diameter pin at the top of this link, this pin standing out beyond the

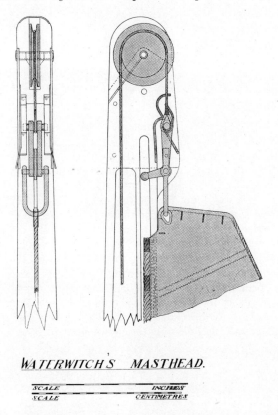

WATERWITCH'S MASTHEAD.

SCALE   INCHES
SCALE   CENTIMETRES

link $\frac{3}{8}$ in. on either side.   The sail is hoisted and this shoulder pin then engages on its own accord into the shoulder made to take it and to lower it it is hoisted still further when the top guide throws the athwartship bar clear out of the mast head fitting which enables the sail to be lowered down clear of everything, and while this fitting has not been tried out under working conditions it seems to be strong and reliable and one of the neatest mast head arrangements I have yet seen.

F.R.C.D.

MASTING AND RIGGING

THIS subject has been dealt with very fully in my three previous books, where the mast plans and rigging details have been given of all types of racing craft from the " J " class cutters right down to the tiny canoes, and also of all manner of cruisers from the largest to the smallest. In all some 60 complete plans have appeared, and as the subject has there been dealt with so fully, these should be studied with the mast and spar plans of five craft of which plans appear in the following pages.

There is still a great deal to be learnt about the masting and rigging of our vessels. For example, so far no 6-metres or other racers have seen their way to abolishing the rigging above the jib halyard height, as I did with the 6-metre *Nada* some five years ago, for where the topmast is only quarter or less of the total length of the mast above the deck, and where no headsail is set above the jib halyard, I am convinced that the mast will stand without any topmast rigging at all either fore and aft or athwartships. It will be seen in my *Second Book* that *Gallant's* mast on page 115 stands without any rigging above the jib halyard height. The 6-metre *Nada's* mast, five years ago, also stood without any rigging above the jib halyard height. This " six " is the only one in which I rigged a mast and so tried out this idea. Future years will see topmast rigging getting less and less, until the crosstree at the hounds is done away with entirely, and then finally there will be no rigging above the hounds on all craft where the topmast is a quarter or less of the total length of spar, and has only to support the top corner of the mainsail.

HELGOLAND

Helgoland being about the same dimensions as *Roland von Bremen*, last year's trans-Atlantic race winner, which was also designed by Henry Gruber, has the same masting and rigging plan as *Roland*, and as this is given in detail on page 80 of my *Sail and Power*, there is no need to reproduce it here, as excepting for the fact that *Helgoland's* rigging

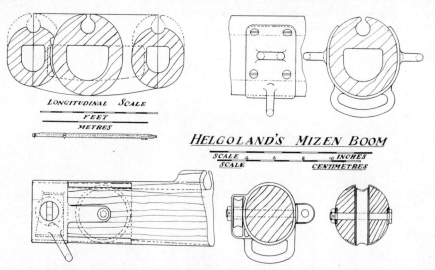

LONGITUDINAL SCALE
FEET
METRES

HELGOLAND'S MIZEN BOOM

SCALE INCHES
SCALE CENTIMETRES

was attached to the mast by fittings and *Roland's* by splices going round the mast, there is no difference in the two, and so in this book we only reproduce *Helgoland's* booms and fittings.

The main boom, a spar 29 ft. in overall length is an oval spar $7\frac{3}{4}$ in. × 7 in. at its greatest point of measurement, which is about one-third from the outer end. From this point it tapers to 6 in. × $5\frac{1}{4}$ in. at the outer end and to $5\frac{1}{4}$ in. × $4\frac{3}{4}$ in. at the inner end, the wall throughout remaining constant at $1\frac{1}{8}$ in., all of which is seen from the plan.

The mizen boom is 11 ft. 7 in. overall and is $4\frac{3}{8}$ in. × 4 in. at middle length tapering to 4 in. × 3 in. at each end, the wall again remaining constant throughout the boom, but this time only $\frac{3}{4}$ in. in thickness.   As will be seen from the plan this boom is grooved to take the foot rope of the mizen, and this has much to recommend it, for it is simple

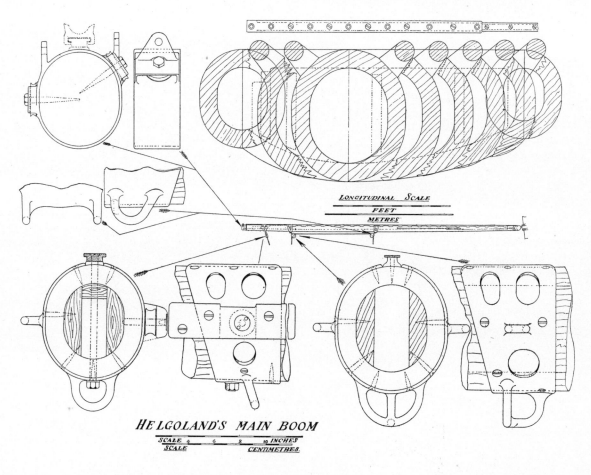

HELGOLAND'S MAIN BOOM

and strong, its only disadvantage being that when the sail is soaking wet the foot rope swells and so binds and sticks in the groove until it is dried and once more reduced to its normal size.   A fairly heavily-tarred rope should therefore be used which would tend to stop excessive swelling.

MAID OF MALHAM

Maid of Malham's mainmast stands 57 ft. 6 in. above the deck and is 10 in. × 8 in. with $1\frac{5}{8}$ in. walls at a spot half-way between the staysail halyard block and the deck and tapers away into a circular spar at the top where the walls are $1\frac{1}{8}$ in. in thickness, and to $8\frac{1}{2}$ in. × 8 in. at the heel.   It is a solid spar from the heel to a spot 3 ft. 6 in. above the deck.

Her main boom which is a solid spar is 21 ft. 3 in. overall, and is 7 in. × $3\frac{1}{2}$ in. at mid length and tapers to $4\frac{1}{2}$ in. × $3\frac{1}{4}$ in. at the inner end, and to $5\frac{1}{2}$ in. × $3\frac{1}{2}$ in. at the outer end, while her twin spinnaker booms which are 18 ft. 7 in. overall are $4\frac{3}{8}$ in. diameter in the centre tapering to $2\frac{3}{4}$ in. at the ends, the walls throughout remaining constant at $\frac{3}{4}$ in. thickness.

The *Maid's* mast was fitted with two crosstrees only, the upper at the staysail halyard block being 5 ft. in length and the second crosstree 16 ft. below this being 4 ft. 6 in. in length, and there would seem to be little wrong with her rig, for it stood up to its work well throughout the 1937 season.

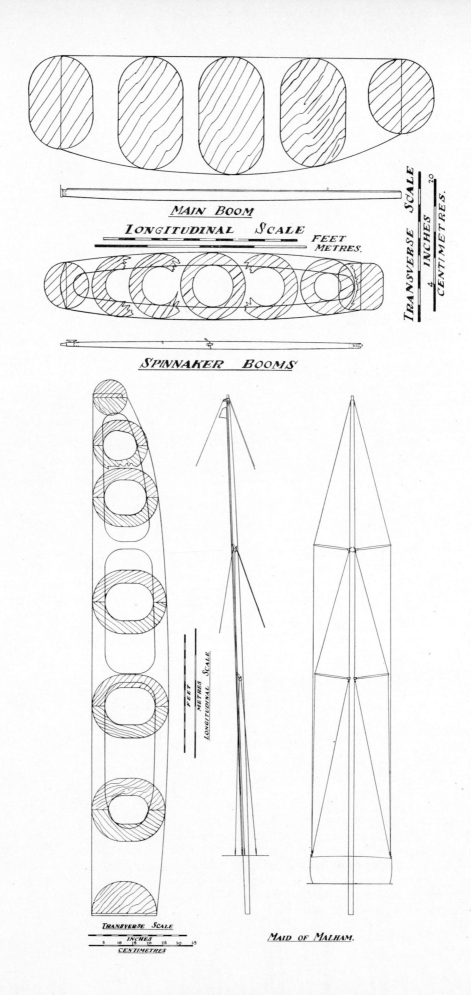

MAIN BOOM

LONGITUDINAL SCALE
FEET
METRES.

SPINNAKER BOOMS

Transverse Scale
4 INCHES 20
CENTIMETRES.

FEET
METRES
Longitudinal Scale

Transverse Scale
INCHES
5 10 15 20 25 30 35
CENTIMETRES

MAID OF MALHAM.

SEA SAGA

The mast of this light displacement racing cruiser is supported by three crosstrees abreast, a jumper strut forward at the jib halyard height, a forestay 42 ft. 6 in. above the deck and a pair of runners leading aft from this spot. As well as this there is a topmast stay to the stemhead and a topmast backstay running aft to her counter, the top of the mast being 58 ft. above the deck.   This spar is 9 in. × 7 in. at its largest place, which is half-way between the jib halyard height and the deck.   Here the wall is $1\frac{1}{2}$ in. in thickness, the spar tapering to $8\frac{1}{2}$ in. × $6\frac{3}{4}$ in. at the deck, the

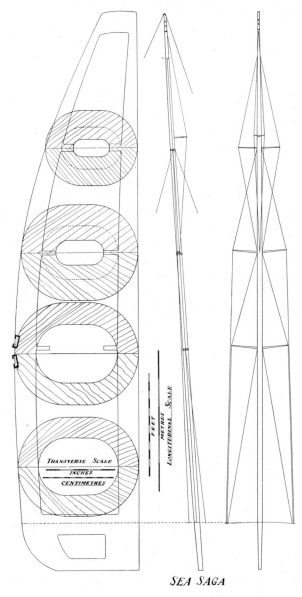

SEA SAGA

walls remaining $1\frac{1}{2}$ in. all through the lower part of this mast, and while the mast is solid where it passes through the deck it is hollow again between the deck and the heel.

This mast tapers away to $2\frac{5}{8}$ in. × 2 in. at the head where the wall is $\frac{5}{8}$ in. in thickness.

As will be seen two female tracks were designed to go on this mast, and if we look at *Sea Saga's* sail plan we see that she has a full length luff trysail, which, with its hollow leech, has only half the area of her mainsail, and to set this sail a second track was designed for the after side of the mainmast.   However, when *Sea Saga* was built this track for some reason or another was not fitted, which seems a pity, for the idea is a good one, for if it did nothing else it gave an auxiliary track so that if any damage occurred to one there would always be a second to fall back on.

ORTAC

Ortac's cutter rig stands 55 ft. above the deck and her oval mast is $9\frac{3}{4}$ in. $\times$ $7\frac{1}{2}$ in. tapering at the top to $4\frac{7}{8}$ in. $\times$ $3\frac{3}{4}$ in. and to $9\frac{1}{4}$ in. $\times$ 7 in. at the gooseneck band.

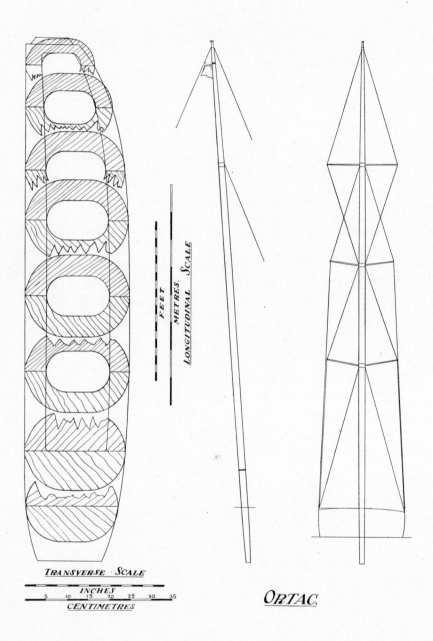

FEET

METRES.

LONGITUDINAL SCALE

TRANSVERSE SCALE

INCHES
5   10   15   20   25   30   35
CENTIMETRES

ORTAC.

From just above the gooseneck band to the heel this mast is solid, and has $1\frac{7}{8}$ in. walls, which taper to $1\frac{1}{4}$ in. at the top, but as will be noticed from the plan an extra $\frac{1}{8}$ in. has been left on all the way up the after side of this mast to take the track.

Athwartships the mast is supported by three crosstrees, the upper at the staysail halyard height being 4 ft. in width, the middle crosstree 3 ft. 6 in. and the lower again 4 ft.

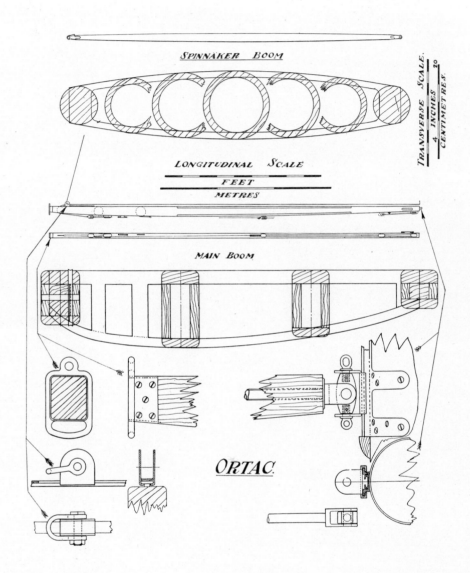

SPINNAKER BOOM

TRANSVERSE SCALE
4 INCHES 20
CENTIMETRES

LONGITUDINAL SCALE
FEET
METRES

MAIN BOOM

ORTAC

Ortac's 21 ft. 6 in. main boom is a rectangular-shaped spar built in the form of a hollow box being $6\frac{1}{2}$ in. $\times 3\frac{1}{4}$ in. throughout, the walls being $\frac{3}{4}$ in. except the upper one, which takes the track and this is $1\frac{1}{8}$ in. in thickness, so once again the designer has left extra wood to take the track and its fastenings.

Her spinnaker booms are circular spars 19 ft. in length overall and $5\frac{3}{4}$ in. in diameter at their middle tapering to 3 in. at the ends ; $\frac{1}{2}$ in. wall being used throughout.

TROMP II

Tromp II's mainmast stands 63 ft. 2 in. above the deck and this spar is $10\frac{9}{16}$ in. $\times 7\frac{5}{8}$ in. at a spot half-way between the jib halyard block and the deck from where it tapers away to $5\frac{1}{4}$ in. $\times 3\frac{3}{4}$ in. at the head to 10 in. $\times 7$ in. at the foot.

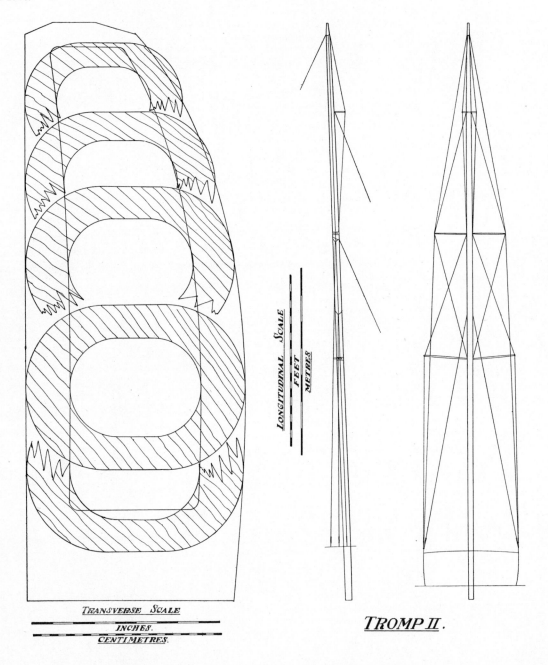

TRANSVERSE SCALE

INCHES.

CENTIMETRES.

LONGITUDINAL SCALE

FEET

METRES

TROMP II.

It will be noticed by the section that the wall of this mast differs in thickness. Fore and aft, it is $2\frac{1}{8}$ in. in thickness, but athwartships the mast is only $1\frac{1}{2}$ in. in thickness at its largest place, and it carries this wall thickness down to a spot 5 ft. above the deck from whence the spar is solid to the heel while at the top the wall thickness is $1\frac{1}{4}$ in. fore and aft on its fore and aft edges, but only $\frac{7}{8}$ in. athwartships on its side, while its staying follows the practice usually employed nowadays.

INDEX

ACKNOWLEDGMENT

OF our five senses I have always believed sight to be the most valuable, and because a good picture will convey as much as a page of words I have always endeavoured to illustrate my books well and a glance through the list of photographs and illustrations will show how deeply I am indebted to such world-famed photographers as Frank Beken, Douglas Went, Morris Rosenfietd and all whose photographs have helped me with this book, and also I would like to thank *Yachting World* for allowing me to reproduce the very fine perspective drawing on page 173. Then too, I feel grateful to the various Museums for their help, and those who wrought and also those who preserved that wonderful monument the Bayeux Tapestry.

LIST OF PHOTOGRAPHS

PRINTED IN GREAT BRITAIN BY ROBERT MACLEHOSE AND CO. LTD. THE UNIVERSITY PRESS, GLASGOW